TEACHER'S EDITION

Biology

LAB EXERCISES

Third Edition

Thomas E. Porch
Brad R. Batdorf

BJU PRESS
Greenville, South Carolina

NOTE:
The fact that materials produced by other publishers may be referred to in this volume does not constitute an endorsement of the content or theological position of materials produced by such publishers. Any references and ancillary materials are listed as an aid to the student or the teacher and in an attempt to maintain the accepted academic standards of the publishing industry.

NOTE: You are legally responsible for the safety of your students in the lab. Insist that they follow safe lab practices. Do not leave them unattended while they are working on any experiment or project in the lab.

The law requires that all permanent containers (not beakers, flasks, etc., that are used for less than one week) be labeled with an HMIS (Hazardous Materials Identification System) label. HMIS labels rank the chemical hazard in terms of health, flammability, reactivity, and contact on a scale from 0 to 4 (0 = no hazard; 4 = extreme hazard). The information you will need to prepare these labels can be found in the MSDS (Material Safety Data Sheet) obtained from the chemical supplier.

An MSDS must be on file for each chemical you have on hand, and it must be located in an area that is easily accessible to your students. It would be a valuable use of your instructional time to go over the HMIS/MSDS formats with your students.

Your legal responsibilities as a laboratory instructor are covered for the most part by the following groups of regulations:

1. Occupational Safety and Health Standards, especially OSHA 29 CFR 1910.1200 Hazard communication, and OSHA 29 CFR 1910.1450 Occupational exposure to hazardous chemicals in laboratories.
2. EPA Summary of Small Quantity Hazardous Waste Generator Rules—Resource Conservation and Recovery Act (40 CFR 261.5).

An excellent resource that puts much of this in perspective for the high school is *Investigating Safely: A Guide for High School Teachers* by Juliana Texley, Terry Kwan, and John Summers (2004, NSTA Press).

You may want to consult your school lawyer to determine whether any local or state regulations should be taken into consideration. Rules regarding laboratory safety and chemical disposal are constantly changing. Safety and disposal procedures in this lab manual should be regarded as only generalized suggestions. You should consult the safety and chemical disposal laws in your own state and community, as well as the most recent OSHA guidelines.

Although you may resent the intrusion of the government into your classroom, your example will influence the attitude of your students with regard to personal safety, a Christian's responsibility to government, and our responsibility for the environment.

BIOLOGY Laboratory Exercises Teacher's Edition
Third Edition

Thomas E. Porch, DMD
Brad R. Batdorf, MAEd

Project Manager
Vic Ludlum

Project Editor
Rebecca Moore

Design
Holly Gilbert
Seven Worldwide

Composition
Seven Worldwide

Illustration
Dave Schuppert
Julie Arsenault
Matt Bjerk
Aaron Dickey
Cory Godbey
Preston Gravely
Jim Hargis
Brian D. Johnson, Gooseneck Graphics
Justin Gerard, Portland Studios

Produced in cooperation with the Bob Jones University Division of Natural Science of the College of Arts and Science, the School of Religion, and Bob Jones Academy.

Photo Credit: © Visuals Unlimited, page 5 (L5 reduced student page)

ISBN 9781-57924-935-9

15 14 13 12 11 10 9 8 7 6 5 4 3 2

Suggestions for Using This Teacher's Edition

Those who are looking for a standard high-school laboratory manual may be disappointed in this book. Unlike many manuals, this one does not offer hundreds of different exercises from which you choose the two dozen you want to do. In this manual there are only forty-three main exercises. Some exercises are designed for more than one class day, while others will take only a few minutes of class time. Some of the exercises have major sections that require little or no laboratory apparatus. Other sections require that the student merely observe something and then record his observations. Occasionally instructions are given for conducting library research. In certain cases the student is asked to perform relatively complex tasks, while in other areas the teacher does the majority of the work while the student observes, records, and then thinks through what he has observed. In other cases, the class is divided into groups to perform different tasks, and then each class member observes the outcome of each group's work. Some sections ask students to label drawings in this book, while other sections ask students to make their own drawings and label them.

Considerable variety characterizes the material included here, and not all of it is standard for most high-school laboratory manuals. The reason for the latter is that this book was designed to accomplish the goals outlined on pages A2–A3 with the laboratory facilities of a Christian school in mind. Thus, although many of these exercises are similar to those normally conducted in high-school biology laboratories, some are not. Some common exercises were eliminated, most were greatly modified, and new exercises were developed.

Equipment and skills to be taught to the student have been carefully selected for their value in accomplishing goals. For example, although microscopes are expensive, their value cannot be denied, and

Laboratory Exercises

Contents

the fact that they can be used repeatedly in the course of the school year warrants not only buying microscopes but also spending time in the laboratory teaching microscope skills. On the other hand, bacteriological skills are important to know about, but developing the manual skill in every student is not worth the time and expense. The skill would be useful in only one or two laboratory exercises and would have little value in most students' futures. Thus the exercise on bacteriology calls for the teacher to prepare cultures as a demonstration for the students to observe and answer questions about.

Tailoring the Exercises to Your Needs

Each laboratory exercise has several parts. Not all parts of every exercise will be used by all teachers each year they teach. Occasionally a lack of certain supplies will dictate that a section that you would like to use be omitted in favor of another for which you have the equipment. Some sections may be considered by some teachers to be less valuable than others. For example, in the exercise on plant anatomy (13b) there are sections on making leaf collections and sections dealing with microscopic observation of leaf cross sections. If you have the microscope slides, you may consider it just as valuable to show the students herbarium specimens of leaves with different margins and shapes as part of your lectures and then have them do the microscopic observation of leaves as a laboratory exercise. If you lack the slides, however, you may want to prepare visuals of leaf cross sections and have the students make leaf collections.

Some exercises will require several class hours to complete. Thus it may be best to omit sections of these exercises or permit sections to be done as extra credit. Occasionally a lack of time may require omitting an entire exercise. The "Required / Extra / Omit" boxes found in the margins of the laboratory exercises (see pp. L7–L8 of the student book for explanation) are designed to help you tailor this laboratory manual to your specific needs. In the teacher's notes for each of the laboratory exercises are indications of what sections could be omitted or assigned for extra credit. These are merely suggestions and should be adjusted as your particular situation dictates.

While you are giving the students their assignments, indicate which sections of the laboratory exercise you will require, permit them to do for extra credit, or omit. (See the Introduction in *BIOLOGY Teacher's Edition* for suggestions regarding assignments and assignment length.) Also, the length of your class hour, the rate at which your students complete laboratory work, and the availability of after-school laboratory times will make a considerable difference in the number of sections of an exercise you assign.

Because sections may be omitted or added, you will need to establish the value of each exercise as you assign it. Students should be informed of the value of each of the exercises before they do it. Also, they should know the value of each extra-credit section, if possible. This knowledge will help them to budget their time. At the beginning of each semester you should look over the exercises that are designed to coordinate with the lecture material you plan to cover. (The numbers of the laboratory exercises correspond to chapter numbers in the text. The lettered sections of each exercise, however, do not correspond to the chapter subdivisions in the text.) After determining which sections of the exercises are to be done, you can determine the values of the various required and extra-credit sections. Try to achieve a balance; avoid placing too much value on an easy exercise and too little on a difficult one. If possible, prepare a handout for each grading period, giving the values of the exercises as well as which sections will be required, extra credit, or omitted.

Introduction

Biology can be a bewildering subject. There is a mountain of information, some of it concerning obscure structures and complex processes that take place on an invisible level. Like all science disciplines, it has its own extensive vocabulary seldom used in conversation. Many students become frustrated when they realize how much there is to learn. At the same time, they see God's wonderful creation all around them. It is impossible to be indifferent to the plants and animals God created. And the processes through which these living things develop and maintain themselves are just as fascinating as the actual organisms are.

Christians have an obligation—set forth in Genesis 1:28—to serve as stewards or caretakers of this creation. Effective stewardship depends on knowledge. The laboratory exercises in this manual are designed to provide hands-on exposure to living things—from algae and bacteria to mammals. The end result should be an increase in knowledge and understanding. While the lab experiences alone will not guarantee comprehension, they should clarify material in the text and make the learning come alive.

It is one thing to read about an unfamiliar object, listen to a person talk about it, look at pictures of it, and even memorize facts about it. It is quite another matter to actually look at the object, handle it, or do something with it. Sometimes students do not really understand the object being discussed until they become personally familiar with it. It would not be unusual for a high school biology student to correctly answer every question on a quiz about *Spirogyra* but be surprised to learn that "the stuff in that dish is real *Spirogyra*." But the student who has learned all about *Spirogyra* and then has looked at it, placed some on a slide, and examined it through a microscope does not easily forget the "green stringy stuff," even though he may forget its name.

One of the main purposes of these laboratory exercises is to provide a framework by which you can increase your understanding by becoming personally acquainted with various biological processes and organisms.

A second purpose is to help you study. By asking you to do certain tasks and to answer particular questions (some requiring merely looking up the answer, others requiring thought, and some requiring experimentation), these exercises should help you learn without having to memorize cold facts. It is a well-known educational principle that working with a piece of information not only aids in learning it but also makes it more usable to the learner. This principle lies behind the writing of essays in English class and the working of problems in math class.

Of course, you can learn from your essays and math problems only if you work on them faithfully and carefully. Otherwise, they become a burden and, for some students, a game to see how few they can do yet still pass the course. These students lose the benefit of these exercises because they have the wrong approach to their work. The same is true of laboratory work in a high school science course. If you approach it as "something I don't want to do"

Occasionally you may feel the need to add something to a laboratory exercise. Adding an observation of a specimen you have or a particular activity you wish your students to experience is not difficult. Some teachers may wish to add an entire exercise. For example, if your school is two blocks from the ocean, an analysis of a tidal pool could be a profitable activity. You could write and duplicate a laboratory exercise on tidal pools in a format similar to the ones used in this book.

The introduction for the student (p. L7) states, "Any sections that you do not finish during the classroom laboratory time become part of your homework. If this requires the use of laboratory equipment, you will need to come to the laboratory at announced after-school times or make arrangements with your teacher to finish the work at some other time." Students in Christian schools often travel long distances to attend school, so after-school lab times might be a hardship. As you select those sections of the laboratory exercises that require apparatus, be sure that the time allotted for completing the laboratory work is reasonable. Getting all the work done by working quickly and efficiently should be an attainable goal for the average or slightly above-average student.

As a general guideline, for the sections requiring laboratory equipment, assign as much as you can accomplish in half the time available to the students. The students should have read completely the exercise they are to do before they come to class so that they are ready to begin the exercise upon entering the classroom. If they are not ready, it is understandable that they may not finish, and they should suffer the consequences, no matter how far away they live.

Keep an eye on the students during the in-class laboratory time. If they are spending too much time reading instructions, if they are filling in answers to sections that they

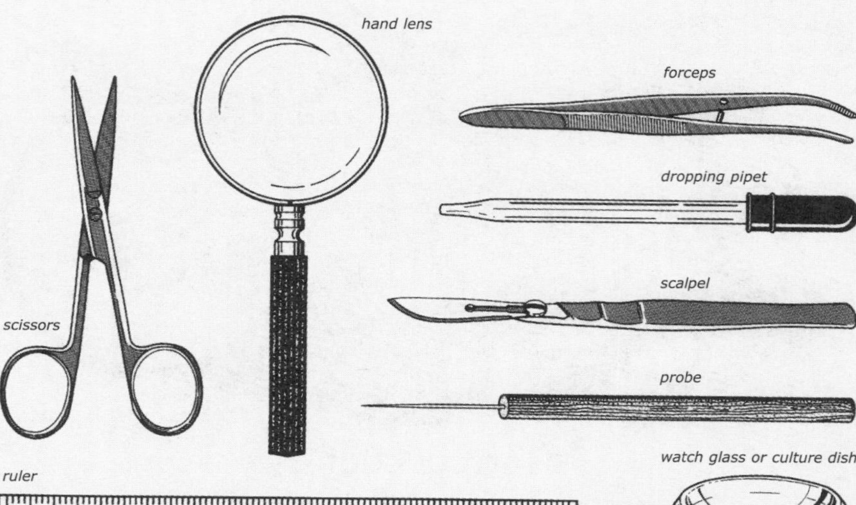

I.1
Student laboratory equipment

or as "something that the teacher requires us to do," you will lose many of its benefits. Your attitude toward the laboratory exercises will greatly influence how much you will benefit from them.

The laboratory exercises in this book are designed to go along with *BIOLOGY*. As you cover the material in this textbook (referred to in the laboratory exercises as the *text*), your teacher will tell you what laboratory exercises (or *labs*) you will be expected to do and when they are to be handed in. A lab is an assignment on which any student, if he is faithful and diligent, can earn a good grade. The teacher will be able to judge the effort you have put forth by looking at how well you did the laboratory exercises. Do your best on them.

Equipment

The laboratory equipment necessary for doing these exercises will be provided. Some of the basic tools frequently used in the biology laboratory are illustrated and named in Diagram I.1. Learn the proper names and uses for these tools. Other pieces of equipment (such as the microscope) will be described in the exercises as each piece is needed.

On laboratory days you should be sure to have the following:

- ❒ *BIOLOGY*
- ❒ A large three-ring binder with lined loose-leaf paper for taking class notes and holding returned laboratory exercises
- ❒ A pencil, an eraser, and extra unlined white paper for laboratory drawings

For certain lab days you may also want to bring a protective garment (an old, large shirt to be worn over your school clothes), colored pencils, and hand cream. These items are optional.

Be sure to report all damaged equipment, even if you are not responsible for breaking it. If you are found using a piece of damaged equipment, it may be assumed you are responsible for breaking the equipment unless you report the damage before you start using it. The policy of your school may be to bill you for such damage or for damage you cause because of carelessness.

Drawings

One of the most common cries echoing through every high school biology laboratory is "But I can't

should have completed before they came to class (those marked by the house icon; see p. L7 of the student book), or if you see them working on conclusions and summaries that do not require laboratory equipment while they still have sections left that require laboratory equipment, speak to them about it. Advise them that they must use their laboratory time wisely or they will suffer the consequences.

Suggestions for Classroom Laboratory Policies

Note carefully the policies and procedures outlined in the introduction for the student. These are suggested policies. This book is designed to be used with these policies; however, other systems of classroom policies will work equally well. If you are going to follow other policies and procedures, you should carefully outline them for your students. If you intend to use the policies suggested in this book, carefully go over them in class, adding your own comments and stressing the important points.

A significant, but often overlooked, aspect of successful laboratory work is the atmosphere of the laboratory on lab days. Before the students walk into the laboratory, the equipment should be set out in an orderly fashion, ready for use. The teacher who is not prepared when he expects the students to be prepared is a poor testimony.

A brief word regarding where things are and comments about special problems (notes about techniques, for example) should immediately follow opening prayer. A brisk, businesslike approach to the laboratory work is important. If you are lackadaisical in your approach to the equipment or the instructions, students will be the same way as they start the laboratory work and will inevitably accomplish little. Set a brisk pace by your opening attitude.

draw!" A lack of artistic ability does not have to be a drawback. A good scientific drawing does not require artistic ability as much as it requires a good eye, a steady hand, and a large eraser.

Let us look at some of the reasons for drawing scientific specimens. Making drawings is one of the best ways to learn some of the complex biological structures and processes. If you feel that a drawing is just bothersome busywork, you will gain little from your drawings. Try a more positive approach. Before attempting a drawing, find out what the text has to say concerning the organism. Look at pictures of the specimen. Then, as you draw the specimen, concentrate on its shape, color, function, name, location, and any other characteristics you think of. By the time you have finished, you should *know* it.

Some drawings are meant to be a challenge. You will occasionally be asked to draw something that your text does not discuss. In such cases you will need to consult other texts in order to find enough information to make an intelligent drawing. Students are commonly tempted to try to draw objects they do not understand. Such a drawing will profit little. If you take the time to find the necessary information for yourself, you will not quickly forget what you have worked to achieve.

Students often find themselves copying. They do not actually put a sheet of paper over a picture and trace the object, but they sit with a textbook drawing in front of them and reproduce it without really thinking about what they are drawing. This method can produce a beautiful drawing, but drawings made without concentration and thought bring little profit. For guidance, consult drawings of the specimens you are working on but never copy the drawings.

Spaces are provided for most of the drawings you will make in these laboratory exercises. Any box with the pencil icon at the top requires you to draw or label something. A box with the eye icon is for your observation and does not require any writing. Occasionally, if you need to begin a drawing again or if you are doing a drawing for which there is not a space, you will need to make a drawing on your own paper. Always use unlined white paper.

I.2
A specimen drawing

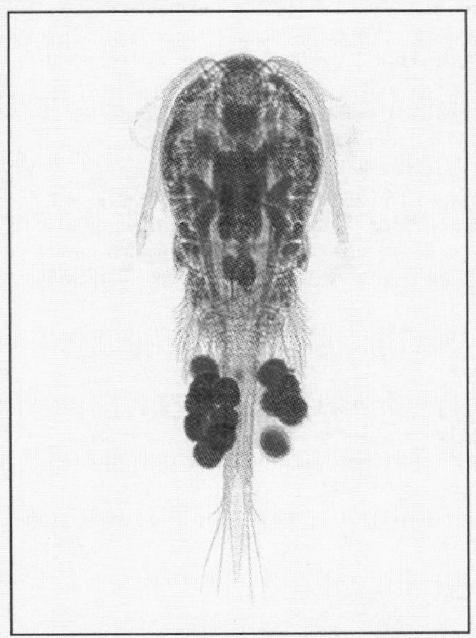

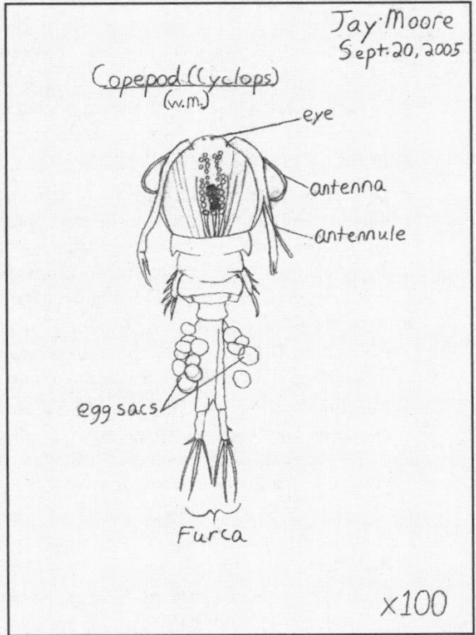

The materials list at the beginning of each laboratory exercise is directed to each student laboratory group. Of course, if sections are omitted, you may not need certain items, and for larger classes you may need more of other items. Look over the materials lists that appear on the student laboratory exercises a month or two in advance so that you can make necessary preparations for obtaining perishables. There are Notes on Materials in the margins of this teacher's edition. They are marked by the scissors icon . These notes offer guidance for securing and setting up the materials. In addition, the Appendix contains extensive information for acquiring and using the materials.

Some students, seeing the list of materials at the beginning of the exercise, will spend the first part of the hour collecting all these items at their desks. Inform the class that this procedure would be unwise, since some of the materials may be for extra-credit or omitted sections. Also, there are not enough of some laboratory items for every laboratory group to have one of its own. For instance, a single dropping bottle of stain is sufficient for an exercise for which every laboratory group needs only one drop of the stain. Since students can observe only one preserved slide at a time, they should be restricted to two slides at a time per microscope. Hoarding slides hinders others from finishing their work. A good policy is to have students return to the proper place any piece of laboratory equipment that is not either in use or about to be used (excluding, of course, those pieces of equipment that are distributed to each laboratory group, such as dissection kits, microscopes, watch glasses, and rulers).

Questions will come up during the laboratory time. The teacher, however, should not answer all of them. The "What do I do now?" after a student has collected the equipment on his desk should be answered with "What does the laboratory exercise tell you to do?" Teaching students to follow directions and to work independently is a

Kinds of Scientific Drawings

Within these laboratory exercises you will be asked to do two different types of drawings.

- The **specimen drawing** is made to show exactly what a specimen looks like. It is drawn from an actual specimen, not from a diagram or a picture in a book.
- The **schematic drawing** is often a stylized representation to show a process or a relationship, and therefore it often does not look exactly like the specimen. On page 127 of your text is a group of schematic diagrams that do not look like the photographs beside them, even though they represent the same process. The schematic drawings explain what is taking place in the process being illustrated.

Requirements for a Good Drawing

- Print all information in the same style. Make all printed material parallel with the bottom edge of the paper.
- Put your name in the upper right-hand corner of the drawing and the date the drawing was made below your name. (If you are making your drawing in the spaces provided in this book, your name and the date on the laboratory exercise sheet are sufficient.)
- Center the name of the specimen above the drawing. If the drawing is of a portion of an organism, indicate the portion in the title or under the title. For example, "Fruit fly, leg" indicates that the drawing is of the leg of a fruit fly. The title "Fruit fly" alone indicates a drawing of the entire fly.
- If the specimen has been prepared in some way before being drawn, indicate this under the name of the specimen. (See Methods of Slide Preparation on the next page.)
- Make the drawing large and center it in the space available.
- Do not use shading and color for specimen drawings. Stippling (holding a pencil in a vertical position and tapping the point on the paper) may be used sparingly. In stippling, the dots are all the same size, and a darkened area is obtained by having many dots. Schematic drawings are often made with colored pencils or pens. A colorful drawing should not be a goal in itself, but color may be used if it aids understanding.
- Add labels after the drawing is complete. The label lines should be straight and never cross each other. They should not have arrowheads on them. They should go directly to the object they indicate and touch it or be drawn onto it.
- Label everything in the drawing. If you are doing a specimen drawing but do not see some object on your specimen that you know should be there, do not take the liberty of drawing it in. In specimen drawings, draw only what you see in the specimen. In schematic drawings, you may take liberties to aid clarity.
- If you used the microscope, indicate the power in the lower right-hand corner. If you used some other type of magnification (such as a hand lens), write "magnified" or "enlarged" in that corner.
- Do not draw the microscope field or the container the specimen is in.

worthy goal that is not accomplished by spoon-feeding them. Slower students may need some help developing such skills. Lazy students, however, should be forced to swim for themselves or watch their grades sink.

Of course, comments like "The book says to do this, but I can't get it to work" demand immediate help. The student obviously has read and followed the directions yet encountered a real problem. Most often you can just look at what the student has done and make a suggestion to solve the problem. This action is much better than doing the lab procedure for the student. Occasionally, doing something for him may be necessary, but do not make a habit of it, or else you will run yourself ragged, and the student will suffer from the lack of experience.

Occasionally students ask questions to try to get the information they need to fill in a blank in the exercises. Try not to give it to them. Instead, encourage them to consult their textbooks or to figure out the answer on their own. Sometimes a prodding question or two will put them on the right track. You do not develop students who can analyze and think for themselves by dispensing answers that they are able to figure out for themselves.

Frequently the laboratory exercises require students to make drawings. Very specific instructions regarding these drawings are given on pages L4–L6 of the student book. A sample of a specimen drawing and a photograph of the specimen from which it was made are shown on page L5. You can use these illustrations to show how a good drawing is done. Emphasize to the students that drawings should be done in pencil and that any erasures they make should be neat. Tell them that they must do the drawing while they are looking at the specimen. They are not to make a sketch and then do the actual drawing at home (most likely while copying from a picture). Students will find it easier to draw if they detach the page on which they are to draw.

Normal Laboratory Procedure

Normally, the sequence for completing the laboratory exercises is as follows:

1. The lab day and the day the exercise is due will be announced a few days in advance.
2. Before you come to class each lab day, you're expected to have **read the assigned laboratory exercise completely** and **to have done as much of the work as possible**. Sections or questions in the laboratory exercises that are marked with the symbol can be done without the use of laboratory equipment and can be completed before the lab day or, in a few cases, will need to be done after lab.
3. On the lab day, you and your laboratory partner will have enough class time to accomplish the work that requires lab equipment if you are prepared and will work efficiently. Sometimes answering questions about your work can be done outside of class, allowing you more in-class time to complete the laboratory work.
4. Any sections that you do not finish during the classroom laboratory time become part of your homework. If this requires the use of laboratory equipment, you will need to come to the laboratory at announced after-school times or make arrangements with your teacher to finish the work at some other time.
5. Remove your completed laboratory exercise from this book and staple it together with any materials that the exercise may call for (such as reports or drawings on your own paper) and hand them in on the date they are due. (This date will usually be one or two days after the lab day.)
6. The laboratory exercise will be graded and handed back in a few days.
7. Place the returned laboratory exercise in a loose-leaf notebook and keep it.
8. At the end of the grading period, the loose-leaf notebook, containing all the laboratory exercises you will have done by then, will be turned in for evaluation. Be careful not to lose these laboratory exercises.

Required / Extra / Omit

When the teacher gives you an assignment, you will need to mark in your laboratory exercise what parts of the assignment your class will be doing. For many sections of the exercise, there are boxes like this:

If your teacher tells you that you are expected to do a particular section of the lab, mark box "R" for "required." If your teacher tells you that you may do a section for extra credit, mark box "E" for "extra." If your teacher tells you that you are not to do a section, mark box "O" for "omit."

The extra credit sections will require additional time, and you may have to return to the laboratory after class time. If you are having difficulty with the

Methods of Slide Preparation

Term	Abbreviation	Description
Whole mount	w.m.	A slide that contains the entire specimen (e.g., flea) or the entire part of a specimen (e.g., fly leg)
Wet mount	W.M.	A temporary slide on which the specimen is placed in water
Preserved slide		A slide on which the specimen is mounted in a medium that permanently keeps the specimen
Cross section	c.s. or c.x.	A specimen that has been cut crosswise
Longitudinal section	l.s. or l.x.	A specimen that has been cut lengthwise
Teased		A specimen that has been shredded into pieces
Smeared		A specimen that has been smeared across the slide
Stained		A specimen that has been exposed to dyes in order to color structures

Most of the drawings the students are asked to do in the laboratory exercises have spaces allotted for them in the book. Occasionally you may ask them to do more drawings than there are spaces in the exercise, or they may make mistakes in an area given to them and need another space. Sometimes a drawing will not fit inside one of these boxes (depending on their skills). If they need more spaces (for whatever reason), they should use their own white, unlined paper.

If you are a new teacher or a teacher who is teaching some of the exercises in this book for the first time, do the exercise yourself a few days in advance. In the privacy of an empty classroom, get out the equipment and follow the instructions in the laboratory exercise. If you have difficulty because of your equipment or your specimens, make adjustments. You can then inform your class what they should do to obtain good results, or you can tell them what kind of results to expect. You will save time and avoid frustration by making necessary announcements at the beginning of class.

Grading Laboratory Exercises

Because each exercise has many unequal parts, and each response is worth considerably less than one point, some teachers may have difficulty deciding how to grade them. There are two methods that can be used. The first is simply to mark any incorrect parts, poor or incomplete drawings, or failure to follow directions and to give a subjective grade based on the number and severity of the marks.

In the second method the value of the exercise is divided among the responses the student is asked to make. Thus a simple yes/no response may be worth 0.1 point, an explanation 0.8, and a difficult drawing 1.0. The point value that the student loses for an incorrect response is recorded next to the response. The score is arrived at by totaling the number of points the student missed and subtracting it from the value of the exercise.

tests, if your last lab grade was not as good as you had wanted, or if you have been doing poorly on quizzes, you are encouraged to do some of the extra credit sections to gain points. If you are doing well in the course, you should do an extra credit exercise only if it sounds exceptionally interesting. Extra credit sections must be done before the laboratory exercise is handed in; they may not be done at the end of the course to improve your grade.

Late Laboratory Work

Points will be deducted from the score of a laboratory exercise for each day it is late. Normally, laboratory exercises will not be accepted if they are more than three days late. If you experience unusual difficulties, talk to your teacher to find out whether an exception can be made.

The loose-leaf notebook containing all the graded laboratory exercises is due at the end of the grading period; it must be handed in on time, or points will be deducted. If exceptional circumstances cause the notebook to be late, see your teacher.

When living organisms are used in a laboratory exercise, you usually must immediately make up any lab work that you miss. The organisms may not be available for an extended time.

Conduct and Honor System

Some of the materials and tools used in the laboratory are extremely dangerous if they are misused. For this reason, **do not engage in horseplay at any time**. Horseplay is using any piece of laboratory equipment for a purpose other than that for which it was intended. Your teacher will impose severe penalties if you commit this offense.

Do your own work for this class. Do not obtain answers from other students or their work. This is cheating. Your teacher may allow students to help each other by discussing the material and sharing sources of information, but you should never tell each other the answer or copy each other's work. Handing in your laboratory exercise is your statement that you have not cheated. If you have difficulties, see your instructor for help. Occasionally, your teacher may give you special permission to use someone else's work as a source when you are making up work.

Tips for Preparing Laboratory Work

- **Mark the drawings you need to make** when you read the laboratory exercise before coming to class. Then check them off as you finish them.
- **Carefully note what you did wrong** when you receive a graded lab and do not make the same mistakes again. For example, if you are told that your label lines are sloppy on your first drawings, use a ruler to draw the lines on other drawings.
- **Carefully follow the instructions** given in the laboratory exercise. They will usually answer your questions. Most of the points you miss on a lab will be for either not doing a section or not following directions carefully.
- **The subpoints under a larger point pertain to that larger point**. Since the subpoints usually explain or give more detailed instruction, be sure to read all of the subpoints before you begin work.
- **Do what you can at home**, either before you come to class on lab day or after lab day (but before the laboratory exercise is due).
- **Consult your text for material concerning your laboratory work**. If the laboratory exercise tells you to read certain pages in the text, do so. Coming to a lab day unprepared to do a laboratory exercise is a waste of time. Do your best to know what you are doing.

Students should not hand in their laboratory work until test day. Unless you can correct the exercise and hand it back before the test (which often requires doing the exercise too early in the teaching unit for it to be profitable), the students will not be able to study from the laboratory work for the test.

It is valuable if students keep all of their returned labs in a notebook. At the end of a grading period, when the laboratory exercises are handed in together, the teacher can glance over the work to see if the student has improved, regressed, or worked consistently. The laboratory notebook can then be evaluated as a separate grade or a separate section of the laboratory grade.

A recommended policy is this: "If you do not hand in a laboratory notebook at the end of each grading period, you will receive an automatic F." In that statement there is no indication either of the point value of the notebook or of the level of the work expected. For some students, requiring the notebook is necessary to convince them that they must do the work. In their previous science classes they probably have not had laboratory work that required effort or counted heavily on their grade. Thus some of the more capable students may expect, by making good grades on tests, to pass the course without the effort required to do laboratory work. These students then miss the benefits of the laboratory work. It is largely the duty of the teacher to make sure that such students are encouraged (perhaps forced) to do what is good for them, even though they may not like it.

In this teacher's edition are notes for each laboratory exercise. Included are suggestions on how to set up the lab, what to do about the major problems students will have, which sections to omit—if necessary—and why, and other helpful advice. The Appendix includes information for preparing a classroom laboratory and for securing the materials (see pp. A2–A20).

Name_______________________________

Date___________________ Hour__________

1a
The Scientific Method

Materials

- meter stick

> Metal, wooden, or plastic meter sticks can be used.

Goals

- To state a problem that can be solved using the scientific method
- To devise an experiment that will supply data to determine an answer to the problem
- To collect and interpret data
- To analyze and interpret data obtained
- To learn the steps of the scientific method

While looking in the newspaper for an article for history class, Laura read a report about the amount of time some young people spend using hand-held electronic games. The article stated that this activity has increased greatly in the last generation and further stated that some believe that use of these devices increases eye-hand coordination. She began to wonder whether there might be some simple way to measure eye-hand coordination.

Laura looked through her textbook and learned that what we see is perceived by light waves entering the eye. These are processed by the retina, which then transmits electrical impulses through the optic nerve to the brain's occipital lobe. This information is then passed to the brain's cerebral cortex, which stimulates muscle movement by transmitting an impulse down the spinal cord to the appropriate muscles. This same process helps you pick up your dinner plate or throw your hands up to avoid being hit in the face by a foul ball.

Because Laura did not have a stopwatch but wanted a consistent way to measure response time, she decided to use a falling meter stick, which the test subject would have to catch after it was released and had begun to fall. The distance it fell before being caught would indirectly measure the response time.

Preliminary Work

Your class will suggest experiments dealing with eye-hand coordination, choose a problem, design and conduct an experiment to supply data that can be used to determine an answer to the problem, and arrive at a conclusion. For this experiment you may use only a meter stick. (Of course, you should also have a pencil, paper, and other classroom materials.) Before you come to class, devise a few problems about eye-hand coordination that you consider interesting and that the class could experiment with. Complete the material below before you come to class so that you can suggest a possible experiment.

I. List several problems dealing with eye-hand coordination that could be used in class.
   - Be sure your problems are worded as questions that have limitations and can be answered with yes, no, or a number.
   - Avoid problems that might involve danger (e.g., dropping a meter stick toward someone's face) and those you would not be able to test (such as comparing red-haired people with blond-haired people when you have only one red-haired person in your class).

1a.1
An illustration of Laura's test for eye-hand coordination. The tester releases the meter stick, after which the test subject must close his fingers as quickly as possible to catch the falling meter stick. Measurements on the meter stick will then indicate, not an actual time, but the distance the stick dropped before it was stopped by the finger closure.

Introduction

The first laboratory exercise is one of the most difficult exercises but also one of the most profitable. Students may find the Preliminary Work a bit confusing. It requires them to come up with a problem, a hypothesis, and an experiment for testing eye-hand coordination, which is discussed in the introduction. Some students may try to adapt the questions to another subject that they are familiar with, while others may try to use an old, standard experiment that does not apply to eye-hand coordination. Some students may complain that they do not understand and will ask you to give them an example. If you do, they will just twist different aspects of your example in order to arrive at other possible experiments. Because the purpose of this exercise is to make them think, it is suggested that you not give students examples of what to put in the blanks under Preliminary Work.

One of the most difficult aspects of this exercise for the students is applying the terms (such as *variable, hypothesis, problem,* and *experiment*) that they have read in their text (pp. 12–14) and have heard from their teacher. In the context of the exercise, the terms seem different. Before students begin, explain that they may not understand the definitions well enough yet and may therefore have problems understanding what the exercise is asking. Usually, if they go back to the text and study the terms and definitions again, they will find the exercise easier.

Doing this exercise as a group project has several advantages. First, it helps you to learn about the students in your class and to spot those who may require extra attention from you in the laboratory. Second, working with other students on the first exercise should help the slower or more inexperienced students to learn what is expected of them.

For this exercise, the answers in the blanks of the Teacher's Edition are examples of what students might write for the problem presented as a guide. (Of course, the answers your students will give will be based

- List possible problems for the experiment. Problems will vary, depending on the student's understanding. Some possible problems include the following: Is the right hand faster in right-handed people? Are the thumb and forefinger faster than other finger combinations? Does it make a difference whether the test subject is seated or standing? Does the level of light in the room make a difference? Will the test subject improve with practice?

II. Develop the problem you consider the best one by answering the following questions.

- What problem do you consider the best? One of the problems devised above should be chosen. This problem will be developed as an example: Is the right hand more responsive in right-handed people?
- What hypothesis would you suggest for this problem? For this example: The right hand is more responsive in right-handed people (and the left hand is quicker in left-handed people).
- Describe the steps of an experiment that will supply data either to support or contradict your hypothesis. (Attach additional paper if necessary.) For this example: (1) Test each person on his dominant hand at least five times. (2) Test the nondominant hand the same way the dominant hand is tested. (3) Compare the average distance the meter stick dropped when the subject used his dominant hand to the average distance it dropped when he used his nondominant hand.
  - What is your experimental variable (single variable)? For this example: the hand (dominant vs. nondominant)
  - List the precautions you would take to limit other variables.
    For this example:
    1. Have the same person test both hands.
    2. Have the test subject seated with the forearm resting on a desk or counter.
    3. Drop the meter stick from the same point each time.
    4. Make sure the test subject begins with his fingers open a fixed distance.
    5. Begin with the dominant hand.
  - What is serving as your control group? For this example: The right hand is the control for the left, and the left is the control for the right.

on the experiment your class chooses.) Below is a sample of the data chart as it would be constructed on the chalkboard. It is followed by a copy of the data summary as compiled by the teacher from the chalkboard information. From this chart, the students are able to fill out the Summary (p. L12). These two charts correspond to the example being used in this exercise.

Required / Extra / Omit

This laboratory exercise should be done completely or not done at all. Have the students read the entire exercise and complete the Preliminary Work (pp. L9–L10) before coming to class on the lab day. The In-Class Procedures (pp. L11–L12) should be done on the lab day in the first twenty minutes of class time. The rest of the class hour should be spent in doing the experiment and recording the data on the chalkboard. On the next class day, give the students the cumulative data in printed form. The students will then be able to complete the Summary for the following day.

Sample Data Chart

Subject	Distances 1–3			1st average	Distances 4–6			2nd average
Ashley	19 cm	22 cm	16 cm	19 cm	17 cm	13 cm	20 cm	16.7 cm
Matt	20 cm	15 cm	16 cm	17 cm	18 cm	14 cm	17 cm	16.3 cm

If you would like to convert the distance dropped to seconds, the formula is t = square root of distance divided by 22.1.

Name________________________

In-Class Procedures

At the beginning of the laboratory period, the class will choose a problem suggested by one of its members. As a group you will then devise an experiment and determine exactly how it will be conducted. The class will then divide into groups and conduct the experiment. Results of the experiment will be recorded on a chart and will be interpreted on the following day. As the class decides which problems to use and devises the experiment to conduct, record this information in the spaces below. (Use additional paper if necessary.)

I. Our problem: For this example: Will eye-hand coordination (as measured by response time) improve with practice?

II. Our hypothesis: For this example: The eye-hand coordination of test subjects will improve with practice.

III. Our experiment: For this example: Test the distance a vertically dropped meter stick falls before being stopped by finger closure six times in a row. The first three trials will be averaged and compared with the last three trials.

- Our experimental variable: For this example: The first three trials compared with the last three trials
- Steps taken to limit the variables: For this example:
  1. Meter stick will start with the 10 cm mark between the test subject's open fingers.
  2. Tester will hold the meter stick at the 60 cm mark and release it without warning or cue to the test subject.
  3. Test subject may not look at the tester during the experiment but must watch only the meter stick.
  4. Thumb and forefinger will be used by each test subject.
  5. Fingers must be open exactly 6 cm at the time of each drop.
  6. The hand that is favored by the test subject should be tested.
- Our procedure for the experiment:
  1. The proper arm is rested on a desk or table.
  2. The hand is hanging over the edge, thumb side up, with the wrist at the desk or table's edge.
  3. The one being tested may not look at the tester.
  4. The test subject's thumb and forefinger must be open exactly 6 cm with the 10 cm mark on the meter stick at the top of the thumb.
  5. The tester will drop the meter stick, whereupon the test subject will close his fingers as quickly as possible to catch the falling stick.
  6. After each catch, the tester will record the centimeter marking at the top of the thumb and subtract 10 cm.
  7. Only the amount of time needed to record the data should pass between trials.

Before class begins, prepare an overhead transparency or chalkboard with the questions and spaces given in the In-Class Procedures.

As the students suggest possible problems, write them on the overhead projector or the chalkboard so that everyone can see them. If a suggested problem statement is poor, ask for a refined statement of the same problem. It may be necessary to remind the students that you need questions that can be answered by yes, no, or a number—not *how* or *why* questions. You can immediately rule out those suggestions that are too difficult to accomplish within an hour, involve too many people of a specific type (redheads, for example), or have other potential problems. From the acceptable problems on your list, have the students choose the one that they would like to experiment with. If necessary, refine the statement of the problem; write it on the transparency or chalkboard.

Work out the hypothesis, experiment, limitations, procedures, and anything else necessary by asking the class the questions given in the exercise and then recording the group answer on the overhead projector or chalkboard.

Conduct the experiment. Have the students record their data on the chalkboard as soon as possible in order to avoid a rush at the end of the class period.

Summary of Data for Exercise 1a

Problem: Does eye-hand coordination as measured by the response time required to catch a falling meter stick improve with practice?

Hypothesis: Eye-hand coordination, as measured by the response time required to catch a falling meter stick, will improve with practice.

Data: Total number of persons tested: 20
Total number of initial tests: 60
Total number of follow-up tests: 60
Average distance of drop for all initial tests: 16.9 cm
Average distance of drop for all follow-up tests: 16.2 cm
Difference between initial and follow-up averages: 0.7 cm

- My observations of problems encountered while conducting the experiment: For this example: Some very competitive people would randomly close their fingers, even before the meter stick was dropped, in order to get a "better score." Sometimes the stick did not fall straight but instead fell into one of the fingers. If the fingers were at all slippery, the stick might still have fallen slightly after initial closure was accomplished.

Summary

The day following the experiment, the class will interpret the data obtained. After your in-class discussion, answer the following questions.

I. Regarding the data
- Does the data tend to support the hypothesis? ☐ yes ☐ no
- What conclusions can be drawn from your data? For this example: There was a slight improvement in reaction time or eye-hand coordination after several trials.

II. Personal observations
- Were limitations to the problem and controls upon the experiment enough to supply reliable data? ☐ yes ☐ no Answers may vary.
- What could you have done to improve the limitations and controls? For this example: Use meter sticks with a rougher surface. Have the testers practice dropping the sticks to get them to fall straight. Disqualify scores from any subjects who closed their fingers in anticipation before the meter stick was released.
- Can you think of any additional changes that need to be made? For this example: Conduct more trials to provide better support for the hypothesis. Improve the lighting in the room. Screen out test subjects who spend extensive time using hand-held games as they may have already improved their eye-hand coordination to the point where further changes are negligible.
- Was the experiment repeated often enough to give reliable data? ☐ yes ☐ no Answers may vary.
- How often would be enough to give reliable data? Answers may vary.
- Based upon your experience, what other experiments dealing with eye-hand coordination would you like to try? Answers will vary. Some students will list experiments suggested in class; others will be very original.

Name____________________________

Date________________ Hour________

1b
The Microscope

Materials

- microscope
- hand lens
- lens paper
- tissue
- preserved slides of colored threads and desmids or diatoms
- illuminator (if not part of microscope)
- immersion oil

Goals

- To learn the basic parts of the microscope
- To learn how to operate a microscope properly
- To become familiar with the theory of magnification
- To make a scientific drawing

As you study biology, you will need various pieces of equipment to test, measure, or observe living things. The microscope is probably the most useful—as well as one of the most technical—pieces of equipment found in the average high-school laboratory. Because of the knowledge that can be obtained by using a modern microscope, today's biology student is frequently better informed in some aspects of biological knowledge than the professional biologist of one hundred years ago.

The microscope is a precision instrument that uses magnification and light refraction to produce an enlarged image. Though durable and easy to handle, the microscope requires proper care. Since repairing or replacing this piece of equipment is expensive, every biology student needs to know how its parts function and how to operate it correctly.

The Structure of a Microscope

R E O

Identify and label the parts of the microscope on Diagram 1b.1. You should be thoroughly familiar with the terms and be able to locate each part on a standard microscope in your classroom.

I. The mechanical parts

- **Body tube.** This long, narrow tube runs half the length of the microscope. The observer looks into one end, and the specimen is placed under the other end. The fixed separation allows the lenses to remain the proper distance apart during viewing. In those microscopes with an inclined body tube, mirrors are used to bend the path of the image.
- **Revolving nosepiece.** A movable disc at the bottom of the body tube allows the interchanging of different sets of lenses (objectives).
- **Coarse adjustment knobs.** There is a large knob on each side of the microscope, usually located directly behind the body tube or at the base of the arm. These knobs provide great movement of the body tube or stage and quick focusing on the specimen.
- **Fine adjustment knobs.** Usually small, these knobs are found underneath the coarse adjustment knobs or near the inclination joint. Occasionally, they are centered on the coarse adjustment knobs. By providing slight movement of the body tube or stage, the fine adjustment produces a sharper focus.
- **Arm.** The "backbone" of the microscope, the arm supports the body tube.
- **Base.** The large rectangular or horseshoe-shaped structure at the bottom of the microscope supports the microscope and keeps it steady.
- **Inclination joint.** Located at the junction between the arm and the base of the microscope, the inclination joint allows the microscope to be tilted. This may be absent on models with inclined body tubes.
- **Stage.** The stage, a platform positioned directly below the objectives and above the mirror or light source, supports the specimen.
- **Stage clips.** The fastenings on top of the stage hold the slide containing the specimen firmly in place.

Check the microscopes before the lab day. Make sure that they work. If there is a problem with a particular microscope, or if there is some unusual feature on a microscope, inform the students using that instrument ahead of time.

Note carefully the slides that the students will be using during this laboratory exercise. If they are cracked but still usable, be sure to write "cracked" on the labels. If they cannot be used, discard them. (This checking should be done before students use preserved slides.)

If your microscopes are old, check to see whether they are parfocal. If your microscopes are not parfocal, you will need to give your students special instructions regarding focusing on higher powers (see box below).

Parfocal Determination

Focus your microscope on a specimen, using low power. Looking at the microscope from the side, slowly turn the revolving nosepiece so that the next higher power objective will be in place. If the objective touches or nearly touches the coverslip either before it is clicked in place or when it is clicked in place, your microscope is not parfocal.

Introduction

Some students may have used microscopes before, but probably many have not. In any case, it is wise to stress that regardless of their previous experience with microscopes, they are expected to follow the procedures and policies set forth in this laboratory exercise and those prescribed by you.

The day before the lab day, discuss some of the points that the students may be inclined to neglect or those that they may not clearly understand. Demonstrate the proper way to carry a microscope. If your microscopes have mirrors, stress that they are never to focus the mirror of the microscope on direct sunlight. Inform them regarding the parfocal or nonparfocal status of the microscopes they will be using. Remind them to report to you anything that is broken and not marked as cracked. Discuss the problems that can result if they attempt to focus their microscopes by turning the coarse adjustment knob so that the body tube goes down. Point out some of the less obvious microscope structures, such as the diaphragm and the substage condenser. Be careful not to give the answers to any questions in the exercise, but include enough information in your lecture to help them figure out the answers.

Required / Extra / Omit

Encourage students to read carefully the complete laboratory exercise (with the possible exception of the section on oil-immersion power on p. L19). They should complete the first section of the exercise (pp. L13–L14) before they come to class.

It is recommended that you require every part of the exercise up to the section on oil-immersion power on page L19. Most students should be able to complete this amount of material within a class period.

The oil-immersion section (p. L19) should be used as extra credit if you have microscopes with this capability. Otherwise it should be omitted. Advanced classes, though, will need oil-immersion information if they are going to do advanced microscope work. Your plans for your class will determine whether you require the oil-immersion section of this exercise. For

II. The optical parts

- **Eyepiece or ocular.** Located at the top of the body tube, the eyepiece contains lenses that help increase magnification of the specimen.
- **Objectives.** Two or three metal pieces extend from the bottom of the revolving nosepiece and contain lenses that produce different magnifications.
- **Diaphragm.** Located between the stage and the light source, the diaphragm regulates the amount of light that passes through the specimen. (Two types of diaphragms are the iris diaphragm, which opens and closes like the iris of an eye, and the disc diaphragm, which is a revolving disc with holes of various sizes.)
- **Substage condenser.** Also located between the stage and the light source, this lens system affects the microscope's resolution by bending and concentrating light before it reaches the specimen. (Some microscopes do not have one.)
- **Light source.** Found on or just above the base, the light source sends light up through the stage and through the specimen. Some microscopes have a mirror instead of an electric light source.

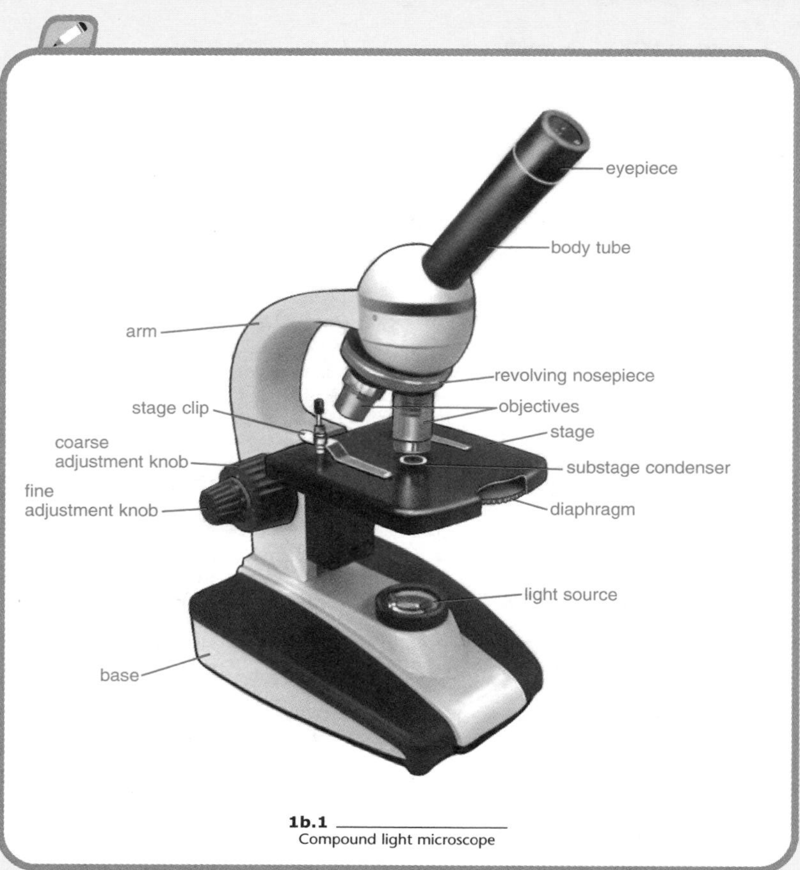

1b.1 ________________
Compound light microscope

most exercises in this manual, you will set up the microscope yourself for any oil-immersion viewing that is necessary.

The section on how a microscope works (p. L20) is recommended as a required section. It is designed to make the students think about how a microscope functions. It requires the use of hand lenses (magnifying glasses) and slides of colored thread. If your class period is short or your students are slow with laboratory work, this could be used as an extra-credit section.

How to Care for a Microscope

I. Carry the microscope properly. Excessive jars and bumps may knock the lenses out of adjustment.
- When taking a microscope out of the cabinet or cupboard, be careful not to bump the microscope against the sides.
- Carry the microscope with one hand underneath the base and the other on the arm.
- Be sure to keep the microscope close to your body in an upright position so that the ocular does not slip out of the body tube.
- Place the microscope gently on the table about three inches from the edge.

II. Prepare the microscope properly. Your microscope may need to be cleaned before you begin to use it.
- Use lens paper to clean lens surfaces and the mirror.
- Wipe the lens in one direction across the diameter of the lens.
- Dust on the lens may be ground in if you use a circular motion and may scratch the lens.
- Consult your instructor if any material remains on your objectives. You may need to use a solvent to remove the material. Never use your fingernail or another object to chip away hardened material.
- Under no circumstances should you attempt to take your microscope apart.

III. Return the microscope properly. When returning a microscope after you have used it, be sure to follow this routine:
- Adjust the inclination joint (if your microscope has one) so that the body tube is straight up and down.
- Remove the slide from the stage.
- Put the low-power objective directly under the body tube.
- Adjust the body tube to its lowest position.
- Carefully return the microscope to the place where you obtained it.
- Cover the microscope with a dust cover if one is available.

R E O

How to Obtain an Image with a Microscope

In order to observe the specimens clearly and easily, you will need to follow carefully the procedures discussed in this section. After you have done these procedures a few times, they will become second nature, and you will be able to do them quickly. Some of the procedures, such as computing the power of your microscope, will need to be done only once; others will need to be done every time you focus on a new specimen. Carefully note all the procedures. If difficulties arise, review these instructions and make sure you have not missed something. Of course, if you have any difficulty, your instructor can help you.

I. Compute the powers available on your microscope.
- Because of the microscope's magnifying powers, you are able to see organisms many times larger than their actual size. Each increase in power reveals a closer look at the specimen.
- You will find numbers that represent *powers* written on the parts of the microscope that have magnifying lenses. *Power* in this case refers to the number of times larger the magnified object will appear. Therefore, the total magnification is the product of the magnifying powers of both the ocular and the objective lenses. (Be sure to use the power of only the objective that is directly above the specimen when computing the total power of your microscope. The other objectives are not in use until they are placed over the specimen.)
- Using the powers and other information found on your microscope, fill in the chart on page L16.

Computing the Magnification of a Microscope

Place the power (number of times it magnifies) of each part of your microscope in the proper space and then compute the total magnification for each objective.

	Ocular		Objective		Total Magnification
Low-power objective	________ ×	times	________ ×	=	________ ×
High-power objective	________ ×	times	________ ×	=	________ ×
Oil-immersion objective	________ ×	times	________ ×	=	________ ×
Other	________ ×	times	________ ×	=	________ ×

(Some microscopes do not have an oil-immersion objective; if yours does not, omit that line of the chart. If your microscope has other objectives, include them on separate lines.)

- Answer the following questions:
  - Why should the substage condenser not be included in computing the magnification? The substage condenser does not affect the light after it has passed through the specimen.
  - What aspect of the microscope does the substage condenser affect? It affects resolution by bending and concentrating light.

II. Obtain the proper light in your microscope.

- You must have proper lighting for satisfactory use of your microscope.
  - Begin by opening the diaphragm so that it admits as much light as possible. Look under the stage to see if the diaphragm is open completely.
    - To adjust an iris diaphragm, move the tiny lever located under the stage forward or backward.
    - To adjust a disc diaphragm, rotate the dial until the largest hole is properly aligned.
  - If your microscope has a built-in light source, simply plug it in and turn the switch on.
  - If your microscope has a mirror, adjust it to provide adequate lighting.
    - Natural light (sunlight) is the best, but not direct sunlight, which could damage the eye, leaving a permanent afterimage.
    - Make sure no object comes between the mirror of your microscope and the light source.
    - Use the curved rather than the flat side of the mirror to obtain an even, unobscured circle of light that fills your field of vision.
    - Look through the eyepiece and adjust the mirror.
- Normally we see light that reflects from an object or light that radiates from something such as a candle flame. In a microscope, however, light is reflected from the mirror and passes through the lenses to our eyes. How are we able to see a specimen placed on the stage of the microscope when no light is reflected from the specimen? Answers may vary. We see a silhouette of the specimen and its parts, not the direct image of the specimen.

III. Position the specimen.

- Obtain a preserved slide of either diatoms or desmids.
- Place the slide on the stage, directly over the opening in the stage.
  - Make sure that the coverslip is on top, or you will have trouble focusing.

Name________________________

Microscope Slides

The specimen is usually mounted on a glass slide and covered with a coverslip.

- Be sure the slide is clean before you use it. Prepared or preserved slides (those professionally made) may be cleaned with a tissue or lens paper. Do not scratch the slide.
- Unless already noted on the label of the slide, all cracks or damage should be reported to your instructor.

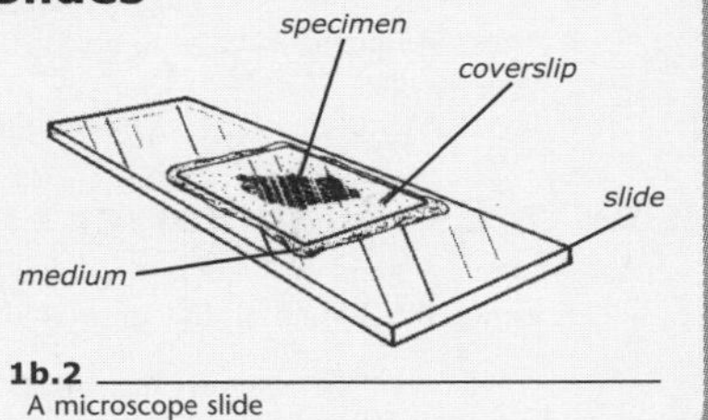

1b.2 A microscope slide

  - Place the stage clips on both ends of the slide (but not on the coverslip) to hold the slide in place.
- Position the slide so that the specimen is centered in the opening of the stage.
  - To move the slide on the stage, place your thumbs on opposite corners of the slide and push or pull the slide into position.
  - Use dry slides on the stage of a microscope. If the lower surface of the slide is wet, it tends to form a suction that makes the slide very difficult to move and may cause damage.

IV. Focus the microscope on low power.

- Focus your microscope, following these steps:
  1. Raise the body tube using the coarse adjustment knob and move the 10× objective clockwise until it fits directly below the body tube. You should hear a click when the objective reaches the correct position.
  2. Looking at your microscope from the side, turn the coarse adjustment knob to move the body tube down toward the stage. Stop when the objective is just above the slide. (Some microscopes have safety devices that will stop the body tube automatically.)
  3. Look into the ocular and carefully move the body tube up slowly until the specimen is brought into view. (NOTE: The body tube usually moves upward when the coarse adjustment knob is turned toward you. Never turn the coarse adjustment knob so that the body tube goes downward while you are looking in the eyepiece. You may damage the slide or lens.)
  4. Now use the fine adjustment knob to get sharper images. One turn in either direction is usually enough to focus properly. Do not spin the knob; you could damage the mechanism.
  5. If no image comes into view by the time you have moved the objective one inch from the coverslip, you probably
     - Tried to focus too fast and passed the point of focus. Start at number 2 above and try again.
     - Did not have a specimen in your field of view. Check to make sure there is something on the slide directly in the center of the hole in the stage. Then try again.
     - Have too much light. Use a slightly smaller opening of your diaphragm and try again.
  6. If you still cannot obtain an image, ask your instructor for help.
- Note some of the effects of using the light microscope.
  - If you move the slide to the right, how does the position of the material change in your field of view? It moves to the left.
  - Turn the fine adjustment knob slowly to move the objective up or down. Describe what happens to the image you are viewing. Answers may vary. You are focusing on different depths of the slide. It is going in and out of focus as the fine adjustment knob is moved.

Students frequently become frustrated while trying to focus their microscopes. You might use this approach as you help them: Have them tell you what to do, and you do it. (They will probably read it out of the book.) Encourage them to watch what you are doing. Sometimes they will immediately recognize what their problem is and indicate that they are ready to try again themselves. If they do, stop and let them continue. If you get as far as focusing the specimen, ask them to look at it. When they have seen it and have focused it adequately for their eyes using the fine adjustment knob, remove the slide, move the body tube up, rotate the objectives, flip the mirror, adjust the diaphragm, and tell them it is now their turn to focus the microscope. If they are reluctant, remind them that they will need to be able to focus the microscope many times during the year and that the purpose of this exercise is to teach them how. You have shown them how the microscope *can* be focused if they follow the directions properly. This type of help will encourage the independence necessary for them to do successful laboratory work.

Some microscopes have adjustment (focus) knobs that move the stage up and down rather than moving the body tube. If this is true of your instruments, let the students know so that they will not be confused by the directions.

You may want to encourage the students to observe the specimens through their microscopes with both eyes open to avoid eye strain. This is not really necessary for most high-school students during these laboratory exercises, however, because they will not use the microscope enough to cause eye strain.

Students with glasses may find it best to take their glasses off to adjust the focus. (Their lab partners will need to readjust the microscope for their own eyes.)

Students are asked to do laboratory drawings for this lab. The drawings to be done for this exercise are all specimen drawings, and spaces have been provided for them. Be strict when grading these drawings; now is the time to establish the type of drawings that you want to see in the future. If a drawing is sketchy, if it is done in ink, if it is too small, if the erasures are poor, if the magnification is not indicated, or if the title is not in the proper place, mark the problem and take off points. When you hand back the exercise, go over the problems you encountered most frequently on the drawings and tell them what you expect in the future.

Point out to the students that the drawing of the five desmids or diatoms should be an outline only.

Because the students have not yet learned cellular structures, tell them that for the drawings in this laboratory exercise, they do not need to label any structures. However, they should have titles on the drawings.

R E O

V. Prepare a specimen drawing of desmids or diatoms. Follow these instructions:
- Draw five specimens in Area A. You may obtain all the specimens from one slide. Draw either desmids or diatoms, whichever you are looking at.
- Make sure you are drawing typical specimens, not just odd globs you find on your slide.
- These specimens have been preserved and stained; they will not appear green as the ones in your text do.
- For this set of drawings, draw only the outlines of your specimens. Ignore the internal structures.

How to Use High Power on Your Microscope

R E O

I. Observe a desmid or diatom using high power (400×–450×).
- Center the desmid or diatom of your choice in your microscope field. Why is it essential to position the specimen in the center? If the specimen is not in the center of the microscope field, it will not be visible in the microscope field when the microscope is changed to a higher power.
- Focus your microscope first on low power and then go to high power, following these instructions:
  - On the nosepiece of most microscopes are several objectives. Most modern microscopes are parfocal: if a microscope is focused on a specimen using one power, all the objectives will be nearly in focus for that specimen (unless the specimen is exceptionally thick). Most parfocal microscopes can be focused on a higher power with only 1/4 turn of the fine adjustment knob.

Focusing Nonparfocal Microscopes on Higher Powers

If the microscopes are not parfocal, tell your students to follow these steps each time they go to a higher power:
1. Raise the body tube slightly.
2. Turn the revolving nosepiece until the desired objective is in place.
3. Looking at the microscope from the side, lower the body tube until the objective almost touches the slide.
4. While looking through the microscope, use the coarse adjustment knob to slowly raise the body tube until you see an image. Bring it into sharp focus, using the fine adjustment knob. Never focus by turning the coarse adjustment knob to lower the objectives.
5. If the objective is raised more than one-half inch above the coverslip, you have gone too far. Start again at Step 3.

- All you need to do to change a parfocal microscope to high power (about 400×–450×, but not oil-immersion power, which is about 1000×) is rotate the nosepiece.
- While you do so, look at the stage from the side to be sure that the objective does not touch the slide as it clicks into place.

II. In Area B prepare a specimen drawing of a section of a desmid or diatom. Include the internal structures.

R E O

How to Use the Oil-Immersion Power on Your Microscope

I. Follow these procedures carefully when using oil-immersion objectives:

- Be sure you have a very bright light source. An illuminator is usually necessary.
- Following the procedures given earlier, focus on low power and then change to high power.
- Make sure that what you wish to observe is in the center of the microscope field.
- Raise the tube from the slide using the coarse adjustment knob.
- Place one small drop of immersion oil on the slide.
  - The drop should be centered on the coverslip.
  - Do not get oil on the label of the slide.
- Turn the nosepiece so that the oil-immersion objective (96×–100×) is down.
- Adjust the tube so that the objective touches the drop of oil. Observing from the side, continue adjustment until the objective almost touches the slide.
- Observing through the microscope, adjust the tube very slowly until focus is obtained. The fine adjustment knob is best for this purpose and usually needs to be turned less than one full rotation.
- If the objective is raised so high that the oil separates from the objective, you have passed the point of focus. Repeat the two preceding steps.
- Focus problems often result from too much light. Adjust the diaphragm.
- If the object was centered when you focused using the lower powers, it will be centered under oil-immersion power. If it is not, carefully move the slide to the correct position.
- When you finish, clean the microscope and the slide carefully, following these steps:
  1. Remove excess oil from the slide and objective with a dry tissue.
  2. Clean the slide with a wet tissue, being careful not to wet the label. Dry the slide thoroughly before returning it.
  3. Clean the objective thoroughly with a wet tissue. Pat it dry with a dry tissue.
  4. Polish the objective with lens paper.

II. Using oil-immersion power, observe a desmid or diatom and draw a portion of the specimen in Area C. Include the internal structures.

How a Microscope Works

Microscopes work because light bends as it passes through substances of different densities. However, the higher the magnification is, the more difficulties are encountered with resolution and depth of focus. An understanding of these problems is necessary for good microscope use.

I. Using two lenses causes a reversed image.

- Observe what happens to light rays that are reflected from this paper when they pass through hand lenses by doing the following:
  - Hold two hand lenses, one on top of the other, about four inches from the paper.
  - Hold your head about fourteen inches from the hand lenses.
  - Focus by moving your head.
- Explain why the image is inverted. You may use diagrams if necessary. The light rays are bent as they pass through the lenses so that the image is reversed.

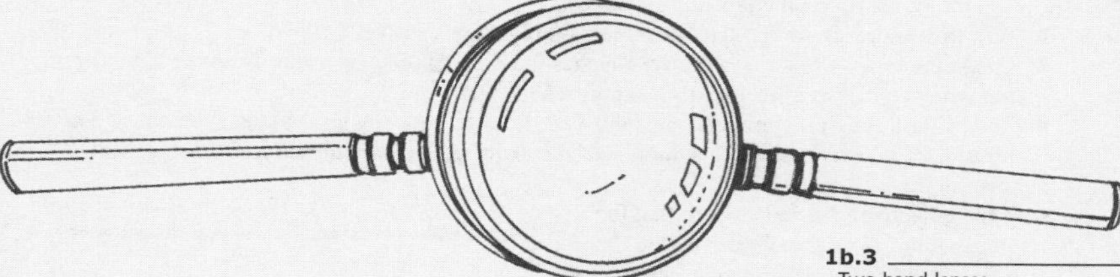

1b.3 ______
Two hand lenses

II. Increasing magnification causes problems with depth of focus.

- Using low power, focus on a slide of three intersecting threads.
  - Why is the intersection of the three threads black? No light passes through the area. The area is too thick to permit light to pass.
  - By adjusting the focus, you should be able to see all of a thread clearly.
- Observe the intersection of the three threads on high power, following these steps:
  - With the microscope on low power, move the slide so that the intersection of the three threads is in the exact center of your field of view.
  - Focus your microscope on high power. Now that you have changed powers, note the different size of the black spot in the center of the junction of the three threads.
    - Adjust the position of your slide until all three threads are visible.
    - You probably will not be able to see all three threads at once because they are stacked and you have limited depth of focus while using high power.
    - Using the fine adjustment knob, determine the sequence of threads at the intersection.

      From top to bottom, they are Answers vary depending on the slide.
  - Although higher powers of the light microscope allow you to see more detail, they present other difficulties. What are they? You cannot see the entire specimen if it is thick. Instead, you must focus on different depths of the specimen and thus see it only in layers.

Name________________________

Date____________ Hour________

2 Osmosis and Digestion

Materials

- osmometer (a semipermeable membrane, a thistle-shaped osmometer bulb, a tube, and a beaker)
- wax marking pencil
- distilled water
- sucrose solutions
- sucrose solutions with invertase
- plastic squeeze bottles
- dropping pipets
- reagent test strips for glucose in urine
- metric ruler

Goals

- To observe a demonstration of osmosis
- To observe various factors affecting the rate of osmosis
- To learn about the action of an enzyme

An osmometer is a device used to measure the rate of osmosis. A semipermeable membrane is stretched across the large open end of a bulb and filled with a solution. When the bulb is suspended in another solution, the osmosis that occurs can be measured by observing the rise or fall of the solution in the tube above the bulb. (See Diagram 2.1.) In this exercise several osmometers, containing different solutions, will be set up. The rates of osmosis for these solutions will be compared. The data will be collected, and you will then form a conclusion about osmosis and digestion.

A Demonstration of Osmosis

I. Set up the osmometer properly.

- Assemble the bulb and tube.
  - The osmometer bulbs will be soaking in water before you come to class so that the membranes will be ready to use.
  - Shake the osmometer bulb to remove all water.
  - Using a plastic squeeze bottle with a narrow spout, completely fill the osmometer bulb with the proper solution. Set the bulb on a wet paper towel.
  - Remove the cap from a plastic squeeze bottle of the same solution you used to fill the osmometer bulb. Insert the tube into the bottle until it is two inches into the solution. Put your finger over the open end of the tube to keep the solution in the tube as you transfer it to the osmometer bulb.
  - Place the tube into the neck of the osmometer bulb, releasing your finger just as the tube is inserted into the bulb. An inch or more of the solution should remain in the tube.
  - Tap the bottom of the membrane to remove any air trapped in the bulb. There should be no air spaces in the solution in either the bulb or the tube. If there are gaps that cannot be removed by tapping, take the tube out and start again.

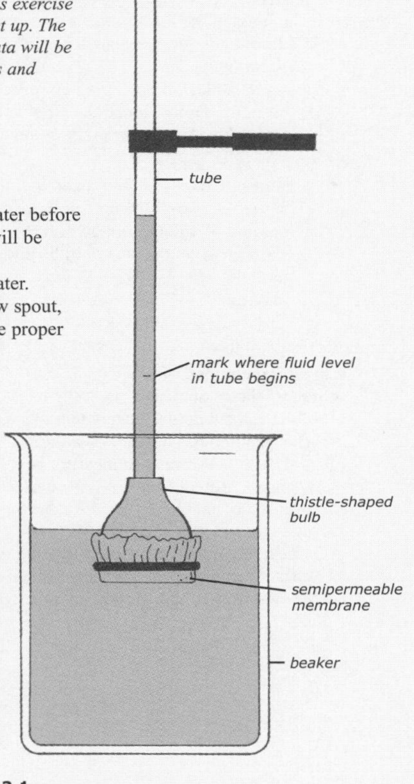

2.1 Osmometer

See page 23 for Notes on Materials.

This experiment should take the entire class hour, if possible. If you need to save time, demonstrate for the students how to set up an osmometer the day before the lab day. You may also want the students to practice setting up the osmometers using plain water so that on the lab day they can proceed without additional instructions. This is important if you choose to have the students set up the osmometers rather than doing this as a pre-set demonstration.

This exercise is designed to be set up in about the first five minutes of class and then to be observed every ten minutes throughout the hour. Observations should take about one minute each. Draw the data charts on the chalkboard or on an overhead transparency and fill them in as the observations are made. Once the experiment has been set up, you can continue your lecture as usual. Set a timer for ten minutes or instruct a student with a watch to interrupt the lecture every ten minutes in order to ensure that the observations are made on time.

Students may have difficulty filling the thistle-shaped bulbs with solution. Repeatedly pumping the squeeze bottle works best. This can be messy, so have paper towels ready or do it over a sink.

Label the squeeze bottles containing solutions with a wax pencil and then cover the labels with tape so that they do not smear.

Be sure that the tube is vertical, not tilted, once the osmometer is set up.

Once the osmometer is assembled, do not move it until it is to be disassembled.

Introduction

This exercise demonstrates the processes of osmosis and digestion. The exercise is not difficult, and the data is easily recorded on the charts. Students may have difficulty answering some of the questions, however. If they think carefully, analyze the data, and read the suggested pages, they should be able to come up with satisfactory answers.

When explaining osmosis, use any type of example except the osmometer discussed in this exercise. When explaining digestion, use any enzyme and substrate example except invertase and sucrose. The goal is to get the students to transfer the general knowledge they gained from the text and class lectures to the specific case set forth in this exercise.

Combining two different concepts (osmosis and digestion) in one experiment occasionally confuses some students. This combination thoroughly tests their understanding of the concepts being presented. Once they have arrived at proper answers to the questions, they usually understand and retain the concepts. Avoid "spoon-feeding" this exercise to the students; allow them to think through the problem and answer the questions on their own.

Because invertase is sometimes difficult to obtain and must be purchased in much larger quantities than are needed for one year's labs, you may choose to omit the digestion portion. If you decide to omit this part but would still like to demonstrate the chemical process of digestion, there are a number of simple demonstrations using milk with lemon juice (acid) or meat tenderizer (enzyme) added that will show the chemical process in at least a qualitative way.

It is recommended that this lab be done as a demonstration. You can have three of the four osmometer bulbs filled and ready to be put in the water before class. Demonstrate the filling of one osmometer bulb and then have four students put their bulbs into the beakers of water at the same time. Have each of these students perform the needed observations on one beaker and report to

Remind the students to measure from the starting mark on the tube to the water level in the tube and not from the bulb to the water level.

- Using a paper towel, dry the joint between the bulb and the tube. If the joint leaks, ask your instructor for help.
- Rinse the outside of the bulb with clean water.
- Fill the beaker of the osmometer with water to a depth of about two inches.
- Suspend the osmometer bulb in the water so that the membrane is covered but the water does not come near the joint of the bulb and tube. (Several methods of suspension can be used. Your instructor will demonstrate the method you should use.)
- Mark with a wax pencil the level of the solution in the tube.

II. Test for the presence of sugar.

- Some substances change color in the presence of certain chemicals. Often these substances are used to test for the presence of the chemicals.
- A reagent test strip is usually a piece of absorbent material containing a substance that changes color when a solution containing the proper chemical is placed on it.
- For this laboratory exercise, use the reagent test strip that tests for sugar in urine. The strip changes color in the presence of sugar.
- Each group must establish a set of controls for its reagent test strip.
    - Using a clean dropping pipet, place a single drop of distilled water on a reagent test strip. Do not touch the pipet to the test strip. Note the color of the strip after ten seconds. This procedure should demonstrate a negative reaction (no change in color) since there should be no sugar in the water.
    - Using a clean dropping pipet, place a single drop of sugar solution (Solution A) on a reagent test strip. Do not touch the pipet to the test strip. Note the color of the strip after ten seconds. Since there was sugar in the solution, you should see a positive reaction (change in color).

III. Set up the experiment.

- Solutions of sucrose (table sugar, a disaccharide) will be placed in the bulbs.
    - There are two different concentrations of sucrose: Solution A contains twice as much sucrose per unit of volume as Solution B.
    - Each group in the class will be given one of the following solutions to place in its osmometer bulb.
        1. Group 1—Solution A
        2. Group 2—Solution B
- The bottom container (beaker) will hold distilled water.

IV. Run the experiment.

- Set up the osmometers, mark the level of the fluid in the tubes, and test the fluid in the beakers of the osmometers to ensure that the water is sugar-free.
- After ten minutes do the following:
    - Use a metric ruler to measure how far the fluid has risen in the tubes.
    - Test a drop of fluid from the beakers for the presence of sugar.
    - Record your results on the chart on page L23. Check *P* if the sugar test was positive, *N* if the sugar test was negative.
- Repeat the above procedure every ten minutes until the class hour ends.
- Toward the end of the class hour, the data from the groups will be exchanged. You will need all the data from all the groups in order to answer the following questions.

the class (while you record the data on the chalkboard or the overhead).

This lab can easily be done as a dummy demonstration. Set up all the equipment, but use only water—no sugar or invertase. After you have done the setup, give the students data for their chart on page L23. Of course, you will need to fabricate measurements that support the results that would be obtained using the prescribed solutions. Briefly discuss the data as you present it, but do not answer the questions on pages L23–L24. Have the students answer the questions.

Required / Extra / Omit

You can shorten the exercise by eliminating the digestion section—that is, use only Solution A and Solution B without the invertase.

Name________________________________

	Start	10 min	20 min	30 min	40 min	50 min
Solution A	0 mm ☐P ☐N Sugar	______ mm ☐P ☐N Sugar	______ mm ☐P ☐N Sugar	______ mm ☐P ☐N Sugar	______ mm ☐P ☐N Sugar	______ mm ☐P ☐N Sugar
Solution B	0 mm ☐P ☐N Sugar	______ mm ☐P ☐N Sugar	______ mm ☐P ☐N Sugar	______ mm ☐P ☐N Sugar	______ mm ☐P ☐N Sugar	______ mm ☐P ☐N Sugar

Questions to Answer After the Experiment

Carefully read the discussions in your text on the following topics: diffusion and osmosis, pages 49–51; catalysts and enzymes, pages 46, 56–57; and sugars, pages 58–59.

I. From the results of the experiment, what can you conclude about the permeability of the membrane to sucrose? The membrane is not readily permeable to sucrose.

II. Was there a difference between the increase of Solution A and the increase of Solution B in the tubes? ☐ yes ☐ no If so, what would account for the difference? Answers may vary. Since Solution A has twice the concentration of Solution B, there is more osmotic pressure, and the level of Solution A should rise faster than that of Solution B.

III. If you let the experiment run long enough, could all of the water from the beaker enter the osmometer? Why or why not? No, because equilibrium would occur when gravity and other forces equal the diffusion pressure. There would still be some movement of molecules through the membrane, but no net change.

IV. If you were to slowly heat the water in either beaker, what might happen to the rate of osmosis and why? It would probably accelerate because of the increased activity of the molecules, and equilibrium would be reached more quickly.

V. If you were to set up the osmometers using salt instead of sucrose, would you expect similar results? Why or why not? Answers may vary. Because salt dissolves into ions that are much smaller than the sucrose molecules, they are able to pass through the membrane. This means that there will not be osmotic pressure to raise the solution in the tube.

A Demonstration of Digestion

I. Set up the osmometers as in the initial experiment above.
- Substitute Solution A with invertase and Solution B with invertase.
- Invertase (an enzyme also called sucrase) will be added to some of the sucrose solutions before they are placed in the bulbs. The sucrose solutions that contain invertase have equal concentrations of this enzyme.

II. Run the experiment as you did in the first experiment, still using the reagent strips to check for sugar in the beaker at each ten-minute interval when you measure the solution level in the tube.

The solutions used for this exercise are approximately 1 molal (Solution A with or without invertase) and 0.5 molal (Solution B with or without invertase) solutions of sucrose. They can easily be made following the formulas in the box below.

Formulas for Solutions

Solution A
25.0 g sucrose (table sugar) ◊
75.0 ml distilled water

Solution A with invertase
25.0 g sucrose (table sugar) ◊
75.0 ml distilled water
0.05 g invertase †

Solution B
15.0 g sucrose (table sugar) ‡
85.0 mL distilled water

Solution B with invertase
15.0 g sucrose (table sugar) ‡
85.0 ml distilled water
0.05 g invertase †

◊ 25 g of sugar is about 2 tablespoons (level).
† 0.05 g of invertase is a little less than 1/16 teaspoon.
‡ 15 g of sugar is about 1 tablespoon, 1 teaspoon, and 1/8 teaspoon (all level).

It is not as significant that you have exactly 0.05 grams as that you have equal amounts of invertase in Solution A with invertase and Solution B with invertase. However, you should not put much more than about 0.05 grams of invertase in the specified solutions.

The sugar solutions may be mixed in advance and left in covered containers. **Do not add the invertase until a few moments before the class begins.** After adding the invertase, cover the container and shake until the invertase has dissolved.

Invertase may be a bit difficult to purchase. It is a perishable chemical, and many of the standard suppliers used by high schools do not stock this enzyme. Sargent-Welch (www.sargentwelch.com) does stock invertase and sells it in fairly small quantities. Although there are higher quality grades of invertase available, grade V, practical invertase obtained from baker's yeast, is suitable for this exercise. If refrigerated, invertase lasts for months. If you are going to use an old supply, try the experiment in advance. If you find that your invertase is no longer active, you can order more.

Semipermeable membranes suitable for this exercise can be purchased from scientific suppliers. The membranes available from Carolina Biological Supply (catalog number 68-4030; www.carolina.com) are recommended. These semipermeable membranes or similar ones are of a quality difficult to duplicate. If properly cared for, they can be stored and reused repeatedly. Chicken skin,

Notes on Materials is continued on the next page.

if carefully cleaned, can be used also. However, small holes in the membrane (usually caused by the papillae of feathers) can ruin the test results.

You will need four osmometers per class for this exercise if you do both osmosis and digestion.

Osmometer assemblies vary widely. The instructions in this book are for a type of osmometer that has the membrane already attached to the thistle-shaped bulb and that has a detachable tube. You can purchase these osmometers from Carolina Biological Supply (catalog number 68-4025). These are inexpensive, come with a semipermeable membrane, and are ideal for this exercise. If you are going to use another design of osmometer, you may need to modify the directions given in the student book.

If the joint between the thistle-shaped bulb and the tube leaks, a few layers of tape wrapped around the tube before it is inserted into the neck of the bulb will usually stop the leak.

The beaker (jar) used to contain the water outside the osmometer bulb should be relatively small (250 mL or 8 oz) and should contain only about 3 to 4 oz of water. If it contains too much water, the sugar solution that passes through the membrane will become too diluted to register when tested.

The reagent test strips needed for this exercise are those used to test for sugar in urine. Clinistix by Bayer Diagnostic or a similar product is available at most drugstores and serves well for this experiment. You should check early with your pharmacist. If he does not have this product in stock, he can easily obtain it or recommend another product.

	Start	10 min	20 min	30 min	40 min	50 min
Solution A with Invertase	0 mm ☐ P ☐ N Sugar	_____ mm ☐ P ☐ N Sugar	_____ mm ☐ P ☐ N Sugar	_____ mm ☐ P ☐ N Sugar	_____ mm ☐ P ☐ N Sugar	_____ mm ☐ P ☐ N Sugar
Solution B with Invertase	0 mm ☐ P ☐ N Sugar	_____ mm ☐ P ☐ N Sugar	_____ mm ☐ P ☐ N Sugar	_____ mm ☐ P ☐ N Sugar	_____ mm ☐ P ☐ N Sugar	_____ mm ☐ P ☐ N Sugar

Questions to Answer After the Experiment

I. How does invertase affect sucrose? (Base your answer on the results of the experiment and on information in the laboratory exercise and text. You have enough information to figure out the answer.) It breaks down sucrose to monosaccharides (glucose and fructose).

Explain how you reached that conclusion. Disaccharide sucrose did not go through the membrane in the first experiment, but sucrose with invertase does permit sugar to pass through the membrane. It can be assumed that sucrose is broken down to monosaccharides by invertase.

II. Was there a difference between the sugar content in the beaker of Solution A and in the beaker of Solution A with invertase? ☒ yes ☐ no If so, what would account for the difference? Invertase broke down sucrose to monosaccharides, which passed through the membrane. Thus the beaker below Solution A did not have sugar in it, while the beaker below Solution A with invertase did.

III. Was there a difference between the increase in the tubes of Solution A and Solution A with invertase? ☒ yes ☐ no If so, what would account for the difference? Solution A with invertase was constantly breaking down the sucrose, which resulted in twice as many molecules in the solution. This would cause more concentration of molecules and therefore a greater rate of osmosis than in Solution A. In time, as the simple sugars pass through the membrane, the rate should decrease because the number of dissolved particles decreases.

IV. What comparisons can you make between the results obtained from Solution A with invertase and those obtained from Solution B with invertase? Both solutions should yield the same basic results, but Solution B with invertase should have reacted more slowly.

Can you account for these differences? Since the sugar concentration of Solution B is only half the sugar concentration of Solution A, Solution B should react more slowly, even though it has the same concentration of enzyme.

Name_______________ Date_______________ Hour_______________

3a
Basic Cytology

Materials

- cotton swabs
- cork
- coverslips
- dissection kit
- glass slides
- methylene blue
- microscope
- large hexagonal metal nut
- onion
- single-edged razor blade

Goals

- To learn the basic technique of preparing a wet mount
- To observe cell walls
- To observe whole cells
- To observe the effect of stains on specimens for the microscope

In your biological studies, you will need to know how to prepare a wet mount, a temporary microscope slide on which the specimen is mounted in water or some other fluid. After you have read about how to prepare a wet mount, you will practice the technique by doing what Hooke did to observe for the first time what he called cells.

Cells are the basic structural and functional units of all living organisms. Whether an organism is microscopic and single celled (like an amoeba or a bacterium) or multicellular (like your body), a study of an organism's cells is important.

Cells from both plants and animals can be easily studied in the laboratory. The onion will represent plants for this laboratory exercise. Though it may appear dead, the onion is a living bulb that produces roots and leaves when planted. The cells in the lining of your own mouth will represent living "animal" cells.

How to Prepare a Wet Mount

I. Prepare the slides and coverslips.
- Hold glass slides and coverslips by their edges so that you do not leave fingerprints on them.
- Thoroughly rinse a glass slide and a coverslip by following these instructions:
  - Be careful not to bend plastic coverslips. If you are using a glass coverslip, handle it gently; splinters from shattered glass coverslips easily enter the fingers and may require surgical removal.
  - Inspect plastic coverslips for excessive scratches. If there are too many scratches, discard the coverslip.
  - Use only water when washing the slides and coverslips. Soap film may kill or damage living specimens. If you cannot clean your slide completely by rinsing it in water, take it to your instructor and obtain another slide.
- Thoroughly dry the slide.
  - Shake excess water into the sink.
  - Blot the slide and coverslip with a paper towel.
  - Finish drying with a soft tissue.
- Set the glass slide and the coverslip on the edge of a book or table so that you can pick them up by the edges without getting fingerprints on them.

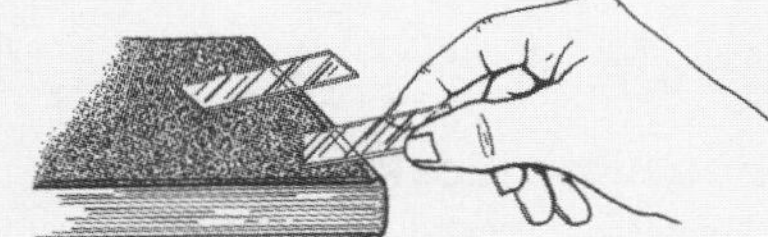

3a.1 Handling glass slides

II. Mount the specimen.
- Place the specimen on the slide by following one of these techniques.
  - *If the specimen is small (unicellular or colonial) and already in a fluid medium,* use a dropping pipet to place a single drop of the specimen-containing medium on the center of the slide.

Having a place for students to return wet slides and coverslips is essential. If the students are expected to dry the slides completely before returning them, they will lose much lab time, and you will have scratched plastic coverslips. Even completely dry slides, if stacked, frequently become inseparable. Place a towel in the bottom of a tray and then put a small piece of wood (a 1" × 2" board several inches long is good) on the towel. Slides that have had the excess water shaken off into the sink should be placed in the tray with one end resting on the wood and the other end on the towel. Wet coverslips should be placed on a paper towel. The tray of slides and the coverslips placed on the paper towel can then be put away until the next time they are needed.

Scratches on coverslips, if relatively few, do not significantly affect the focus of the microscope. Stains, if not completely rinsed off, often get into minor scratches and discolor the plastic.

Soap film on a slide can be removed by rinsing the slide in alcohol.

Encourage the students to use the stain at their desks but to return the stain immediately to the counter so that the next group needing the stain does not have to search the room to find it.

Stains other than methylene blue can be used, but try them before you have the students use them.

Methylene blue is a common stain, often used in treating sick tropical fish. Sometimes a small amount of it can be obtained from the better pet shops.

Introduction

This exercise begins with the presentation of techniques for preparing wet mounts to be used in observing cellular structures. The instructions are relatively straightforward and give your students an opportunity to show that they can follow directions. Do not go over these techniques in class. Let the students proceed on their own. If they have difficulty, help them. The observation of living cells is relatively easy if students have mastered the use of the microscope and the procedures for making a wet mount.

Methylene blue is a permanent stain that will not come out of clothing. Suggest that students wear protective garments in class. The best way to prevent spills is to place the stains in small dropping bottles. Although methylene blue will stain the hands, normal washings over a few days will remove the stain.

Required / Extra / Omit

The primary reason for having students observe cork cells is to help them gain experience in making wet mounts, using microscope techniques, and doing drawings. The repeating of Hooke's experiment for its historical significance may not be worth the class time and the effort students would need for it. If your students are skilled in microscope work and have all the drawing skills you deem necessary, you may wish to omit the section dealing with the observation and drawing of cork cells and to have them do their first wet mount on onion epidermis.

It is recommended that you have your students observe onion epidermal cells. Even if you decide not to have them stain and observe stained onion epidermal cells, the viewing of the cells can be a profitable activity. Normally students can easily find onion epidermal cells.

Observing the human cheek epithelial cells cannot be successfully done without staining. Students sometimes have problems determining what is debris and what are cells,

Tell the students that not all the bubbles on a wet mount need to be eliminated.

- *If the specimen is large (a tissue or a clump of organisms)*, follow these steps:
  1. Using a dropping pipet, place a small drop of water (or culture medium) on the slide.
  2. Using forceps, place the specimen in the drop of water. In some cases, your teacher may provide a special concavity slide that has a shallow "well" to hold larger specimens.
  3. If necessary, prepare (smear or tease) the specimen.
  4. If the specimen remains dry on top, place another drop of water (or culture medium) on top of the specimen.

3a.2 Preparing a wet mount

- Place the coverslip on top of the specimen by following these instructions:
  - Place the coverslip so that one edge is touching the slide and the coverslip is at a 45° angle above the drop of water.
  - Slowly lay the coverslip down on top of the water and specimen.
  - If bubbles appear in the area you are going to view, tap the coverslip with the tip of a probe in order to remove the bubbles.
  - If there are too many bubbles, take the wet mount apart and start again.
  - If you have used too much water, you may need to blot dry the bottom of the slide before placing it on the microscope stage. You may also need to remove excess water from around the coverslip by lightly touching a paper towel to the water. Absorption will remove the water.

III. Clean up and put away the wet mount.

- When you finish observing the slide, remove the coverslip and specimen. (If a stain was used, it is wise to use forceps.)
  - If the specimen is microscopic in size, rinse it down the drain.
  - If the specimen is large (a tissue or clump of organisms), wrap it in a paper towel and put the paper towel in the trash can.
- Rinse the slide and coverslip in running water.
- Shake the excess water into the sink.
- Place the slides and coverslips in the places provided.
  - You do not need to dry the slide and coverslip completely.
  - Do not stack the slides or coverslips. When dry, they will be impossible to separate.

Observing Cork Cells

R E O

Over three hundred years ago Robert Hooke discovered that certain plant tissues are made up of what he called "cells." To get a proper perspective of cytology, you will repeat his experiment. To see cork cells well, you must use a very thin slice of cork only one to two cells thick. If suitable slices of cork are provided for you, begin at Section II below. If you must cut your own, begin at Section I.

I. Cut a sliver of cork by following these instructions:

- Insert the small cork stopper (piece of cork) into a hexagonal metal nut.
  - Twist it carefully so that the flat surface of the cork does not become crooked inside the nut.
  - As the cork reaches the other side, continue to turn it until it barely protrudes beyond the nut.

and the activity may require extra time merely to be sure they are observing the right thing. Nevertheless, it is an interesting activity, and some teachers may want students to do it rather than the onion epidermis activity.

If you have your students do only the onion or cheek cells, you will not be able to have them answer the questions in the final section comparing the onion and cheek cells.

Scheduling Laboratory Exercises

Laboratory Exercises 3a and 3b can be considered a set and can be tailored to fit in a single class period. Consider having students do the following:

- Read about how to prepare a wet mount (3a).
- Observe, answer questions about, and draw the onion epidermal cells (3a).
- Observe, answer questions about, and draw the Anacharis cells (3b).
- Answer the questions about leucoplasts (3b).

For extra credit, students could do the following:

- Observe, answer questions about, and draw cork cells (3a).
- Observe, answer questions about, and draw cheek epithelial cells (3a).
- Observe, answer questions about, and draw banana cells (3b).

- Run a single-edged razor blade along the surface of the nut, carefully cutting into the cork. You do not need to get an entire cross section of the cork, but the section you use must be very thin.

3a.3 Slicing cork

II. Prepare a wet mount of cork by following these instructions:
- Pick up your cork slice carefully (it may crumble) and position it on top of the water of your wet mount.
- Add another drop of water on top of the cork slice before putting on the coverslip.
- If your coverslip "teeter-totters" on the cork, your slice of cork is too thick. Start again.

III. Observe the wet mount of cork on low power.
- Your slice is probably thinnest along one of the edges, so you might want to start exploring there first.
- When you observe wet mounts, remember that the microscope stage must remain parallel to the floor. Why is this necessary? The fluid medium will drain off the slide if the slide is not level.
- Can you see any internal cellular structures in the cork cells? ☐ yes ☒ no

  Explain. Only the cell walls remain.
- You are, of course, observing dead cork. What cellular structure are you observing? cell walls

Observing Onion Epidermal Cells

R E O

I. Observe onion epidermal cells.
- Obtain the scale of a small onion.
  - A scale is one of the layers of the onion.
  - The thin, transparent skin on the inside surface of the scale is the epidermis of the onion.
- Remove a layer of onion epidermis by following these instructions:
  - Break the scale. At the edges of the broken scale, you should be able to see a portion of the epidermis.
  - Use your forceps to remove the thin sheet of cells.
  - Do not crush or wrinkle the epidermis. Otherwise, cells become damaged and air bubbles get trapped between the layers, making it hard to observe.

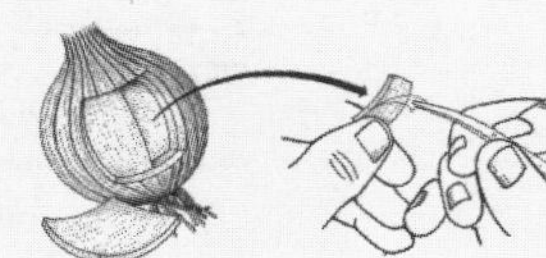

3a.4 Removing the onion epidermis

- Prepare a wet mount, using a small piece of onion epidermis no larger than the drop of water on your slide.
  - Place the onion epidermis so that it lies flat. If it begins to fold or curl, use probes to straighten it.
  - Put the second drop of water on it and then put the coverslip on. You may need your lab partner's help.
- Observe the onion epidermis cells under low power.
  - What is the general shape of one onion epidermal cell? Answers may vary. Rectangular

    Of a group? Answers may vary. A brick wall
  - What do the cork and onion cells have in common? Answers may vary. Characteristics include shape of cells, cell walls, and regularity of cell shapes.

3a.5 Straightening the onion epidermis

  - Mark the terms that apply to onion epidermis.

    ☐ unicellular ☒ multicellular ☒ tissue ☐ organ ☐ system

Have each student rest the nut with the cork in it on a table or counter and slice the cork by moving the razor blade away from his body. A sharp new blade is necessary to get good slices. (It would be wise to have first-aid equipment available.)

It may be necessary to use concavity slides for viewing cork.

Students often have difficulty obtaining the onion epidermis and instead try to observe an entire onion scale. A word of instruction before they begin is helpful. If the coverslip "teeter-totters" on the specimen, something is wrong.

To reduce the odor in the room, cut an onion into medium-sized sections. Put these into a dish of water and cover it with glass, aluminum foil, or plastic. Cutting the onion in advance will save the students time. Stress that they need only a small piece, not enough for a hamburger.

Staining the onion epidermal cellular structures is often a challenge. Common problems include too much water (thus diluting the stain) or tough onion cells. The stain must work its way through pores in the cell wall and then through the plasma membrane. If the nuclear materials do not darken within ten minutes, the student should start over with a fresh specimen. It is necessary to have water both beneath and above the epidermal cells for clear focusing.

R E O

II. Stain your onion epidermal cells and observe them again.

- Stain the cells by following these steps:
  - Carefully remove the slide from the stage and place it next to the microscope.
  - Place one drop of methylene blue on the slide at the very edge of the coverslip, in contact with the water under the coverslip. At the opposite side, touch a paper towel to the water under the edge of the coverslip, allowing the paper to absorb the water. The stain will be drawn under the coverslip. (If the stain runs over the outside edges of the coverslip, you probably used too much water when you made your wet mount. Use paper towels to absorb the excess water and try again.)
  - When the stain has contacted the onion epidermis, blot away any excess fluids on the slide or coverslip.
  - Allow the stain to remain on the slide three to five minutes before observing the specimen. This permits the stain to enter the cells. If you don't see changes after five minutes, you may need to add another drop of stain or wait a little longer.

3a.6 ____________
Staining cells in a wet mount

- Observe the stained onion epidermis on low and on high power.
  - What can you see that differs from your observation of an unstained onion epidermis? structures inside the now colored cell walls
  - Look among the cells until you find a dark, circular structure inside one of them. What is it? nucleus
  - Frequently, darker spots can be seen within this dark structure. What are they? nucleoli

R E O

- In Area A, make a drawing of one onion cell with a few adjoining cells to show how the cells fit together. Follow these instructions:
  - Draw the internal structures for the main cell only.
  - Label only the structures you see in your specimen.
  - Use the power you feel is best, but be sure to indicate which power you used to prepare your drawing.

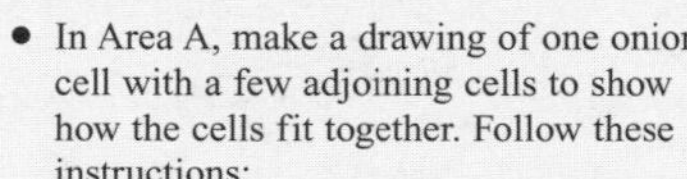

A

Observing Human Cheek Epithelial Cells

R E O

I. Prepare a wet mount of your cheek cells (or those of your lab partner) by following these instructions:

- Collect some mucous epithelial cells by rubbing the blunt end of a toothpick back and forth inside your cheek.
  - You should collect cells from only your own mouth.
  - To get the greatest concentration of cells, do not twirl the toothpick around, but use only one side.
- Remove the toothpick carefully, collecting as little saliva as possible.
- Put one drop of methylene blue stain on the center of the microscope slide.
- Immediately tap the edge of the toothpick several times in the stain.
- After this is done, carefully add the coverslip. Why do you need to be careful when you place the coverslip on top? Answers may vary. So that you will not get stain on your fingers or so that your cells will not get flushed off the slide.

II. View the cheek cells under low power.

- Look for isolated cells, not clumps.
- How can you tell the epithelial cells from the other debris that appears on the slide? The cells have a distinct shape, and only the cells will have nuclei inside.
- These cells are called *mucous epithelial cells*. What does the word *mucous* tell us about the functions of these cells? (For help, use the index of your textbook.) Answers may vary. They are part of the tissue that manufactures mucus. They help to lubricate and protect the mouth.

R E O

III. Draw a single cheek epithelial cell in Area B.

- After you have found the cell you wish to draw, center it and then adjust your microscope to high power.
- Draw one epithelial cell and label all the parts you see.

In obtaining cheek epidermal cells, the blunt end of a flat wooden toothpick works well. If not carefully coached, however, some overzealous students will bring blood as well as cheek cells. Cotton swabs may be a safer method, but they sometimes fail to provide enough cells.

If students follow the instructions properly, they should be able to obtain cheek cells. If they have eaten or brushed their teeth very recently, however, the cells may be scarce.

Comparing Onion Epidermal and Cheek Epithelial Cells

R E O

I. What are some of the similarities between the onion epidermal cells and the cheek epithelial cells? Answers may vary. Both may form tissues. They both cover (epidermal/epithelial) tissues. They both have nuclei.

II. What are some of their differences? Answers may vary. Onion cells are larger and have cell walls. Cheek cells are not as regular in shape.

III. If you stained both types of cells, which stained more quickly and why? The cheek cells stain more readily as they have no cell walls to slow the movement of the stain.

Name______________________________

Date________________ Hour__________

3b
Cellular Organelles and Processes

Materials

- Anacharis (or *Elodea*) leaves
- banana
- methylene blue
- dissection kit
- cotton swabs
- salt solution
- microscope (with illuminator)
- glass slides
- coverslips
- concavity slides
- iodine

Goals

- To study some specific cellular organelles
- To observe cellular reaction to a salt solution

Anacharis is a common freshwater plant noted for its photosynthetic abilities. The edges of this plant's young leaves are thin enough to make possible microscopic viewing of living plant cells. You can see some colored organelles by observing these living plant cells. Also, you can observe some cellular processes and reactions. Other plant organelles not visible in Anacharis can be seen in stained banana cells.

Observing Anacharis (*Elodea*) Cells

R E O

I. Prepare a wet mount of an Anacharis leaf by following these instructions:
   - Use only young light-green leaves from the ends of the stem.
   - Use a concavity slide (a slide with a concave depression in it). This type of slide will permit the thick leaf to be mounted and will allow the coverslip to lie flat. Use enough water to fill the concave portion of the slide.
   - Be careful not to crush the leaf as you pick it up or mount it. (Often scissors and forceps help.)

II. Observe Anacharis cells, using both the high power and the low power of the microscope.
   - Be sure you are focused on cells on the margin (edge) of the leaf.
   - The green chloroplasts make the clear, unstained nucleus difficult to see.
   - By focusing at different depths in one cell, locate the large, clear area in the center of the cell (not the nucleus). What is this area called? central vacuole
   - Observe the cytoplasmic streaming (carrying with it the chloroplasts) in the Anacharis cells.
   - If your specimen is not demonstrating any streaming, place the slide under an illuminator or bright desk lamp for two to five minutes. (Sometimes even this procedure does not help.)
   - If your specimen does exhibit cytoplasmic streaming, tell the instructor so that others can observe yours.
   - Why would cytoplasmic streaming be valuable for cells that have many chloroplasts? Answers may vary. Streaming exposes different chloroplasts to the most direct sunlight.

R E O

III. In Area A make a drawing of two or three adjacent Anacharis cells. Use the power you think best for drawing them and state which power you used.

R E O

IV. Place the Anacharis leaf in a concentrated salt solution.
   - Because the cells may react quickly, do not remove the slide from the stage. One lab partner should observe the specimen while the other performs the following operations:
     - Using the same procedure used to stain onion epidermal cells in Lab 3a, draw a concentrated salt solution under the coverslip.
     - You may need to use two or three drops. The change may take up to two minutes.
   - Describe the change in the appearance of the cells. The cytoplasm collapses to the center of the cell, moving the chloroplasts with it.

Concavity slides (hanging-drop slides) are good for thick specimens, such as the Anacharis leaf. Remind students that they must use the side with the concave portion. Using the flat side defeats the purpose of the slide.

Iodine is a permanent stain that will not come out of clothing. See the teacher's notes for Exercise 3a regarding stains. The iodine needed for this experiment is the same used for treating minor wounds and can be purchased in drugstores. Mercurochrome and other substances used to disinfect wounds, however, will not work.

The salt solution should be saturated. Put in more salt than can be dissolved in the water. The solution should be placed in a small bottle with a dropping pipet since the undissolved salt grains will clog a dropping bottle.

Remind the students that they are to use leaves from the tip of the Anacharis and that they should look at only the cells on the edge (margin) of the leaf.

Introduction

The observation of Anacharis and banana cells is relatively easy. Students can usually observe Anacharis cells go through plasmolysis. However, the cells do not always cooperate by going through cytoplasmic streaming. Conditions in the culture dish (or pond or wherever your supply came from) must be like those on a warm spring day in order for the cells to cooperate. Water temperature should be 65–68 °F, and the water needs to have small amounts of minerals in it (a spoonful of a rich soil in the culture or a weak soluble fertilizer can be used, but water from a pond or aged aquarium is best). Often, in an attempt to get enough light, students move lamps too close, causing the water temperature to rise too high and cytoplasmic streaming to stop.

The Anacharis can be ordered from science suppliers, but is probably better if purchased locally from a pet store dealing in live plants. Pick a bunch that has the richest green color and the least amount of brown edges. If you order from a supplier, you should purchase the tips rather than the plants sold for rooting in an aquarium. The plant sold for aquariums and by most science suppliers is usually *Egeria densa,* the Brazilian elodea. One of the most available of all aquarium plants, it has become naturalized in most of the United States, often with devastating consequences for native plants. In several states where the Brazilian elodea is an aquatic nuisance, only our native plant, *Elodea canadensis,* is available. Either will work for these procedures. Please do not place any leftover plants of this or any other type out in nature unless you took them from there initially.

Required / Extra / Omit

See the teacher's notes for Laboratory Exercise 3a for information that may be useful in deciding what sections of this exercise you wish to have your students do.

It is recommended that you have your students observe the Anacharis cells and put the cells in a salt solution, causing plasmolysis. Warn them that observing cytoplasmic

Most students have problems with too much banana on their slide. The coverslip should not teeter-totter on the banana. You should not see yellow banana on the slide, only a smear of banana. Even if some streaks are too thick to permit the viewing of individual cells, there is usually an area on the slide in which a thin streak can be found.

- Describe the reasons for the change within the Anacharis cells. (You may need to do research in your text to explain the change.) Plasmolysis occurred (see text, p. 90).

Observing Leucoplasts in Banana Cells

I. Answer the following questions before beginning:

- What are leucoplasts? clear plastids found in certain plant cells
- What is the major function of leucoplasts? storage, usually of starch
- In what plant structures would you expect to find leucoplasts? fruits as well as fleshy roots and stems

II. Observe leucoplasts in banana cells.

- Using the broken end of a cotton swab (or a toothpick), make a smear wet mount of a small amount of mashed banana.
- Observe the slide on both the low power and the high power of your microscope. What do you see? Answers may vary. Clear, odd-shaped cells
- Stain the slide with an iodine stain. (NOTE: Iodine turns starch dark.)
  - Use the same procedure for staining as was used to stain the onion epidermis in Lab 3a.
  - Observe the slide. What do you see now? The leucoplasts, which were clear before, are now dark oval structures inside the cell.

III. Prepare a drawing of a stained banana cell in Area B and label as many parts as you can.

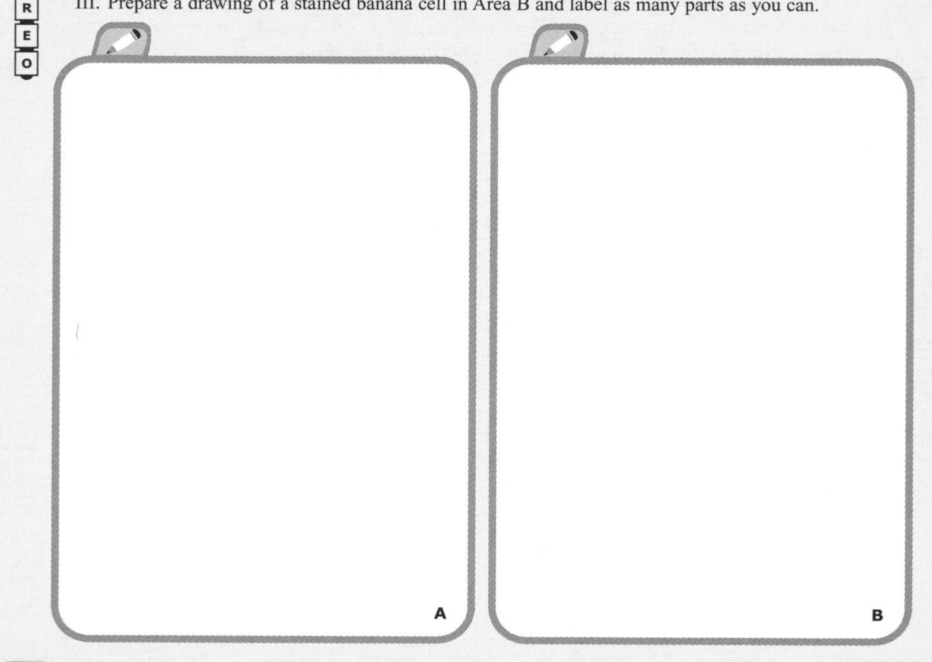

streaming may be difficult and ask them to inform you if they notice it happening.

It is relatively easy to observe banana cells. The usual problem is failing to make the smear thin enough.

Name________________________________

Date____________________ Hour__________

4 Photosynthesis

Materials

- live Anacharis
- glass funnels
- glass beakers
- test tubes
- metal or plastic blocks (nonfloating material)
- metric ruler
- thermometers
- desk lamp (or other illuminator)
- pH test papers
- dilute acetic acid (vinegar)
- baking soda

Goals

- To observe the results of photosynthesis in an aquatic plant
- To determine the conditions for photosynthesis in a plant

Anacharis is also known for its rapid growth and oxygen-producing ability. It produces stems that are ten to thirteen feet long and covered with short, flat leaves that grow in whorls of four. The most actively growing parts are the ends of the stems. The stem tips are composed of a rosette of immature leaves.

As photosynthesis takes place in many aquatic plants, the oxygen produced travels along tubes in the stem. The rate of photosynthesis can be measured by the amount of oxygen produced. If the stem of Anacharis is cut, the oxygen produced during photosynthesis escapes and bubbles to the surface.

In this exercise you will measure the amount of photosynthesis occurring in Anacharis by measuring the oxygen given off. By setting up the same experiment under different conditions, you should be able to draw some conclusions regarding the ideal conditions for photosynthesis in Anacharis.

An Apparatus to Measure Photosynthesis

I. Prepare the apparatus (Diagram 4.1).
- Prepare a large quantity of the proper medium (see below) in a container with a large opening.
- Fill the beaker with the proper medium.
- Place three or more blocks on the bottom of the beaker to support the funnel.
- Place the funnel in the beaker so that it rests on the blocks. (NOTE: The funnel's stem should be lower than the surface of the medium.)
- Fill the test tube with medium and place it above the funnel by following these instructions.
  - Place the test tube in the large container of the medium.
  - While the test tube is under the medium, cover the end of the test tube. (A glass plate can be used, but using your thumb to cover the end of the test tube works best.)
  - Remove the test tube from the medium, holding the cover in place so that no medium escapes.
  - Place the covered end of the test tube in the beaker under the level of the medium and

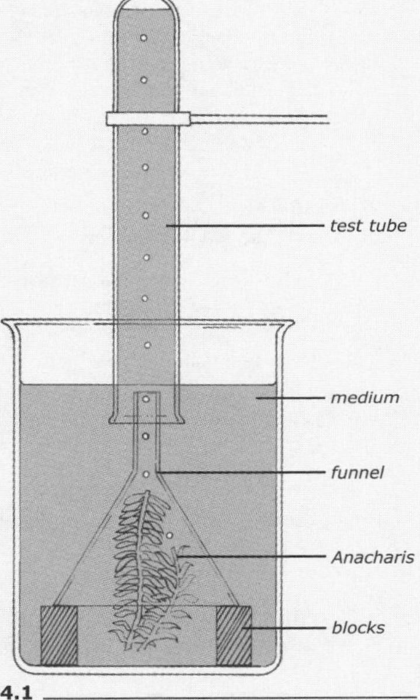

4.1 Apparatus to measure photosynthesis

Many science suppliers sell Anacharis tips (the freshest, most active part of the plant). These work the best for photosynthesis experiments.

Anacharis grows at 16–20 °C (60–68 °F) with its ideal temperature in the upper limit of that range. Above these temperatures it stops growing. That does not mean that it will not carry on photosynthesis above that temperature. Healthy specimens will carry on limited photosynthesis up to about 25 °C (77 °F).

Anacharis grows well in full sunlight but will tolerate various lesser degrees of light. The biggest problem with using direct sunlight in these experiments is that the small quantity of water in the apparatus quickly heats above the range the plant can tolerate.

Once Anacharis has started carrying on photosynthesis, the light must become rather dim for photosynthesis to stop completely. However, when coming from a low light level, it appears not to start carrying on photosynthesis until the illumination is greatly increased. It is, therefore, best to have the Anacharis in nearly ideal conditions before the experiment is begun.

Anacharis grows best in slight alkalinity (pH 7–8). Going much beyond this range will stop photosynthesis. For this reason, the medium for this exercise should have a pH measurement in that range. You can start with tap water, check the pH and then add vinegar to lower the pH or baking soda to raise it.

The larger the amount of Anacharis you can put into your funnel, the better. If, however, you pack the Anacharis tightly, the experiment will not work properly. All of the Anacharis leaves need to be loose and exposed to light, and the cut stem end should be exposed. The ideal is a glass funnel as large as the rest of your apparatus with a comfortable amount of Anacharis in it.

***Notes on Materials** is continued on page 35.*

Introduction

Photosynthesis has a tendency to be abstract. It is one thing to know that plants are carrying on photosynthesis; it is quite another to realize photosynthesis is happening because you can see something to verify it. Since most people assume that plants that are green are very slowly growing, it is natural to assume that photosynthesis is constantly, slowly occurring. In this activity the transient nature of the conditions necessary for the very active process of photosynthesis can be seen quite easily.

Required / Extra / Omit

It is recommended that you do this exercise as a demonstration. The tricks of setting up the apparatus are easily learned, but the time spent learning them is not as important as watching the results. Even if you do not set up several apparatus with different conditions in each one, the mere observation of photosynthesis-caused bubbles coming from the Anacharis stem is interesting.

If your Anacharis is in good condition and the conditions in your laboratory culture and apparatus are just right, a slow, steady stream of bubbles can be observed coming from the cut stem. At such times the number of bubbles produced in a period of time (thirty seconds is adequate) can gauge the rate of photosynthesis. By dimming the lights, waiting a few minutes for the plant to adjust, and then again counting the bubbles, you can observe that photosynthesis has slowed. Photosynthesis, of course, is not rare, but it often does not happen at the time you want to do the demonstration. For this reason the exercise described involves catching and measuring the oxygen produced over an undetermined period of time. Run the experiment as long as needed to get measurable results.

You may find that a classroom discussion of the results of the demonstration is more profitable than having students write out the answers on pages L34–L35.

Cut the Anacharis stem just prior to running the experiment. The Anacharis will, in time, begin to heal itself, blocking the tube through which the oxygen escapes.

Use sharp, pointed scissors to cut the stem without damaging leaves.

Handle the Anacharis as little as possible to avoid damaging it. Use forceps (whenever possible) to hold areas that are not being used in the experiment.

It is recommended that you have your entire class do a single set of experiments: four different light intensities or four different pH's or four different temperatures. (You may, of course, choose to do three, five, or six different ones, depending on the availability of equipment.)

It is not essential that you begin all the various experiments at once, but you should take the measurements at the same intervals. In other words, all experiments should be measured after a specified period of time (e.g., twenty minutes) rather than measured all at the same time on the clock.

Maintaining light intensity, unless you are using the sun, can be done with relative ease. Measure the temperature periodically if you deal with light intensity to be sure the temperature does not change greatly during your experiment. If it does, consider adding ice or hot water. Placing the beaker in a large water bath (must be a clear container) will slow the heating or cooling of the apparatus. Darkness can be created by covering the entire apparatus with an overturned trash can and just removing it to take a reading. Different shades of colored cellophane may be an interesting variable as they will permit only certain wavelengths of light to pass through.

Maintaining the pH is relatively easy, but the results are not as dramatic until the pH levels of the media are very different.

Maintaining the water at different temperatures is difficult. If the Anacharis is producing oxygen at a high rate and a set of different temperatures of water can be quickly obtained, the results can be quick and dramatic. If, however, the Anacharis is carrying on photosynthesis slowly, the medium may not maintain its temperature long enough for you to obtain measurable results. You may need to maintain the temperature by adding hot or ice water or by using a water bath.

remove the covering. If air gets into the top of the test tube, remove the test tube and repeat the process until your test tube contains no air.

- Move the test tube so that it covers the end of the funnel and can be suspended as shown in the diagram.

II. Prepare the Anacharis.

- Cut a 5–8 cm section (or sections, if your glass funnels are large enough) of the growing end of an Anacharis stem.
- Place the Anacharis sections in the medium in the beaker and gently shake them until all air bubbles are freed. (Gas introduced into the funnel with the Anacharis will spoil the results of the experiment.)
- While holding the funnel in place, use forceps to place the Anacharis section(s) in the funnel from the bottom. The cut end should be pointing up the tube.
- When you set up experiments to compare the quantity of photosynthesis taking place, be sure you use Anacharis pieces that are similar in length, quantity of leaves, and color.

Experiments to Determine Conditions for Photosynthesis

I. Devise a set of experiments to determine under which conditions Anacharis carries on photosynthesis best.

- Choose from the following list a condition with which your class wishes to experiment.
  - *Light intensity.* Use different areas that naturally receive different light intensities such as a dim corner, a window ledge, a desk in the classroom, or under a bright lamp; or you may use a light meter to set up areas with different light intensities.
  - *pH.* Use vinegar and baking soda to arrive at media that have different pH values. Test papers or a pH meter will be needed to determine their pH.
  - *Temperature.* Various temperatures can be established and maintained by using ice, hot water, or other methods.
- Be sure you design an experiment that will involve only one experimental variable.
  - The light intensity can affect the temperature if steps are not taken to prevent it.
  - The experiment may need to be carried on for several hours, and constant temperatures are often difficult to maintain for that length of time without careful supervision.
- Plan to observe your experiments every thirty to sixty minutes for several hours.

II. Run the experiments and record your data on the chart on page L35.

III. Answer the following questions.

- What factor (experimental variable) did you test? Answers may vary. ____________________
- Based on your data, is photosynthesis affected by the factor you were testing? ☐ yes ☐ no
- At what range of the factor did photosynthesis happen at the fastest rate? ____________________
- At what range of the factor did photosynthesis happen at the slowest rate? ____________________
- What can you summarize regarding the rate of photosynthesis and the factor you were testing? ____________________

Name________________________

Conditions for Photosynthesis			
Experimental variable	**Time**	**Oxygen in test tube**	**Temperature**
Experiment 1 ______	______	______ mm	______
	______	______ mm	______
	______	______ mm	______
	______	______ mm	______
Experiment 2 ______	______	______ mm	______
	______	______ mm	______
	______	______ mm	______
	______	______ mm	______
Experiment 3 ______	______	______ mm	______
	______	______ mm	______
	______	______ mm	______
	______	______ mm	______
Experiment 4 ______	______	______ mm	______
	______	______ mm	______
	______	______ mm	______
	______	______ mm	______

- Were the other factors held constant? ☐ yes ☐ no Were these factors held within acceptable limits to give reliable data? ☐ yes ☐ no
  Answers may vary.
- If no, indicate which ones fluctuated too far. ______
- If yes and the factor was not constant, indicate why you feel the fluctuation is acceptable. ______
- What steps would you recommend to improve the experiment you performed? ______

Continued from page 33

Funnels must be glass or clear plastic to permit light to reach the Anacharis.

All of the test tubes used in all of the apparatus must be identical in order for you to use a ruler to gauge the amount of oxygen produced. The similarity of other pieces of the apparatus (beaker, funnel, etc.) is not crucial, but they should be as alike as possible.

Use a test tube as slender as the end of your funnel tube. Thus less oxygen is needed to obtain a measurable amount; this procedure will increase the measurable differences in the oxygen produced.

Decide how you will measure the rounded end of a test tube with a ruler. How it is done is not as important as being consistent about the way measurements are taken.

It is possible to place the Anacharis tips (properly shaken to rid them of air bubbles) in the medium before you put the funnel over it.

The blocks can be any size, as long as the funnel's tube can be kept under the level of the medium in the beaker. They should be of a nonsoluble material. Children's small plastic building blocks work well.

If the experiment is being set up as a short-term demonstration, the blocks under the funnel can be omitted. The water in the funnel should contain adequate CO_2 to maintain photosynthesis for a class period.

Name________________________

Date________________ Hour__________

5a
Mitosis and Meiosis

Materials
- microscope
- preserved slides of *Allium* root tips, l.s.
- preserved slides of whitefish embryos prepared for viewing mitosis

Goals
- To understand mitosis and learn its stages by drawing progressive diagrams
- To observe cells in various stages of mitosis
- To compare mitosis and meiosis
- To understand meiosis

Cell division is one of the basic biological processes. To thoroughly understand what happens during mitosis, however, you must understand what happens to the chromosomes in each of the phases.

After you master the process and significance of mitosis, you can understand meiosis (which forms gametes) and fertilization (which unites gametes). In order to grasp genetics and the concepts involved in the debate between biological evolution and Creationism, you must understand the basic processes of mitosis and meiosis.

You will need to have one *Allium* root tip slide per microscope since most of the students will be doing this section at the same time.

There are many different stains that can be used on plants. Be sure that you have slides stained for viewing mitosis.

In order to get a better image, students may want to use oil-immersion power. This does not help, however, because the field of view becomes too small.

A Description of Mitosis

R E O

To help your understanding of mitosis, use your text as a reference and fill in the following descriptions of the phases of animal mitosis before you begin your observations and drawings.

I. Prophase
- Outside the nucleus
  - The centrosomes with their centrioles divide and migrate to opposite sides.
  - The centrosomes form the mitotic spindle.
  - The nuclear membrane disintegrates.
- Inside the nucleus
  - The chromosomes begin to coil, becoming shorter and thicker.
  - The nucleolus disappears.
  - The kinetochore appears as a pinched-together point of sister chromatids.

II. Metaphase
- The centromeres of the chromosomes are located on the equatorial plane.
- Metaphase ends as the centromeres separate.

III. Anaphase
- The sister chromatids separate to form daughter chromosomes.
- The kinetochore fibers appear to pull the chromosomes.
- The polar fibers push the centrosomes apart to elongate the cell.

IV. Telophase
- Forming the nuclei
  - The daughter chromosomes begin to uncoil at the ends of the spindle.
  - At each pole of the cell a new nucleus forms.

Introduction

The main purpose of this exercise is to show the students what happens to chromosomal material during mitosis. Observing the slides of these processes should help to reinforce their study.

Students frequently try to copy mitosis diagrams from the text. They may be confused after their first encounter with the onion tip cells and find it much easier to copy the schematic diagrams of mitosis. Be on the lookout for diagram copying and stop it immediately. Watch for structures in their drawings that are too accurate or too nearly perfect. If you see centrioles in student diagrams of onions, you can be sure that the student is copying from the text rather than drawing from the onion cells he should be observing. Since they are plants, onion cells do not have centrioles. Even in whitefish embryos, centrioles viewed through classroom light microscopes do not look like those illustrated in the text.

Much of this exercise can be completed either before or after the students have spent time in the laboratory. Encourage students to use most of their class time on their drawings and to complete the other sections at home.

The main purpose of the second part of this exercise (beginning with A Description of Meiosis) is to show students what happens to chromosomal material during meiosis and to compare this to what happens during mitosis. Laboratory observation of this comparison is somewhat difficult. Students, therefore, are asked to describe the changes by completing statements and to compare the differences between mitosis and meiosis on a chart.

You may wish to use the second part of this exercise as a review of your presentation of meiosis. Used in this way, the entire exercise can be completed as homework, and you can collect and grade the exercise. You may wish to have the students fill out the information at home and then use their work as the foundation of a classroom discussion of these processes. There are other profitable uses for this material.

If students have difficulty figuring out how the *Allium* root tip slide was made, encourage them to look on the label and to use the chart on page L7.

You may need to hint to some students that they should use the index to find out that the root area that they are looking at is the meristematic region. Ask them what they are looking at. When they look up *root* and find *root cap,* they are on the right track. On the page that discusses these structures, the region is diagrammed and is said to carry on mitosis (p. 353). Do not give this information to them; they should learn to discover such information for themselves. Do, however, give helpful suggestions to guide them in the right direction.

Students may become frustrated when trying to count chromosomes. Explain to them that they will encounter problems but they should still try.

- The nuclear membrane re-forms.
- The nucleoli reappear.

- Outside the nucleus
  - The mitotic spindle disappears.
  - The centrosomes remain just outside the nuclear membranes.
  - The plasma membrane pinches in (invaginates).
  - The cytoplasm divides.

Mitosis in Plant Cells

R E O

In certain plant parts, almost all the cells carry on mitosis. If these areas are properly stained, chromosomes in the various phases of mitosis are easy to see.

I. Observe mitosis in a prepared root tip of *Allium* (onion).
- Obtain a preserved slide of an *Allium* root tip.
  - Notice the way the root tip has been sectioned (see p. L7). Name and describe this type of sectioning. Longitudinal section (l.s.): the specimen is cut lengthwise.
  - Mitosis is carried on in an area just above the root cap, a protective group of cells located at the very tip of the root. What is the name of this area? (Research in your text may be necessary.) the meristematic region (p. 346)
- Examine your slide under the microscope.
  - Using low power, locate the root cap and the area where mitosis is carried on.
  - Using high power, observe various stages of mitosis.
    - ❖ Why do some of the root cells have no chromatin material? (Hint: How was the onion root cut to make this type of slide?) Some of the cells were cut in such a way that the nucleus is in another slice.
    - ❖ Find a cell in anaphase and tell, as accurately as possible, how many chromosomes are found in an onion cell. Answers may vary.
    - ❖ You will probably not see all the chromosomes. How many chromosomes are in an onion cell? (Research in your text.) 16 (p. 125)
    - ❖ Account for the difference between the number you saw and the actual number. Some may have been cut off as the section was made; others may have been overlapping and thus not visible.

R E O

II. Draw a series of specimen drawings showing mitosis in *Allium* root tips.
- Make sure you draw typical specimens of the various stages of mitosis. If the first one you find is not good, look for another.
- Draw one cell in each of the following phases in the spaces provided on the next page.

1. Interphase	2. Prophase
3. Metaphase	4. Anaphase
5. Telophase	6. Daughter cells

- All the drawings must be individually labeled.
- A timesaving tip: It is not necessary for you to draw the interphase first. If you find a good metaphase, draw it in the metaphase space; then look for another phase. The drawings, however, must be in the proper boxes.

Required / Extra / Omit

A Description of Mitosis—This section can be completed by all students. Even if you do not have them do the microscopic viewing of mitosis, it is recommended that you have your students do this part of the exercise. It can be done at home, and if you are going to have students use microscopes, you should encourage them to do this section before they come to the lab.

Mitosis in Plant Cells—This section comes in two parts: answering questions and making drawings. You can do one without the other. If you plan to have the students observe or draw other parts of the lab and your time is limited, you may wish to have them merely answer the questions regarding the root tip mitosis. The easier drawings are those of the onion root tip. You may want to make the whitefish embryo drawings extra credit or omit them entirely if your time is limited.

Mitosis in Animal Cells—This section has three parts. You may have your students do the observations asked for in the first part and not do the drawings asked for in the second part. The third part asks students to compare animal and plant mitosis. This can be done without observing either plant or animal cells, since the necessary materials are in the text.

Some teachers have students do only the description of mitosis (pp. L37–L38) and the comparing of mitosis in animals and plants (p. L40). Doing these sections does not require any laboratory apparatus, but the sections can be useful in teaching students about mitosis.

The two sections dealing with meiosis can be used independently.

Other sections could be done by students for extra credit, or they can be omitted.

Name________________________________

1.

Interphase

2.

Prophase

3.

Metaphase

4.

Anaphase

5.

Telophase

6.

Daughter Cells

- Randomly pick twenty cells from the slide and assign each to one of the six stages. Are some phases more frequently seen than others? ☒ yes ☐ no
- Why do you think this is so? Some phases, such as interphase, take much longer than the actual mitotic phases.

Mitosis in Animal Cells

R E O

In embryos mitosis happens rapidly. Thus a slide of an embryo, if properly prepared, will reveal phases of mitosis.

I. Observe animal mitosis in a whitefish embryo.

- Obtain a preserved slide of a whitefish embryo.
- Observe the slide on high power, looking for the various stages of mitosis. You should find all the phases. In the proper spaces check the phases you find.

☐ Interphase	☐ Prophase
☐ Metaphase	☐ Anaphase
☐ Telophase	☐ Daughter Cells

- How many chromosomes do you think a cell of a whitefish has? Answers may vary.

  Based on your observations, can you be sure of this answer? ☐ yes ☒ no

- Explain why you can or cannot be sure. Answers may vary. Chromosomes may have been cut off or may be overlapping.

R E O

II. Draw a series of specimen drawings on page L41, showing mitosis in whitefish embryos.

- Make sure you draw typical specimens of the various stages of mitosis.
- Draw and label one cell in each of the following points in the process.

1. Interphase	2. Prophase
3. Metaphase	4. Anaphase
5. Telophase	6. Daughter cells

R E O

III. Compare mitosis in animals and plants. List several differences between mitosis in plants and animals by filling in the spaces below.

- In plants the centrioles are not present,

  while in animals the centrioles are present.

- In plants the daughter cells are divided by the formation of a division plate,

  while in animals the daughter cells are divided by invagination.

- In plants the mitosis process usually takes a shorter time,

  while in animals the mitosis process usually takes a longer time.

Name________________________

1.

Interphase

2.

Prophase

3.

Metaphase

4.

Anaphase

5.

Telophase

6.

Daughter Cells

A Description of Meiosis

To help your understanding of meiosis, use your text as a reference and fill in the following descriptions of the phases of meiosis in animals.

I. First Division

- Prophase
  - Before going through meiosis, the mother cells must have the __di__-ploid chromosome number.
  - The homologous chromosomes pair up, forming a tetrad.
- Metaphase
  - The tetrads line up in homologous pairs on the equatorial plane.
- Anaphase
  - The sister chromatids do not separate.
  - The homologous pairs of chromosomes separate, traveling to different ends of the spindle.
- Telophase
  - The chromosomes arrive at the ends of the spindle.
  - The cytoplasm divides.
  - The result of the first division of meiosis is two __ha__-ploid cells, each containing __one__ of each homologous pair of chromosomes found in the mother cell.

II. Second Division

- Prophase
  - Since the chromosomes do not uncoil after the first division of meiosis, the cells are ready to undergo the rest of the phases of meiosis almost immediately following the first division.
- Metaphase
  - The chromosomes in each cell (location) line up on the equatorial plane.
- Anaphase
  - The sister chromatids in each cell travel toward opposite ends of the spindle.
- Telophase
  - The nuclei are re-formed.
  - The cytoplasm in each cell divides.
  - At the end of the second division of mitosis there are __four__ cells, each of which contains the __ha__-ploid number of chromosomes. These cells are called the __gametes__.

Name________________________________

Comparison of Mitosis and Meiosis

Mitosis is the asexual reproduction of cells. Meiosis is the formation of gametes in preparation for sexual reproduction. The processes, while similar, have noticeable differences.

I. Compare the phases.

- Compare mitosis and meiosis by filling in the chart below. All the information you need is in your text (see diagrams on pp. 127–28 and 130–32); however, some of the answers will require thought.

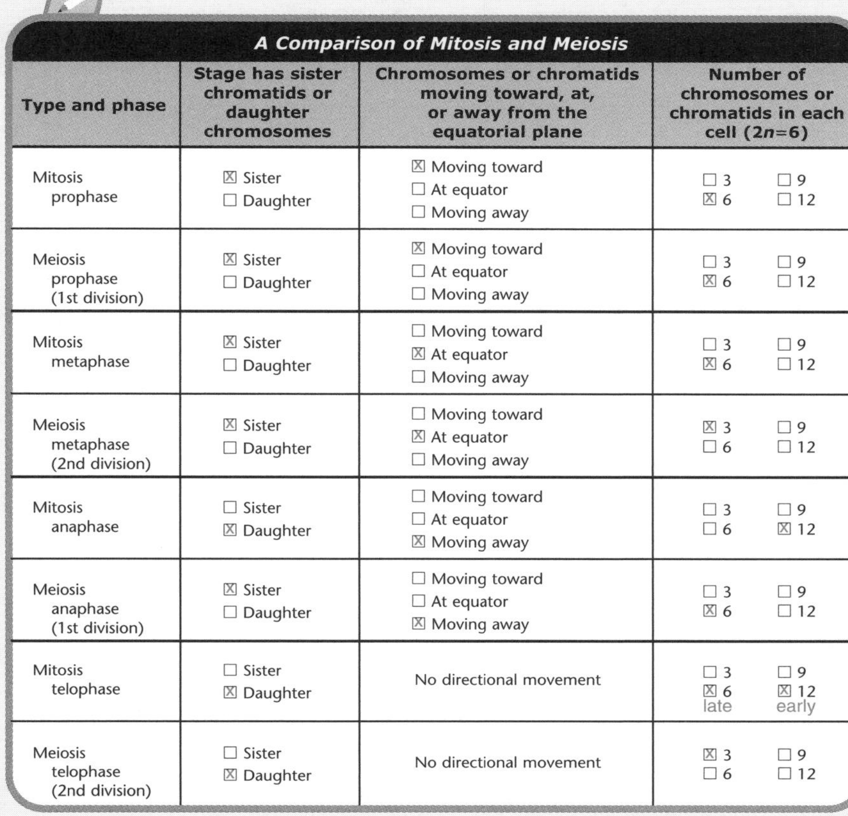

A Comparison of Mitosis and Meiosis

Type and phase	Stage has sister chromatids or daughter chromosomes	Chromosomes or chromatids moving toward, at, or away from the equatorial plane	Number of chromosomes or chromatids in each cell (2*n*=6)
Mitosis prophase	☒ Sister ☐ Daughter	☒ Moving toward ☐ At equator ☐ Moving away	☐ 3 ☐ 9 ☒ 6 ☐ 12
Meiosis prophase (1st division)	☒ Sister ☐ Daughter	☒ Moving toward ☐ At equator ☐ Moving away	☐ 3 ☐ 9 ☒ 6 ☐ 12
Mitosis metaphase	☒ Sister ☐ Daughter	☐ Moving toward ☒ At equator ☐ Moving away	☐ 3 ☐ 9 ☒ 6 ☐ 12
Meiosis metaphase (2nd division)	☒ Sister ☐ Daughter	☐ Moving toward ☒ At equator ☐ Moving away	☒ 3 ☐ 9 ☐ 6 ☐ 12
Mitosis anaphase	☐ Sister ☒ Daughter	☐ Moving toward ☐ At equator ☒ Moving away	☐ 3 ☐ 9 ☐ 6 ☒ 12
Meiosis anaphase (1st division)	☒ Sister ☐ Daughter	☐ Moving toward ☐ At equator ☒ Moving away	☐ 3 ☐ 9 ☒ 6 ☐ 12
Mitosis telophase	☐ Sister ☒ Daughter	No directional movement	☐ 3 ☐ 9 ☒ 6 ☒ 12 late early
Meiosis telophase (2nd division)	☐ Sister ☒ Daughter	No directional movement	☒ 3 ☐ 9 ☐ 6 ☐ 12

This chart is difficult for some students. If they understand the processes of mitosis and meiosis, they should be able to use their text to figure out the answers. You may need to help slower students complete the first phase (mitosis, prophase) in order to get them going. Students should decide for themselves how to complete the rest of the chart. Not all the phases are asked for in the chart, but all are illustrated in the text. Remind them that the number of chromosomes or chromatids asked for in the last column is for *each cell.* (When a cell divides, it becomes two cells, and *each* resulting cell is discussed in the chart.)

II. Answer the following questions comparing mitosis and meiosis.

- In metaphase, what is the name of the chromatin material that lines up on the equatorial plane for
  - mitosis? sister chromatids
  - meiosis, first division? sister chromatids and homologous pairs of chromosomes
  - meiosis, second division? sister chromatids
- In anaphase, what is the name of the chromatin material that is moving toward opposite poles in
  - mitosis? daughter chromosomes
  - meiosis, first division? separated homologous pairs of chromosomes (sister chromatids still attached)
  - meiosis, second division? daughter chromosomes

Name______________________________

Date__________________ Hour__________

5b Genetics

Part I Monohybrid Problems with Simple Dominance

Goals

- To work lab problems to increase understanding of genetics
- To measure knowledge and understanding of basic genetic principles

Materials *(none)*

It is easy to watch someone else work on a solution to a problem. Often, however, it is quite another thing to take a similar problem and work it out yourself. Only when you thoroughly understand the process can you work a problem "from scratch." If you can work the series of problems in this laboratory exercise outside of class, you probably understand the simple genetics presented in BIOLOGY. *If you cannot figure them out, you need more study and instruction. If you have difficulty with these problems, seek help from your teacher. Many of the problems in this lab are study problems and will not be graded, but do not discuss your answers with anyone.*

In order to increase interest in this exercise, consider distributing PTC test papers and control papers (available from scientific suppliers). All students should have the control paper in one hand and the PTC paper in the other. Do not tell them what is happening until after the experiment. Have all of them taste their control paper simultaneously. Then have them all taste their PTC paper at the same time. The students' faces usually tell who the tasters are.

If possible, permit the students to take home PTC test papers and control papers to test members of their immediate families. Have them draw pedigrees.

Determining Genotypes from Phenotypes

R E O

In humans, the ability to taste the chemical phenylthiocarbamide (PTC) is an inherited, dominant characteristic. For these exercises use the symbol *T* to represent the dominant allele and *t* to represent the recessive allele.

I. The genotype for a person who cannot taste PTC would be written __tt__.

II. The genotype for a person who can taste PTC would be written as either __TT__ or __Tt*__.

III. Put a star in the answer above by the genotype for a person who is heterozygous.

- Is there any difference between the phenotypes of these two people? ☐ yes ☒ no
- Explain. Answers may vary. Both can taste PTC because both have the dominant allele.

Once you have discussed a particular genetic concept and have assigned a section of the exercise dealing with that concept, you can expect that some students will have difficulty with it. However, your working other similar problems in class will help them master the concept. The idea is not to work the exact problem presented in the exercise but to get the students to transfer concepts from one situation to another. If students still do not catch on, encourage them to see you individually.

Tell the students to write in pencil. They may need to change their answers.

How to Fill In a Punnett Square

- Female genotypes are written on top of a Punnett square; male genotypes are written along the left side.
- The symbols used on the top and side of the Punnett square are possible gametes, not genotypes for individuals.
- The symbols you write inside the Punnett square are possible gamete combinations or the possible genotypes of the offspring.

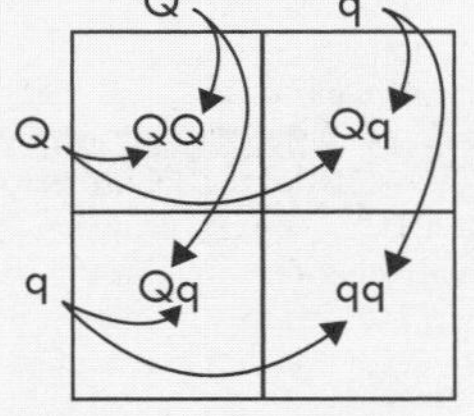

Emphasize the importance of working Punnett squares as a means of solving problems even when they are not called for in the exercise. A Punnett square will show all possible genotypes, and students can thus know the possible phenotypes that can result from a given cross.

Students frequently need to be reminded that the gametes placed on the top and side of a Punnett square are not genotypes. Genotypes are listed within the Punnett square.

Emphasize that the possible gametes produced by the female go across the top of the Punnett square and the possible gametes from the male go down the left side. This becomes important when working with sex-linked traits.

INTRODUCTION

When teaching genetics, you may find that no matter how much you lecture or how many notes the students take, they have difficulty working a simple genetics problem. This exercise is designed to reinforce what the text teaches and to give the students a working knowledge of the terms and concepts of simple genetics.

Before you assign any of this exercise, make sure that the students have a thorough understanding of the terms *genotype, phenotype, allele, gamete, homozygous, heterozygous, dominant,* and *recessive.* In class, work several problems similar to the ones they are to do at home. Go over the examples in the text and the teacher's notes and then assign an exercise. Tell the students that if they have problems with the exercise, they probably have misunderstood the definition of one of these terms and should try to work out the problem using their text.

Required / Extra / Omit

This exercise is designed to be done at home after you cover the concepts in class. You should, of course, either omit or permit the students to do for extra credit any section that deals with material you do not cover in class. It is recommended that you cover all the material and have the students do the entire exercise. Once you have given the students adequate time to complete one of the parts of the exercise and to seek help if they need it, have them hand it in. Grade the exercise section quickly and return the papers to the students, insisting that those who did not do well on the exercise see you for extra help.

The challenging incomplete dominance problem on page L50 should be done for extra credit or should be omitted if students are having difficulty with genetics.

Some teachers merely discuss dihybrid crosses but prefer not to have students work the problems (pp. L53–L54). If that is the case, have the students do these problems for extra credit or omit them.

Using Punnett Squares

R E O

I. Using the Punnett square on the right, cross a homozygous male taster with a female nontaster. In this Punnett square, is it possible to have the following offspring:

A. A heterozygous taster? ☒ yes ☐ no
B. A heterozygous nontaster? ☐ yes ☒ no
C. A homozygous taster? ☐ yes ☒ no
D. A homozygous nontaster? ☐ yes ☒ no

	t	t
T	Tt	Tt
T	Tt	Tt

R E O

II. One of the offspring of the cross done above marries a person who is known to be heterozygous.

- Is there any possibility of there being a nontaster in the next generation? ☒ yes ☐ no
- To prove your answer, diagram the cross on the Punnett square to the right and circle the genotype of the nontaster (if there is one).
- What is the phenotypic ratio of this cross? (Give the numbers and the description of what the numbers stand for.) 3 tasters (dominant trait) : 1 nontaster (recessive trait)
- What is the genotypic ratio of this cross? (Give the numbers and the descriptions of what the numbers stand for.) 1 TT (homozygous dominant) : 2 Tt (heterozygous) : 1 tt (homozygous recessive)

	T	t
T	TT	Tt
t	Tt	(tt)

Suggestions for Solving Genetics Problems

1. Determine as many genotypes as you can.
   - Since a person who has the recessive phenotype must have the recessive genotype, you know the genotype of that person.
   - Since a person who has the dominant phenotype must have at least one dominant allele, note that as part of that person's genotype.
2. Determine whether the person's parents or offspring tell you anything about the person's genotype.
   - If the parents are known to be purebred (homozygous) for a trait, that may give you some information regarding the individual's genotype.
   - If the offspring are known to be purebred (homozygous) for a trait, that may also give you information regarding the individual's genotype.
3. Put the information you have on a Punnett square.
4. Determine what you can, based on the information you have.

R E O

III. Mr. Johnson cannot taste PTC, but his wife can. Mrs. Johnson's mother cannot taste PTC, but her father can.

- Is it possible for the Johnsons to have a child that can taste PTC? ☒ yes ☐ no
- Is it possible for the Johnsons to have a child that cannot taste PTC? ☒ yes ☐ no
- Demonstrate your answers on a Punnett square.

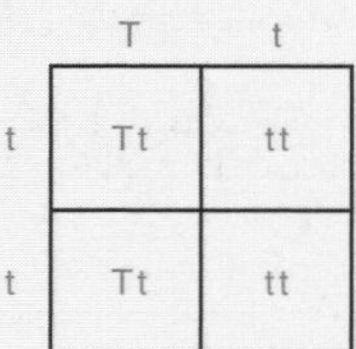

	T	t
t	Tt	tt
t	Tt	tt

Name________________________

Date________________ Hour__________

5b
Genetics

Part II Problems with Pedigree Charts

Examine the Pedigree Chart below. It shows several generations of tasters and nontasters of PTC. Some of the genotypes are supplied. As you work out the problems below, you may need to fill in the genotypes of individuals on the pedigree chart.

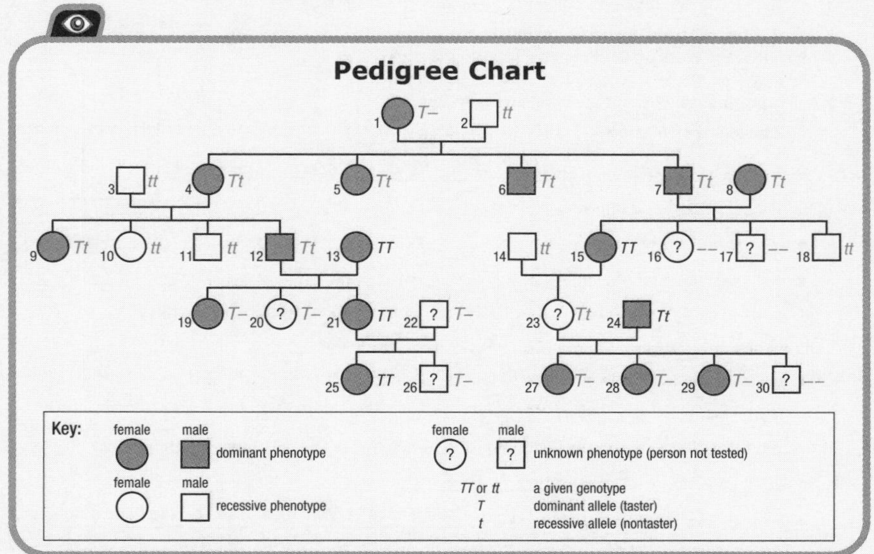

Be sure you have read the material about pedigrees in your text (p. 140).

I. Answer the following questions regarding the pedigrees of tasters and nontasters.

- What is the phenotype of individual 1? ___taster___
- What are the possible genotypes of individual 1? ___TT or Tt___
- What is the phenotype of individual 2? ___nontaster___
- What is the genotype of individual 2? ___tt___
- Diagram the possible crosses for individuals 1 and 2 on the Punnett squares below.

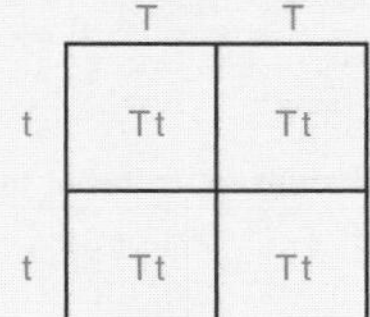

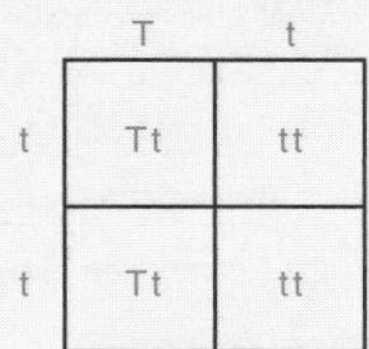

Remind the students that a question mark on the pedigree chart indicates an unknown phenotype. It does not mean that it is impossible to figure out the phenotype (and the genotype) of the person by using other information given on the pedigree.

- Note carefully the phenotypes of the offspring of individuals 1 and 2 as given on the pedigree. Give the genotypes for the following individuals:

  4 Tt 5 Tt 6 Tt 7 Tt

- Would it be possible for any of their future brothers or sisters to exhibit the recessive trait?

  ☒ yes ☐ no Explain your answer. The information given in the pedigree is not enough to tell whether individual 1 is Tt or TT. If she is Tt, she could have a nontaster offspring.

- Enter the genotypes for individuals 1, 2, 4, 5, 6, and 7 on the pedigree. Be sure to indicate those alleles you are not sure of by a dash (example: "*T* –" or "– –").

R E O

II. What is the expected phenotype ratio for the crossing of individuals 3 and 4?
- Fill in the cross on the Punnett square to the right.
- Enter the phenotypic ratio from the Punnett square, being sure to tell what the numbers stand for.

  2 tasters: 2 nontasters

	T	t
t	Tt	tt
t	Tt	tt

III. What is the genotype of individual 12? Tt

IV. Individual 20 died in infancy.
- Is it possible to tell the child's phenotype? ☒ yes ☐ no If so, what is it? taster
- Is it possible to tell the child's genotype? ☐ yes ☒ no If so, what is it? T–

V. From the information given on the pedigree, is it possible to determine the phenotype of individual 22? ☒ yes ☐ no If so, what is it? taster
- Is it possible to tell the genotype of his son (individual 26)? ☐ yes ☒ no

  If so, what is it? T–

VI. From information given on the pedigree, is it possible to tell the genotype of individual 8?

☒ yes ☐ no If so, what is it? Tt
- Explain how you know or do not know. Husband is Tt. Wife must also be Tt to have a nontaster (tt) child (individual 18).

VII. Is it possible to know the phenotype
- of individual 16? ☐ yes ☒ no
- of individual 17? ☐ yes ☒ no
- If so, what are they? 16 – – 17 – –
- Explain how you know or do not know. Because of the genotypes of their parents, these offspring could be either tasters or nontasters.

VIII. What must be the phenotype and genotype of individual 23? taster, Tt

IX. Is it possible that individual 30 expresses the recessive trait? ☒ yes ☐ no

Is it possible that he expresses the dominant trait? ☒ yes ☐ no
- Which is more likely? Dominant taster
- Explain your choice. The expected ratio is 3 tasters (dominant) to 1 nontaster (recessive). Thus this individual has a 3 to 1 chance of being a taster.

Name________________________

Date______________ Hour________

5b
Genetics

Part III Problems with Incomplete Dominance

Read carefully the information about incomplete dominance in your text (pp. 141–42). Incomplete dominance problems can be worked easily on Punnett squares.

R E O

Simple Incomplete Dominance Problems

When a homozygous red radish plant is crossed with a homozygous white radish plant, purple radishes result.

I. Determine the alleles in radishes.

- In incomplete dominance, both alleles are usually expressed with the same uppercase (capital) letter. We will use *C* for this cross.
- The possible traits are shown with lowercase superscripts.
  - Give the genotype of a white radish. C^wC^w
  - Give the genotype of a red radish. C^rC^r
- Determine the possible gametes of
  - A white radish w
  - A red radish r

II. Complete these radish crosses.

- If the pollen from a white radish fertilizes the egg of a red radish, what will be the genotypes and the phenotypes of the offspring? Prove your answer on the Punnett square to the right. All will be C^rC^w, purple.

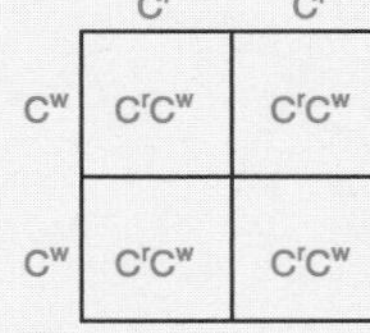

- If pollen from a red radish flower fertilizes the egg of another flower on the same plant, what will be the genotypes and phenotypes of the offspring? Why? all red (C^rC^r) because the cross of $C^rC^r \times C^rC^r$ can produce only C^rC^r offspring
- If two purple radishes are cross-pollinated, what are the genotypic and phenotypic ratios of the F_1 generation? Prove your answer by making the proper cross on the Punnett square to the right.

  Genotypic: 1 C^rC^r: 2 C^rC^w: 1 C^wC^w

  Phenotypic: 1 red: 2 purple: 1 white

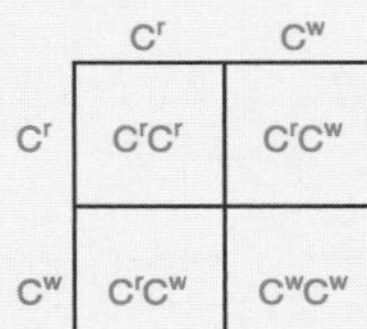

- If a red radish and a purple radish are cross-pollinated, what will be the phenotypic and genotypic ratios?

  Genotypic: 2 C^rC^r: 2 C^rC^w

  Phenotypic: 2 red: 2 purple

Remind students that in plants, the pollen contains the male cells while the egg is the female part.

- Will the ratios given in the preceding question be the same if a white radish and a purple radish are crossed? Explain. The ratios are the same (although the characteristics are different)—two C^wC^w : two C^rC^w; two white : two purple

A Challenging Incomplete Dominance Problem

R E O

This problem is more complex, but if you understand the material already discussed, you can figure it out.

The litter resulting from the mating of two short-tailed cats contains three kittens without tails, two with long tails, and six with short tails.

I. Diagram a cross that will show the above results on the Punnett square to the right. First, however, you will need to give a key for the letters you choose to represent the alleles.

Key: C^l = allele for long tail

C^s = allele for no tail

C^sC^l = genotype for short tail

(Students' symbols may vary.)

	C^s	C^l
C^s	C^sC^s	C^sC^l
C^l	C^sC^l	C^lC^l

II. What is the genotype of the parents? ☐ homozygous ☒ heterozygous ☐ one of each

III. Does the ratio of the kittens given in the statement agree with the ratio obtained from the Punnett square? Is it close enough for you to be sure you used the proper genotypes when you diagrammed the cross? It does not agree exactly, but it is close enough that the ratio is accurate. The expected ratio is 1 long, 2 short, 1 tailless. The ratio given in the problem is 2: 6: 3.

Name____________________

Date____________ Hour________

5b
Genetics

Part IV Problems with Multiple Alleles

Occasionally there will be more than one set (a pair) of alleles at a single locus. Three or more alleles, rather than just one set of contrasting traits, may be possible. Read carefully the material in your text regarding multiple alleles (p. 143–44).

Inheritance of the ABO Blood Types

The human blood types—A, B, AB, and O—are determined by multiple alleles, two dominant alleles and one recessive. They are often written

Dominants: I^A I^B Recessive: i

In this example the *I* represents the chromosome, and the A and B the gene. Of course, *i* represents the recessive gene on a chromosome.

R E O

I. Using the above symbols, indicate all the possible genotypes for the phenotypes given below. (NOTE: Two of the blood types have two possible genotypes; the others have only one.)

- Blood type A I^AI^A, I^Ai
- Blood type AB I^AI^B
- Blood type B I^BI^B, I^Bi
- Blood type O ii

II. A man who is heterozygous for blood type A marries a woman who is heterozygous for blood type B.

- Write their genotypes below.
  - ○ Man I^Ai
  - ○ Woman I^Bi
- Could a child with blood type O be born into this family?
  ☒ yes ☐ no
  Prove your answer on the Punnett square to the right.
- Could a child with blood type A be born into this family?
  ☒ yes ☐ no
- Could a child with blood type B be born into this family?
  ☒ yes ☐ no
- Could a child with blood type AB be born into this family?
  ☒ yes ☐ no

	I^B	i
I^A	I^AI^B	I^Ai
i	I^Bi	ii

Additional Multiple Allele Problems

R E O

I. Is it possible for a woman with blood type O to have a child with blood type AB? ☐ yes ☒ no
Explain your answer. (You may need to use a Punnett square to demonstrate the proper cross.)

Since the woman must be homozygous recessive (ii) to have O blood, she can give neither the A nor the B allele to her children. In order for a child to have AB blood, he must have one of the two dominant alleles (A or B) from his mother.

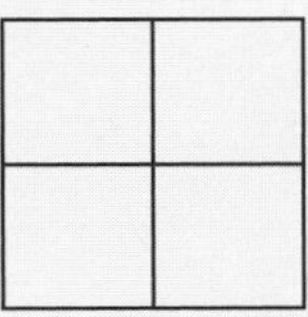

R E O

II. Is it possible for a man with blood type AB to have a child with type O blood? ☐ yes ☒ no
Explain your answer. (You may need to use a Punnett square to demonstrate the proper cross.)
The man's genotype must be I^AI^B. He must give either the A or the B allele to his offspring. Since a person with type O blood has neither the A nor the B allele, a man with blood type AB cannot have a child with type O blood.

R E O

III. Is it possible for a woman with type A blood to have a child with type O blood? ☒ yes ☐ no
Explain your answer. (You may need to use a Punnet square to demonstrate the proper cross.)
If the woman is heterozygous (I^Ai), she can have a type O child if she marries a man with a recessive allele (I^Ai, I^Bi, or ii).

	I^A	i
i, I^B, or I^A	I^AI^A	I^Ai
i	I^Ai	ii

Name______________________________

Date____________________ Hour__________

5b Genetics

Part V Problems with Dihybrid Crosses

A dihybrid cross deals with two sets of characteristics at the same time. Read carefully the material on dihybrid crosses in your text (pp. 144–45).

The abilities of some people to taste PTC and roll their tongue into a U shape when it is extended from the mouth are dominant characteristics. We will call those who exhibit the dominant traits "tasters" and "rollers," and we will call those who exhibit the recessive traits "nontasters" and "nonrollers." The capital letters T *and* R *will be used for the dominant alleles, and the lowercase letters* t *and* r *for the recessive alleles in this exercise.*

A Simple Dihybrid Cross

R E O

I. A man who is homozygous for tongue rolling and homozygous for the ability to taste PTC (genotype *RRTT*) marries a woman who is homozygous for both recessive traits.

- Write the genotype for his recessive wife.

  rrtt

- What possible gametes can the husband form? (Remember that a gamete will have one of every homologous pair of chromosomes. It is thus impossible to have an *RR* gamete or a *TT* gamete.)

  RT

- What possible gametes can the wife form?

  rt

- On the Punnett square on the right, cross these two people. What is the genotype of their offspring? NOTE: You should have only one genotype for the offspring, and that genotype must have four letters. If yours does not work this way, go back and check your work.

roller (*RR* or *Rr*)

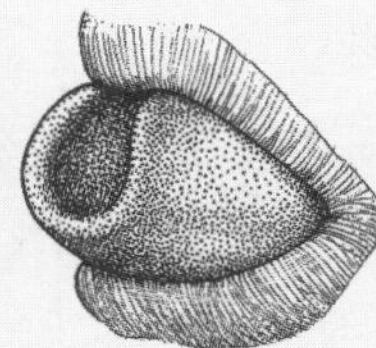

nonroller (*rr*)

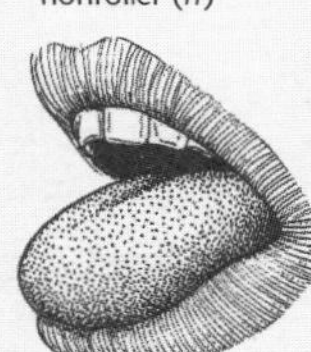

5b.1 Tongues of a roller and a nonroller

	rt	rt	rt	rt
RT	RrTt	RrTt		
RT	RrTt	RrTt		
RT				
RT				

When doing dihybrid crosses, students frequently have difficulty coming up with the gametes. Chalkboard diagrams help. Remind the students that gametes go on the top and side of a Punnett square.

When working dihybrid crosses, the students should use a sixteen-box Punnett square regardless of how many boxes are needed for the cross. The fact that there are sixteen boxes in the Punnett square for this example, all of which will be filled in with the same genotype, is confusing to some students. It is suggested that you work out a similar problem ahead of time in class, pointing out that although not all the boxes are needed, they are usually all drawn.

II. A man who is heterozygous for both rolling his tongue and tasting PTC marries a woman with the same genotype.

- Write the genotypes for them:

  man RrTt woman RrTt

- What are the possible gametes they can form?

  man RT, Rt, rT, rt woman RT, Rt, rT, rt

- Cross this couple on the Punnett square to the right.
- Give the resulting phenotypic ratio in the proper spaces.

  9 roller-taster(s)

  3 roller-nontaster(s)

  3 nonroller-taster(s)

  1 nonroller-nontaster(s)

	RT	Rt	rT	rt
RT	RRTT	RRTt	RrTT	RrTt
Rt	RRTt	RRtt	RrTt	Rrtt
rT	RrTT	RrTt	rrTT	rrTt
rt	RrTt	Rrtt	rrTt	rrtt

Another Dihybrid Cross

In fruit flies, vestigial wings and hairy bodies are recessive traits that are caused by recessive genes located on different chromosomes. The normal alleles (long wings and hairless body) are dominant.

I. Using the above information, fill in the following chart with symbols for the alleles.

l is the allele for vestigial wings.

L is the allele for long wings.

H is the allele for hairless bodies.

h is the allele for hairy bodies.

II. Suppose a vestigial-winged, hairy-bodied male is crossed with a homozygous dominant female. (Work the Punnett squares for these questions on a separate sheet of paper. You will not turn it in.)

- What offspring would be expected? (Show genotypes and phenotypes as ratios.)
  - Genotype: 4 LlHh : 0 any other type
  - Phenotype: 4 long-winged, hairless-bodied fruit flies : 0 any other
- If these F_1 offspring are permitted to mate freely, what would you expect their offspring (the F_2) to be like? Show genotypes and phenotypes as ratios.
  - Genotype: 1 LLHH : 2 LLHh : 2 LlHH : 4 LlHh : l LLhh : 2 Llhh : 1llHH : 2 llHh : 1 llhh (These may be in any order.)
  - Phenotype: 9 long-winged, hairless-bodied : 3 long-winged, hairy-bodied : 3 vestigial-winged, hairless-bodied : 1 vestigial-winged, hairy-bodied (These may be in any order.)

Name________________ Date________ Hour________

5b
Genetics

Part VI Problems with Sex-Linked Traits

Carefully study the pedigree of Queen Victoria and Prince Albert on pages 149–50 of your text and read the material regarding sex-linked traits on pages 148–49. Hemophilia, a recessive trait found on the X chromosome, is sometimes called "bleeder's disease." Traits on the X chromosome that are not found on the Y chromosome are usually written as superscripts (above and to the right) of the symbol for the chromosome—the X. The Y, which lacks the gene for this trait, is left without a superscript. Since hemophilia is recessive, we will use the letter h *for the hemophilia gene and* H *for the normal, dominant gene.*

I. Write the genotypes for the people described below. One phenotype given below is impossible and does not have a genotype. Put a star (*) in the blank for the impossible phenotype.

- A normal female who carries the gene for hemophilia: X^HX^h
- A normal male who carries the gene for hemophilia: *
- A normal female without a gene for hemophilia: X^HX^H
- A normal male without a gene for hemophilia: X^HY
- A hemophiliac female: X^hX^h
- A hemophiliac male: X^hY

II. Answer the following.

- What is Queen Victoria's genotype? X^HX^h
- What is Prince Albert's genotype? X^HY
- Cross Queen Victoria and Prince Albert on Punnett Square A.
  - In the proper boxes of the Punnett square, write names of their offspring.
  - Is it possible to have a noncarrier female from Victoria and Albert? ☒ yes ☐ no
- On Punnett Square B, cross Beatrice of the first generation with Henry of Battenburg.
  - Show how they were able to have Alexander and Maurice, both males, but one with hemophilia and the other without the disease. (Write their names in the proper boxes.)
  - Is it possible to have a hemophiliac female from this cross? ☐ yes ☒ no

A

	X^H	X^h
X^H	X^HX^H Victoria, Helena, Louise	X^HX^h Alice, Beatrice
Y	X^HY Edward VII, Alfred, Arthur	X^hY Leopold

B

	X^H	X^h
X^H	X^HX^H	X^HX^h
Y	X^HY Alexander	X^hY Maurice

Students may try to do these sex-linked crosses without using the X chromosomes and Y chromosomes. Consider solving the problem with this three-step method: (1) Have them list in the proper spaces on page L55 the X and Y chromosomes to indicate whether the person is male or female. (2) Have them go back and add the proper superscript to the X chromosomes. (3) Then tell them to add superscripts to the Y chromosomes, if needed. If they indicate that superscripts are needed, you should explain what a sex-linked trait is. If they indicate that superscripts are not needed, ask them to explain why. (You may still need to explain what a sex-linked trait is.)

- On Punnett Square C, cross Alice of the first generation and Louis IV.
  - To show how they can have Elizabeth and Irene, both females, but one a carrier and the other a noncarrier, write their names in the proper spaces of the Punnett square.
  - Is it possible to have a hemophiliac female from this cross? ☐ yes ☒ no

	X^H	X^h
X^H	X^HX^H Elizabeth	X^HX^h Irene
Y	X^HY	X^hY

C

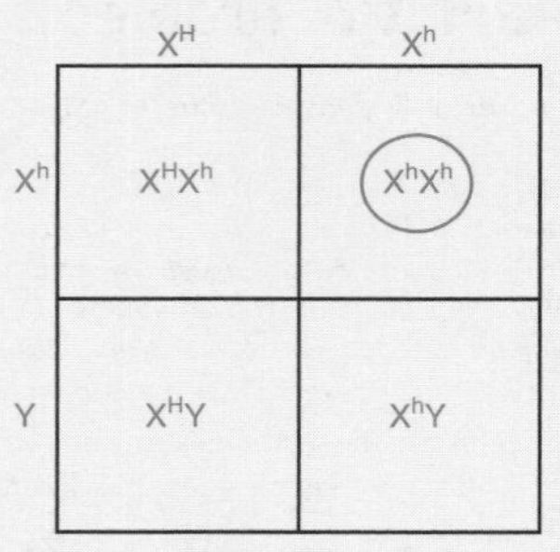

- If Frederick William married his cousin Alice (both of the second generation), could they produce a hemophiliac female? ☒ yes ☐ no
- Prove your answer on Punnett Square D. If there is a hemophiliac female, circle her genotype.
- Since there is no difference between the phenotype of a female carrier and the phenotype of a normal female, how have the people who compiled this chart been able to determine who were carriers and who were not? by studying the offspring

- The current English ruling family (Queen Elizabeth II, fourth generation) has gone for five generations without a hemophiliac individual. This is because Edward VII, Victoria's son, did not have hemophilia. Explain how this fact eliminated the hemophilia gene from the current line of English rulers. Since Edward VII did not inherit the gene from his mother (and his father could not give him this gene), Edward could not pass it on to his offspring.

Name______________________

Date______________ Hour________

6 Genetic Research

Materials

- library

Goals

- To learn about the current topics of genetic research
- To make some decisions regarding genetic research

Genetic research makes headlines today more frequently than ever before. Scientists are not yet ready to announce cures for all kinds of cancer or a way to replace a worn-out heart or liver with a cloned (genetically identical) replacement/transplant. Nor have they engineered a plant that will withstand heat, frost, drought, and flood and still produce abundant, edible, nutritious fruit. But many of the experiments being done today yield information that brings those and other genetic dreams closer to reality.

With all abilities come not only opportunities but also responsibilities. For example, when you begin to drive a car, you have not only the opportunity to drive the car for good purposes (going to school or church, doing errands for the family) but also the opportunity to improperly use the car (going places you should not go, driving recklessly). It is your responsibility to use the car as it should be used.

The same principle holds true for scientific information. Most people would rejoice at the announcement that scientists had learned to use a few blood cells to grow kidneys that can be implanted when needed and will not be rejected. Such information, however, could also permit people to do things that might not meet with such universal approval and might even violate scriptural principles of morality.

In this exercise you will be asked to read about a current area of genetic research or application of genetic knowledge and to speculate about the good and the bad that could result from the information's being learned and used.

Research

I. In a periodical that has come out within the past two years, find an article that deals with current genetic research and/or application.
- The article may deal with any of the following.
  - Recombinant DNA
  - Genetic screening
  - Cloning
  - Gene therapy
  - Stem cell research
  - Genetically modified organisms or crops
  - Artificial reproduction (artificial insemination, test tube fertilization, surrogate motherhood)
- The article may deal with humans, plants, animals, protists, bacteria, or the release of genetically altered organisms into the environment.

II. If possible, find other articles dealing with the same genetic research or application of knowledge.
- Look in other periodicals that came out about the same time.
- Use the Internet to search for additional information or recent developments.
- Look for reactions of scientists, physicians, scientific groups, activist groups, political leaders, government agencies, and other groups regarding this or closely related research or applications.

This activity should not become an exercise in learning how to use the library. It is often difficult for some students to find appropriate information on these topics in the *Reader's Guide to Periodical Literature.* The list of topics given in the Research section should help if you plan to send students to the library to conduct their own research.

Some teachers find it advisable to make a list of specific genetic topics or reports they have read that would lend themselves to the kind of analysis being asked for in this exercise. By offering this list of selected topics to the students, the teacher is sure that the students will be spending their time on significant topics that will permit good analysis. You may wish to offer the students a short selected bibliography on the genetic research or applications.

Some teachers find it advisable to collect articles about various genetic topics for the students (or groups). In this way the exercise stresses the analysis of the topic rather than the finding of articles. Also, not all articles on genetic research lend themselves to the kind of analysis that is asked for in this exercise.

Introduction

Today it is impossible for any textbook to remain current when it deals with genetics. By the time a sentence dealing with genetic research is written and makes it into a classroom, it is out of date. This exercise is, in part, designed to deal with major genetic advances that are not a part of this text.

The other reason for this exercise is more important. It is one thing for the text and the teacher to speak about current genetic trends and the possible scriptural or moral principles that may be violated. It is quite another for the student to make these judgments himself. The experience of doing so, however, is important. When one has made these sorts of judgments several times and has had the experience of analyzing not only his own conclusions but also the conclusions of others, he will be more likely to make good judgments. The Christian classroom is the ideal place for a young person to practice making good judgments. This exercise is designed to help guide him through an early decision-making experience so that he will be prepared to make good decisions in the future.

Required / Extra / Omit

It is suggested that you either require the entire exercise or omit it completely.

It is recommended that you do this exercise as group projects. Each group should select (or be assigned) a particular genetic issue and should prepare a single written report (set of answers). You may wish to have the reports given orally.

You may wish to have the students (or groups) present their findings and analyses as oral reports. Classroom discussions of the Analysis section should greatly improve the students' ability to evaluate scientific study and the use of scientific information.

R E O

Analysis

In some of the following spaces you may need to indicate "none." In those answers where you deal with scriptural matters, be sure to give references. Answer the questions in outline sections II–V on your own paper.

I. Describe the genetic research or application.

- Who or what group did the research or experimentation? ______

- What organisms are currently involved in this genetic research or application? ______

- What part of the organism(s) is currently involved? ______

- What has been done? (Summarize the process of doing it, not the results.) ______

- What results have been achieved? ______

R E O

II. What are the projected outcomes of this genetic research or application?
- What is projected as the immediate outcome (benefits) of this genetic research or application? Mention any time frame that is given.
- What are the projected long-range benefits of this genetic research or application? Mention any time frame that is given.
- What drawbacks or potential problems connected with this genetic research or application are mentioned?

III. What is your analysis of the present research and its present application?
- Were any scriptural principles violated in the discovery of the information (research)? If so, explain.
- Is the present application(s) of the information in violation of scriptural principles? If so, explain.
- What advantages or drawbacks not mentioned above might emerge regarding the present use of the information?

IV. What is your analysis of the future uses of this genetic research or application?
- To what studies might this information contribute?
- What potential scriptural problems might arise from the use of this information?
- What advantages or drawbacks not mentioned above might arise regarding the future use of the information?

V. What can you recommend to prevent present and/or future abuse of this knowledge and/or unacceptable applications of the knowledge?

Name____________________
Date__________ Hour________

7 DNA Extraction

Materials

- distilled water
- small clear plastic cup
- graduated cylinder
- 6% salt solution
- 25% solution of liquid dish soap
- rubbing (isopropyl or ethyl) alcohol or denatured alcohol
- glass or wooden stirring rod
- test tube
- phenol red indicator

Goals

- To perform a simple DNA extraction using cheek epithelial cells
- To observe DNA strands separated from the nucleus

DNA can be found in most cell types in your body. Although the amount in a single cell is microscopic, it is a simple process to collect a quantity that is visible without magnification. In an earlier lab, stains were used to make the nuclear material more obvious. In this lab, you will be painlessly removing cells from your own mouth and, with some simple chemical and physical reactions, releasing the DNA from the nucleus and separating it from the other cellular contents.

The extraction and analysis of DNA in professional labs requires the use of enzymes and is conducted under very controlled conditions. After extraction, the DNA molecules are separated through a process called gel electrophoresis. The end result is an image of light and dark bands that is unique to each individual organism.

I. Collect your cheek cells.
- Use the graduated cylinder to measure 15 mL of water and pour it into your plastic cup.
- Swirl this water around in your mouth for at least thirty seconds. The more vigorously you swirl, the more cheek cells you will collect.
- Spit this swirled water back into the cup.
- What type of cells have you just collected? (Hint: see lab 3A) mucous epithelial cells
- Observe and describe the appearance of your solution. probably slightly cloudy with some bubbles

II. Treat the cell solution.
- Using a graduated cylinder, measure out 5 mL of the salt solution and add it to the contents of the cup.
- Using the same graduated cylinder, measure out 5 mL of the soap solution and add it also to the contents of the cup.
- Why is soap used to release DNA? (Hint: Soap cleans dishes because it breaks fats apart.) The cell membrane and the nuclear membrane contain lipids bonded together. The soap loosens these bonds, allowing the DNA material to escape.
- Swirl the cup around to mix the salt and soap solutions with the water and cells.
- Observe and describe the appearance of your solution at this point. about the same as the last description

You need to use clear plastic cups instead of translucent ones. Large test tubes may work better if they are available.

The 6% salt solution is made by adding 1 tbsp of salt to 8 oz of water.

Noniodized salt works best.

The 25% soap solution is made by mixing 1 part soap to 3 parts water.

If you have plastic squeeze bottles for the solutions, it will be easier for the students to dispense the right amount.

Most rubbing alcohol is 70% isopropyl alcohol (C_3H_7OH), and this should work well. If a higher concentration is available, it may yield clearer results. A similar solution of ethyl alcohol (C_2H_5OH) will also work.

A large wooden match or toothpick may work to gather the DNA, but it must be long enough to reach the bottom of the test tube if you are going to do the final step.

Phenol red indicator is sometimes called phenolsulfonphthalein. It is sold as a 0.02% aqueous solution that ranges from yellow at 6.8 pH to red at 8.2 pH.

If you do not have thoroughly clean graduated cylinders with which to measure the water that will be swirled in the mouth, calculate where the water should come up to in the cup and pre-mark each cup.

Encourage students to vigorously swirl the water in their mouths to increase the cell load in their sample. If a student has brushed his teeth or drunk recently, he might have more difficulty getting enough cells to yield significant amounts of DNA. A cotton-tipped applicator can also be used to obtain a sample. Scrub the cheek with the cotton-tipped end and then swirl the cotton tip in the 15 mL of water.

Introduction

This exercise allows students to collect some of their own cells and, through a series of simple steps, extract the DNA for observation. It makes the esoteric discussion of the double helix of DNA relevant, because the students actually get to look at a visible sample of their own genetic material. The entire procedure could be done in much less than one class period, allowing time for lecture.

A quick Internet search yields many other DNA extraction labs that are done in a similar manner. Most of them extract DNA from plant cells of onions, bananas, or dried split peas. This particular lab is probably more satisfying for students since they are seeing their own DNA.

Some advanced high-school biology lab courses use gel electrophoresis to analyze DNA in a manner similar to biomedical labs. These kits are available from many science supply companies. While this may be fascinating for some students, it involves costly equipment and supplies, and the value gained is not commensurate with the cost.

Required / Extra / Omit

Because of the brevity of this lab, it is recommended that you complete all of the sections. You can save even more time by having the salt and soap solutions prepared in advance, using the directions under Notes on Materials.

If you do not have phenol red indicator, it would be possible to skip the last step. However, this confirms the acid content of the sample, indicating the presence of DNA.

It is critical that the alcohol be added slowly. Pour it carefully down the side of the cup. If it becomes mixed, the separation of the DNA is seldom successful.

Some labs specify that the alcohol be chilled in an ice bath to accelerate the DNA separation and decrease the amount of mixing that might occur with the solution already in the cup. You should try it at room temperature first to determine whether this is necessary.

The phenol red indicator turns the solution a yellow color, showing that acid is present. This is the deoxyribonucleic **acid** of DNA.

III. Separate the DNA from the solution.
- Use a graduated cylinder to measure out 15 mL of the alcohol.
- After tilting the cup, slowly pour the alcohol down the side so that it forms a separate layer on top of the solution already in the cup. It is important to do this slowly. If you allow mixing to occur, your results will be affected.
- Gently put the cup down without mixing the layers.
- Allow it to sit for two to three minutes.
- Hold the cup up toward a light and look for a cloudy layer of stringy material separating out just below the alcohol layer.
- If you see bubbles rising through the alcohol, observe them carefully. They may be drawing white "strings" of thousands of DNA molecules along with them as they rise.
- Why does the DNA material collect here between the water and the alcohol? The alcohol stays on top because it is less dense than water. The lipids and DNA material rise to the top of the water because of their lower density, and the DNA is even less dense than alcohol, causing it to rise into the alcohol.

IV. Physically remove a DNA sample from the cup.
- Insert a glass or wooden rod into the cup, putting it the whole way down so that it touches the bottom of the cup.
- Slowly turn it in one direction, but *do not stir*.
- Look for the white strings to be collecting around the rod as you turn it.
- Gently remove the rod. There should be clumps containing many DNA molecules wound around the rod.

R E O

V. Verify the presence of DNA.
- Insert the rod containing the DNA strings into a test tube containing 15 mL of the 6% NaCl solution.
- Spin the rod to dislodge the DNA into the water.
- What happens to your DNA molecules when you place them in the water? They should clump together if enough are present.
- Add five drops of phenol red indicator to the solution. (Be careful with the indicator as it may permanently stain clothing.)
- Phenol red indicator ranges in color from yellow at a pH of 6.8 to red at 8.2.
- What color change, if any, did you observe when phenol red was added to your water and cell solution? (It should have turned yellow if enough of the DNA was present.)
- What does this tell you about your solution and the type of materials it contains? DNA is essentially an acid, and that caused the pH of the solution to become acidic, turning to yellow.
- Extraction is defined as removing a substance using chemical and/or physical means. What chemical means did you use to extract your DNA? the addition of soap to break down the membranes
- What physical means did you use? the addition of alcohol to aid separation, the swirling of the mixture

Name________________________________

Date____________________ Hour__________

8
Creationism: My Beliefs and Their Defense

Materials
- a Bible

Goals
- To think through information about Creation and decide upon a biblical position
- To defend a position on Creationism biblically and logically

It is one thing to read and hear about Creation and quite another to know what you believe. It is one thing to know what you believe and still another to defend your position. In this exercise you are asked to state your position on various Creationist topics and to give your reasons for taking these positions. As you do this lab, think about how you would use this information to help a person who has not been taught about Creation or has not taken the time to think through it.

My Creationist Creed

A creed is a short statement of belief. It normally lists, without explanation, what a person (or group) believes. Of course, for a Christian, any creed must reflect biblical positions. In the space below, write your personal creed regarding Creationism. Using your own words, cover the main aspects of this view. After each statement, list in parentheses the Scripture passages that support it.

I believe Answers will vary. Look for statements dealing with God's direct action at Creation and with the accuracy of the biblical account. The creed may also include statements about a young earth, the various interpretations of Genesis 1–3, and similar thoughts.

My Answers to Some Evolutionist Statements

Below are several statements frequently used to defend evolutionary theory. Based on the information you find in Chapter 8 and other areas in the text (as well as outside references if necessary), answer the following arguments with logical, scientific, and if possible, scriptural statements. Use additional paper if necessary.

I. According to many evolutionists, reptiles are the evolutionary ancestors of birds. Microscopic examination shows that scales and feathers have a similar chemical composition. Evolutionists use this fact to support their argument that scales evolved into feathers. Evolutionists disregard the fact that there is no fossil evidence of such evolution; they claim that fossils of feather evolution simply have not been located. What arguments would you use to support the Creationist position that birds did not evolve from reptiles? Answers may vary. It is more logical to think that scales and feathers originating from similar skin tissues indicate similarity of design than it is to think that they indicate evolution. Students might use these supporting arguments: the improbability of necessary mutations; the uselessness of the "half feathers/half scales" found during the process; and the statement in Scripture that reptiles and birds were created on different days of Creation (Gen. 1:20–25). The lack of fossil evidence for feather evolution is significant, although most evolutionists would not like to admit such an argument.

Introduction

This exercise can be used in several ways. It can be assigned as homework to be collected and graded. Although worthwhile, this method is probably not the best use of the exercise because the students' ideas and opinions are not as quickly put to the test, evaluated, and changed as they are with some other methods.

A more profitable method is to assign groups of students to different sections of the exercise—one group to the creed and one group to each of the four questions. The group that is assigned to the creed should present a statement of good Creationist beliefs on which they (and other believers) can agree. When this is presented, the rest of the class should consider adding to or deleting from the creed. Each of the other groups should present a panel discussion of the various aspects of the question they were assigned and then discuss questions from the rest of the class. Using the exercise in this way will probably take most of a class period.

A third method is to assign the students to read the exercise and make notes regarding their answers so that they can discuss them in class the next day. In class, the teacher should lead the discussion, challenging the students to defend their answers. Some teachers may want the students to fill out the exercise after it has been discussed in class and then hand it in.

Yet another method is to assign to each group a particular question that they must answer in an oral report. Let the students have several days to work on their questions. It would be advisable to allow a few minutes at the beginning (or end) of each class for the groups to get together. Then on the appointed day, have each group present an answer in a three-to-five-minute oral report.

II. A visit to the zoo confirms that man shares many characteristics with the primates, especially the great apes. Evolutionists are quick to point out these uncanny similarities. They also delight in the fact that we share 98% of our DNA with chimpanzees. This, they say, is clear proof that we had a common ancestor. How would you refute this? Evolutionists have an underlying belief that similarity is equal to relationship. They apply this when it fits their scenario of how living things evolved but ignore it when similar structures appear on animals that they do not feel are closely related. For instance, the octopus is a mollusk but has a pair of very complex eyes. Evolutionists do not interpret this as a sign that they are closely related to eyed vertebrates but as a coincidental development of a similar structure. Creationists explain the similarities between humans and primates the same way they do similarities between two kinds of animals. Living things that live in similar habitats and have similar diets and needs look alike because they have a common Designer who knows what works best for each situation.

III. Evolutionists often claim that homology indicates common ancestry. The fact that the "arms" of many vertebrates contain the same number of bones (illustration, top of p. 231 in the text) is often used as an example of homology. Fish, frogs, lizards, birds, rats, monkeys, and man all have digestive systems with a liver attached to the intestine by a tube just below the stomach. Evolutionists argue from this similarity that all these organisms can be traced to a common ancestor. How would you argue against this logic? Answers may vary. Evolutionists are forced by their theory to believe that mutations are the mechanism of evolution. Because mutations are random and almost always harmful, the number of mutations necessary to effect the evolution from fish to human would create such a genetic load that the organism could not survive. Evolutionists would answer that survival of the fittest eliminated the organisms with "defective" digestive systems, keeping the superior design that we observe. On the other hand, Creationists believe that the design that we observe is an evidence of an intelligent Designer and Creator, not of evolution based on random mutations.

IV. Almost all the mammals of Australia belong to the order Marsupialia (pouched mammals, such as the kangaroo and koala—see pp. 562–63 in the text). Evolutionists generally believe that these are "lower mammals" because their reproduction does not involve a placenta, which is a complex structure. Some evolutionists claim that there is no environmental pressure upon these marsupial mammals to develop into placental forms. Because of this, these pouched mammals continue to live contentedly in Australia. What arguments can you give against the evolutionary concept that marsupials are a "lower" form? Answers may vary. The opossum, a North American marsupial, shows no evidence of evolving into a placental animal, although it must face the same pressures that supposedly caused other mammals of North America to "become placental." The pressure referred to by evolutionists would have to cause genetic changes, which the animal cannot control. A placental mammal placed in Australia (rabbit—see pp. 576–77 in the text) may thrive and may even replace a marsupial mammal in the ecosystem; however, its survival does not show that placental mammals are more advanced. It is the lack of natural enemies and other controlling factors, not the organism's actual "superiority," that results in its numerical dominance and eventual replacement of the native organism. In the same way, the gypsy moth in North America competes successfully with native insects for a niche, but its success does not prove that the gypsy moth is superior to other insects.

Name________________________

Date____________ Hour________

9 The Use of Biological Keys

Materials

- animal specimens and photographs or illustrations

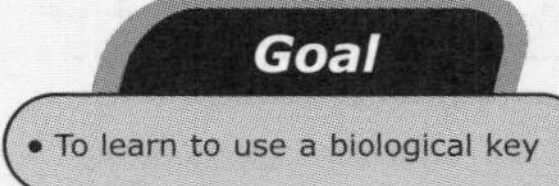

- To learn to use a biological key

Included with this laboratory exercise is A Biological Key for Major Animal Classifications. You will use this general simplified biological key to classify specimens (and some photographs or illustrations of specimens) in the laboratory. You will have a limited amount of time to correctly identify the specimens and properly record all the information regarding your identifications. Before you come to class, carefully read the instructions, study the examples, and do the samples that are presented.

Preliminary Work

I. Read carefully the instructions on using a biological identification key in Facet: What Is It? on pages 244–45 in your text. On page L64 is a glossary of terms used in the key. You may use this glossary while you identify organisms in the laboratory.

II. In order to receive credit for having correctly identified an organism, you will need to fill out all the information requested on the Specimen Identification Chart.
- The Sample Specimen Identification Chart (p. L64) is filled in for Specimen A, a leopard frog (illustrated on p. 524 of the text). Check carefully to see how all the information was obtained from the Biological Key.
- The chart has also been filled in for Specimen B, a grasshopper (illustrated in the top diagram on p. 487 of the text).
  - Note that no subphylum for this example appears in the Biological Key. Thus there is a line drawn in the space marked SP on the Sample Specimen Identification Chart.
  - Draw a line through any blank in the Classification of Specimen column that does not apply.
- Try to identify the organisms listed below and fill in the Sample Specimen Identification Chart for them.
  - Specimen C—the earthworm on page 464 of the text
  - Specimen D—the fish on the bottom of page 511 of the text
  - Specimen E—the timber wolf on page 559 of the text

III. On the lab day be prepared to identify as many of the specimens as you can.
- You may use only the key and the glossary given with this exercise.
- You will have a limited amount of time.
- You must fill in the Specimen Identification Chart accurately and completely to get credit for identifying the organism.
- After completing this exercise, you should know how to use a biological key, not simply be familiar with the divisions of the animal kingdom in the key. This key is highly artificial and does not contain all possible groups. The groupings will be discussed in more detail later.

See page 64 for Notes on Materials.

If you are asking for twenty specimen identifications (the Specimen Identification Chart has twenty blanks), have about twenty-five to thirty different specimens in the classroom. Students should be allowed thirty to forty-five minutes for the exercise. Good students should be able to complete about twenty identifications in this time. Tell the exceptional student who needs more space to use additional paper and to give complete information.

Tell the students how much time they will have to identify the specimens and how many specimens there are. (You should have more specimens than the students can use. This will allow them to eliminate those specimens that are confusing to them.)

Students should be permitted to use only the key, the glossary, and the Specimen Identification Chart (pp. L64–L68) to identify the specimens.

Introduction

Although you may have spent considerable time covering the text material on biological keys (pp. 244–45), when students try to use one, you may see some very unusual identifications (such as elephants in class Aves and cows in phylum Annelida).

The day before doing the exercise, discuss the identification of Specimens A and B shown on page L64. Work out two or three other examples (not the ones suggested in the laboratory exercise) based on pictures in the text or on other pictures or specimens you may have. Try some difficult examples—such as turtle, snake, crayfish, and starfish—as well as easy ones. This will help teach the students some terms they must know in order to use the key (see p. L64). Tell the students to try to identify Specimens C, D, and E as homework. On the following day, before having the students fill in the Specimen Identification Chart for the specimens you have provided, answer questions they may have. Once they begin the exercise, do not allow them to ask questions.

Page L64 contains a list of terms that the students may not know. Go over these terms, giving brief definitions. Since they will learn these terms in detail later, do not spend time on lengthy explanations. The goal at this point is that the students be able to use a biological key.

Remind the students that in order to get credit for any specimen they identify, their entire entry must be correct. Explain that they should go through the key for each specimen, copying down its classification until no further number is given.

Required / Extra / Omit

The main section of this exercise must be done completely or not at all. You may find it best to have the students identify only a few specimens and then to discuss each one. Or you may want to impose a

If you have a large class (or are limiting the time to less than fifteen minutes), use a number of duplicated specimens. For example, you could have a poster of a monarch butterfly (numbered 1) and, in another area, a mounted specimen of a monarch butterfly (also numbered 1). Duplicating specimens will help prevent crowding and copying and will permit a class of thirty students to identify twenty-five specimens without having to waste time waiting to see them. Students may also see clearly in the photograph what they cannot see in the mounted specimen or vice versa. If you do this type of duplication, tell the students that you have done so and that they will get credit for identifying only one of the two specimens numbered 1.

Live or entire preserved specimens are by far the best for this exercise. However, pictures or posters work equally well if they are carefully selected. For example, an elephant can be identified as a member of a particular order by using this key. However, if students cannot see the elephant's foot, they may not know whether it has hooves or not. If you are going to use pictures, be sure you use the key to classify them before you ask the students to do so. When selecting specimens or pictures, be aware that this key is not comprehensive. For example, only seven orders of insects and eight of the twelve orders of mammals that are covered in the text appear on this key. If you run into a set of choices that cannot be made based on the picture you have, find another picture or add a note to the picture. It is best if the students can make the identifications without added notes.

Old calendars, nature magazines, and wildlife websites are all excellent sources of photos and illustrations.

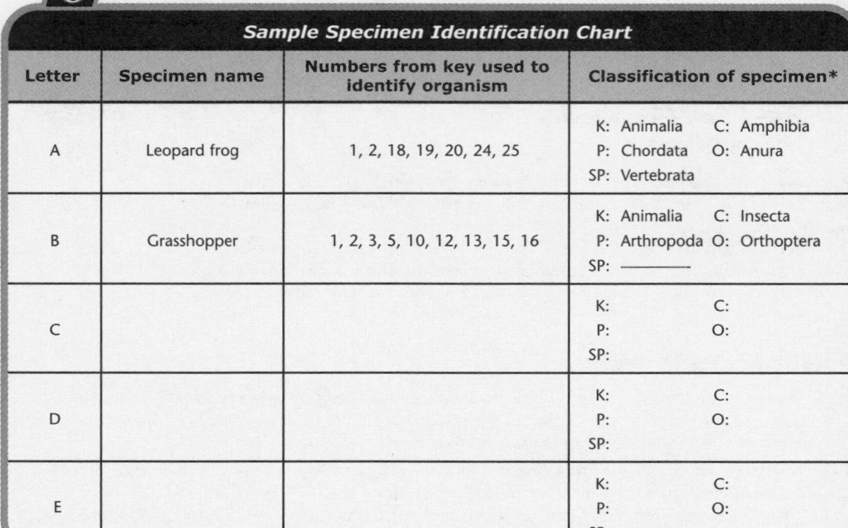

Sample Specimen Identification Chart

Letter	Specimen name	Numbers from key used to identify organism	Classification of specimen*
A	Leopard frog	1, 2, 18, 19, 20, 24, 25	K: Animalia C: Amphibia P: Chordata O: Anura SP: Vertebrata
B	Grasshopper	1, 2, 3, 5, 10, 12, 13, 15, 16	K: Animalia C: Insecta P: Arthropoda O: Orthoptera SP: ———
C			K: C: P: O: SP:
D			K: C: P: O: SP:
E			K: C: P: O: SP:

*Key to symbols used: K—Kingdom P—Phylum SP—Subphylum C—Class O—Order

Glossary for Key to Major Animal Classifications

abdomen *A body region posterior to (below or behind) the thorax in arthropods*

asymmetry *Lack of correspondence of body parts as a result of different shapes, sizes, and structures (animal cannot be divided into like external halves)*

bilateral symmetry *Matching external right and left sides (animal can be divided into matching halves)*

cnidoblast *A stinging cell, characteristic of cnidarians, that contains poisonous barbs, coiled threads, or a sticky substance*

dorsal *Toward the back or upper side of an animal*

epidermal plates *Small, hard plates joined beneath the epidermis to give shape and support*

exoskeleton *A system of external plates that protect and support the animal*

gill *A respiratory structure in aquatic organisms through which oxygen and carbon dioxide are exchanged*

notochord *A tough, flexible rod of cartilage, usually located along the dorsal side of an animal; supports the animal's body*

radial symmetry *Animal can be externally divided in half like a pie; has no right or left side*

tentacle *A long, slender, movable extension of an animal's body*

terminal end *The extreme end of an animal's body*

trunk *A flexible extension of an animal's head used for grasping, feeding, and breathing*

ventral *Toward the underside, or "stomach side," of an animal*

time limit and cut down on the number of specimens or pictures to be identified. (If you do this, you will need duplicate specimens or pictures so that there are enough for all students to be looking at a picture or specimen at the same time.)

Name__________________________

A Biological Key for Major Animal Classifications

This key deals with adult animals, not immature or larval forms. This simplified key is not designed to cover every possible organism but should help you understand the use of biological keys. It is not a field guide but should be used to identify organisms in a laboratory exercise.

1. Autotrophic, perhaps producing flowers and seeds . . . . **Kingdom Plantae**
   Heterotrophic, not producing flowers and seeds . . . . **2** . . **Kingdom Animalia**
2. No backbone (an invertebrate) **3**
   Backbone (a vertebrate) or notochord . . . . **18** . . **Phylum Chordata**
3. Radial symmetry **4**
   Asymmetrical or with bilateral symmetry **5**
4. Soft body, usually transparent; thin tentacles; body with cnidoblasts . . . . **Phylum Cnidaria**
   Firm body with internal support; covered with epidermal plates that often have spines; tiny hollow tube feet protruding from openings in the body covering are used for movement . . . . **Phylum Echinodermata**
5. Exoskeleton . . . . **10** . . **Phylum Arthropoda**
   No exoskeleton; external shell or soft shell-less body **6**
6. External shell . . . . **7** . . **Phylum Mollusca**
   No external shell **8**
7. Coiled shell . . . . **Class Gastropoda**
   Shell of two similar parts . . . . **Class Bivalvia**
8. Wormlike body without sensory tentacles on head . . . . **Phylum Annelida**
   Nonwormlike body, or sensory tentacles on head . . . . **9** . . **Phylum Mollusca**
9. Wormlike body with sensory tentacles on head . . . . **Class Gastropoda**
   Nonwormlike body, but eight or more tentacles used for grasping . . . . **Class Cephalopoda**
10. More than three pairs of legs **11**
    Three pairs of walking legs . . . . **12** . . **Class Insecta**
11. Four pairs of walking legs, body in two divisions . . . . **Class Arachnida**
    More than four pairs of walking legs; perhaps large pincers on some legs; often with large, segmented abdomen; usually aquatic . . . . **Subphylum Crustacea**
12. Wings **13**
    No wings **17**
13. Only transparent wings **14**
    Nontransparent wings **15**
14. Capable of inflicting sting with last abdominal segment . . . . **Order Hymenoptera**
    Not capable of inflicting sting (may be able to bite) . . . . **Order Diptera**
15. Large, often colorful wings covered with scales that easily rub off . . . . **Order Lepidoptera**
    Thick, hard, or leathery wings **16**

16. Pair of hard wings covering a folded pair of thin, transparent wings . . . . Order Coleoptera
    Pair of leathery wings covering a pair of straight, thin, transparent wings . . . . Order Orthoptera

17. Piercing, sucking mouthparts for obtaining blood . . . . Order Siphonaptera
    Chewing mouthparts . . . . Order Hymenoptera

18. No vertebrae (backbone) . . . . Subphylum Cephalochordata
    Vertebrae (backbone) . . . . 19 . . Subphylum Vertebrata

19. Jaws or beak 20
    No jaws or beak . . . . Class Agnatha

20. Skin is covered with scales 21
    Skin lacks scales 24

21. Fins; breathing by means of gills 22
    No fins; breathing by means of lungs . . . . 23 . . Class Reptilia

22. Mouth on ventral (lower) side of body . . . . Class Chondrichthyes
    Mouth at terminal (most anterior) end of body . . . . Class Osteichthyes

23. Legs or legless, no dorsal (top) or ventral (bottom) shell . . . . Order Squamata
    Legs and dorsal (top) and ventral (bottom) shell . . . . Order Testudinata

24. Skin is naked (no hair, scales, or feathers) and slimy . . . . 25 . . Class Amphibia
    Skin with feathers or hair 26

25. Tail . . . . Order Caudata
    No tail . . . . Order Anura

26. Body covered with feathers . . . . Class Aves
    Body covered with hair . . . . 27 . . Class Mammalia

27. Hooves 28
    No hooves 29

28. Odd number of toes, each with a hoof . . . . Order Perissodactyla
    Even number of toes, each with a hoof . . . . Order Artiodactyla

29. Eats other animals 30
    Eats vegetable matter 31

30. Lives on land . . . . Order Carnivora
    Fishlike bodies, some with blowholes . . . . Order Cetacea

31. Enlarged front teeth for gnawing 32
    No enlarged front teeth for gnawing 33

32. Legs suitable for crawling . . . . Order Rodentia
    Hind legs suitable for jumping . . . . Order Lagomorpha

33. Enlarged trunk, used for breathing and for grasping . . . . Order Proboscidea
    Tendency to stand erect on two hind limbs . . . . Order Primates

Name________________________________

Specimen Identification Chart

#	Specimen name	Numbers from key used to identify organism	Classification of specimen*
			K: C: P: O: SP:
			K: C: P: O: SP:
			K: C: P: O: SP:
			K: C: P: O: SP:
			K: C: P: O: SP:
			K: C: P: O: SP:
			K: C: P: O: SP:
			K: C: P: O: SP:
			K: C: P: O: SP:
			K: C: P: O: SP:

*Key to symbols used: K—Kingdom P—Phylum SP—Subphylum C—Class O—Order

To avoid crowding, tell the students that they may start at any of the specimens and enter it in the first blank on the specimen chart. The next one they choose to identify may go in the second blank, and so on.

A grading suggestion: Start with the specimen numbered 1. Go through all the students' papers, grading their classification of that specimen (if they have it). Then do the same for number 2, and so on. This method is actually faster than trying to grade an entire paper (that will have the entries out of order) before going on to the next one.

Another grading suggestion: The student who correctly identifies the most specimens in the time allotted sets the standard for the class. Thus, if twenty-five specimens were available, and the best paper has eighteen right, then nineteen correct is a perfect paper. Other grades should be scaled from that point.

Specimen Identification Chart

#	Specimen name	Numbers from key used to identify organism	Classification of specimen*
			K: C: P: O: SP:
			K: C: P: O: SP:
			K: C: P: O: SP:
			K: C: P: O: SP:
			K: C: P: O: SP:
			K: C: P: O: SP:
			K: C: P: O: SP:
			K: C: P: O: SP:
			K: C: P: O: SP:
			K: C: P: O: SP:

*Key to symbols used: K—Kingdom P—Phylum SP—Subphylum C—Class O—Order

Name________________________

Date______________ Hour________

10a
Bacterial Basics

Materials

- petri dishes
- divided petri dishes
- agar
- nutrient agar (beef extract, peptone)
- test tubes
- transfer loop
- Bunsen burner
- laboratory cultures of *Bacillus cereus*, *B. subtilis*, *Rhodospirillum rubrum*, *Sarcina lutea*, and *S. subflava*
- incubator
- preserved slide of bacteria types
- dropping pipets
- distilled water
- cotton
- autoclave
- microscope
- immersion oil

Goals

- To observe the laboratory techniques for handling and culturing bacteria in an experiment
- To observe bacterial growth rates under different conditions
- To observe different types of bacteria

In this laboratory exercise several types of living bacteria will be cultured under laboratory conditions. These cultures will be prepared one day, and then they will be observed twenty-four, forty-eight, and seventy-two hours later. The instructor will set up the laboratory cultures as a demonstration. You will observe these cultures and record the observations during the first few minutes of class for the next several days.

The species of bacteria used in this lab are nonpathogenic; however, if a culture becomes contaminated with bacteria from the air, pathogenic bacteria could be cultured. Therefore, you must handle live bacteria only under the instructor's supervision. ***Under no circumstances should you open any bacterial culture in the laboratory without the presence and supervision of the instructor.*** *You can easily make your observations for this laboratory exercise through the lid of the culture container.*

Materials Used in Culturing Bacteria

Carefully observe the following pieces of equipment in the laboratory. You should be able to recognize them and know what they are used for.

Equipment

- The **petri dish**, a flat dish with a flat lid, is used for culturing bacteria, molds, and similar organisms on solid culture media.
- The **autoclave**, a piece of equipment used to sterilize materials for culturing bacteria, normally contains a closed chamber that can be heated and will keep its contents under pressure. Adequate heat and pressure will kill even spores.
- The **incubator**, a piece of equipment containing a chamber that can be kept at a specific temperature, is used to culture organisms such as bacteria.
- A **culture slant** is a test tube of solid culture medium that has been cooled at an angle, forming a large surface area of the culture medium on which to grow bacteria.
- A **transfer loop** is a piece of wire with a small loop at one end and a handle on the other. The wire can be heated to destroy bacteria on it and can then be used to transfer bacteria from one culture to another.

(Continued on next page)

See Note B on page A18 for sources and substitutions for the equipment used in this exercise.

Carolina Biological Supply Company stocks the bacteria required for this exercise. Other bacteria, however, may be substituted. Those listed were chosen for their differing growth rates, their visibility, and their variety of appearances. They are also large bacteria that, if you desire, can be stained with a common bacteriological stain (methylene blue, safranine, crystal violet, etc.) and seen relatively easily under a microscope.

Nutrient agar can be made by boiling 3 g of beef extract, 5 g of peptone, and 15 g of agar in 1 L of distilled water until dissolved. However, the dehydrated nutrient agar available from many scientific suppliers is very good and considerably more convenient. It is probably cheaper over a period of time, since beef extract is not usable after a few years of refrigeration. Dehydrated nutrient agar and nutrient broth are available in single-serving pouches from some suppliers.

Introduction

Bacteria are among those organisms that students hear about and see odd-looking photographs of but do not really understand until they have experience with them. For this reason high-school students should be exposed to bacteria culturing. However, having thirty students working in a laboratory with living bacteria cultures could be dangerous. Much time would be spent in explaining the proper techniques in order to ensure that students did not contaminate cultures and possibly expose themselves to pathogens.

This exercise calls for the teacher to set up the bacteria cultures as a demonstration. Thus the risk of contamination and the possibility of culturing a pathogen and exposing students to it are avoided. The cultures are subjected to various growth conditions and observed by students for several days. This exercise exposes students to the equipment and techniques used in culturing bacteria and permits them to observe bacterial growth without spending a long time learning bacteriological skills that they will probably never use.

Required / Extra / Omit

Whether or not you do the experiment, have the students read and be responsible for the information in the sections on materials and techniques used in culturing bacteria (pp. L69–L71).

All of the laboratory exercise should be required.

If you set up these experiments in class on a Monday or Tuesday, the observations can be made on the following three days.

The seventy-two-hour observation of bacterial growth rates (p. L73) may be eliminated, since usually little significant growth follows the forty-eight-hour observation. Thus the demonstration could be done on Wednesday, and the observation could still be completed before the weekend.

Some teachers may find it best to use mock cultures for the demonstration and then to announce that actual cultures were set up the previous day and are ready for the twenty-four-hour observation.

In some situations it may be advisable to have a mock demonstration on Friday and then to set up the actual cultures on Sunday. Thus the first observation would be on Monday.

Culture Media

- **Beef extract** is a paste made of beef. It serves as a nutrient source in culturing many bacteria.
- **Peptone** is an enzyme that digests protein. It is added to many bacterial culture media since many bacteria are not able to digest some proteins.
- **Agar** is an agent obtained from certain algae; it is used to solidify the culture media on which bacteria grow.
- **Nutrient broth** is a mixture of beef extract, peptone, and water that is used for growing certain species of bacteria.
- **Broth culture** is a culture of bacteria in a fluid medium (like nutrient broth).
- **Nutrient agar** is a mixture of beef extract, peptone, water, and agar that is used for growing bacteria on a solid medium.

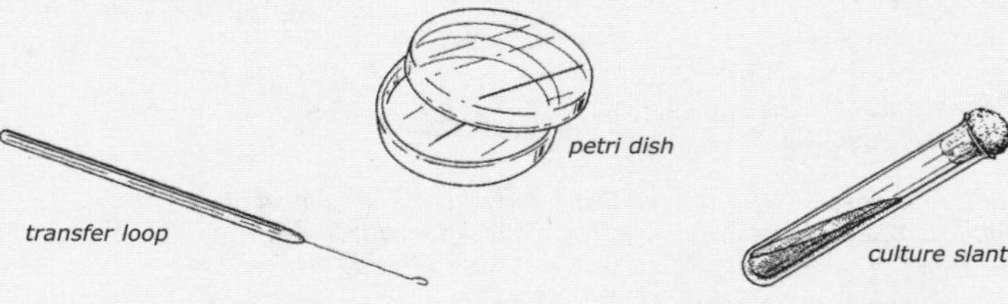

10a.1 ______
Bacteriological equipment

Techniques Used in Culturing Bacteria

The techniques described will be demonstrated while your instructor sets up bacterial cultures for your observation.

I. Prepare the apparatus and the media.
  - After the proper media are set up in the proper containers, they must be sterilized in an autoclave to destroy all living materials in them.
  - After the containers have been removed from the autoclave, they should not be opened until it is time to transfer the culture material into them.

II. Prepare the environment.
  - Close windows and turn off fans and other blowers. The fewer air currents there are, the less chance there is of contamination.

III. Open different containers of bacterial cultures.
  - Open a culture slant.
    - After opening a culture slant, pass the lip of the test tube through a flame to destroy stray bacteria.
    - Keep the open culture slant at an angle or even parallel to the floor to avoid as much as possible having airborne bacteria settle on the agar.
    - Never set the cotton stopper down on a table while working with bacteria; replace it as soon as possible.
    - Just before replacing the stopper, pass the lip of the test tube through a flame to destroy contaminating bacteria.

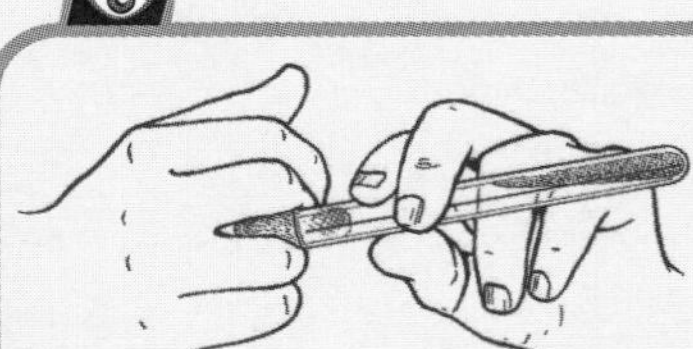

The proper way to hold a culture slant

After opening a culture slant, pass the lip of the test tube through a flame.

10a.2
Opening a culture slant

- Open a petri dish.
  - When opening a petri dish, turn the dish upside down so that the agar is in the upper section of the dish.
  - Open the dish only partway to avoid, as much as possible, having airborne bacteria settle on the agar.
  - When finished with the bacteria, close the petri dish as soon as possible.
- Use a broth culture.
  - Broth cultures pose special problems because they cannot be held at an angle and frequently must be poured.
  - Take special care to leave broth cultures open as little as possible.
  - Pour any excess broth into a strong, bacteria-killing solvent.

IV. Transfer bacteria from one culture to another by using a transfer loop.

- Heat the transfer loop in a flame until it is red-hot. This destroys any living material that may be on it. Allow the loop to cool for a few seconds.
- Touch the loop of wire at the end of the transfer loop to the bacteria being transferred.

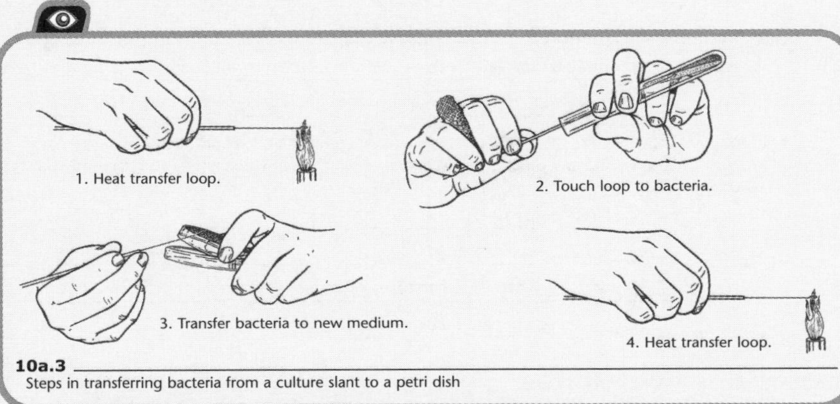

10a.3
Steps in transferring bacteria from a culture slant to a petri dish

- Quickly take the transfer loop to the sterile culture medium prepared to receive the bacteria. Take care not to touch the transfer loop to the dish containing the culture medium.
- The transfer loop should be immediately heated in a flame until it is red-hot to destroy any bacteria that may be left on the loop.

When setting up the bacteria for microscopic observation, be sure to use microscopes with appropriate magnifying powers. Some bacteria are large enough to be seen under 430×. If you do not have oil-immersion objectives on your microscopes, you may want to obtain preserved slides of these bacteria. If you have only one microscope with an oil-immersion objective, introduce a different bacteria type each of the three days that observations are made.

Students sometimes have difficulty understanding that not all the groups of cells they see under the microscope need to be completely typical of the colony that the slide represents. A few diplococcus bacteria clumped together on the side, thus appearing to be a staphylococcus group, indicate a slide manufacturing problem—not bacteria suffering an identity crisis. Stress that the students should indicate on the chart (p. L72) the bacterial colony that is most prevalent on the slide.

Students making observations of the bacteria cultures often have difficulty knowing what to record. There are no right or wrong methods. They do, however, need to be able to answer the obvious questions (e.g., Which culture grew the fastest?). Thus they need to make appropriate, sensible notes. When grading this exercise, you should be satisfied if students record something in the proper spaces on the growth rate observation charts. The answers to the questions following the observations reveal far more about the students' observational abilities.

To make observations easier, put the petri dishes upside down on a dark surface.

When incubating petri dishes, be sure that they are upside down (with the medium on the upper surface). If the culture is incubated with the lid side up, condensation on the lid will drip down, splashing the bacteria cultures.

Observing Bacteria

In this segment you will observe various bacterial cells and colonies through a microscope and then observe living cultures of bacteria.

I. Observe bacteria with the microscope.

- In the lab will be three microscopes on oil-immersion power (940x–1000x), each focused on a different preserved and stained bacterium.
- From your observation, decide on the type of bacterial shape and type of colony in each of the microscopes and record your answers below.

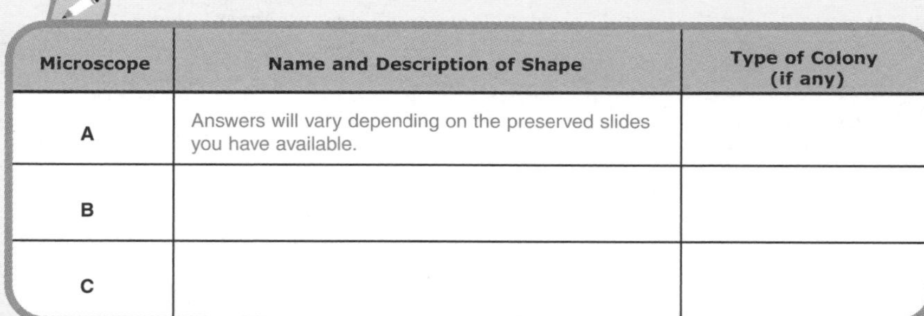

Microscope	Name and Description of Shape	Type of Colony (if any)
A	Answers will vary depending on the preserved slides you have available.	
B		
C		

II. Observe bacterial cultures.

- Observe living cultures of the following bacteria on nutrient agar. Write a detailed description of each bacterial growth, including color, size of growth, texture, shape of growth, and any other visible factors.
  - *Bacillus subtilis*: Answers may vary. A dull white filmlike bacterial growth
  - *Rhodospirillum rubrum*: Answers may vary. A reddish or whitish streak growing in the agar
  - *Sarcina lutea*: Answers may vary. A shiny yellow bacterial growth on top of the agar
  - *Sarcina subflava*: Answers may vary. A shiny white bacterial growth on top of the agar

- From your knowledge of etymologies and bacterial colonies and shapes, determine the shape, the type of colony, and any other characteristics each of the above bacteria has. Record your answers below.
  - *Bacillus subtilis*: rod-shaped
  - *Rhodospirillum rubrum*: spiral-shaped, red
  - *Sarcina lutea*: coccus-shaped, sarcina colony (cube-shaped), yellow
  - *Sarcina subflava*: coccus-shaped, sarcina colony

Bacterial Growth Rates

Two identical culture dishes, each with the same four bacteria *(Bacillus subtilis, Rhodospirillum rubrum, Sarcina lutea,* and *Sarcina subflava)*, will be prepared by your instructor. They will be placed in streaks on nutrient agar in a divided petri dish. The direction of the streaks tells which bacteria is which (see Diagram 10a.4). One petri dish will be kept in a dark incubator at a constant

Name________________________

temperature of about 39 °C. The other will be kept in the classroom near a window so that there will be a change in temperature and amount of light.

I. Read the questions in Part III. These are the questions you will be expected to answer after three days of observing these bacteria.

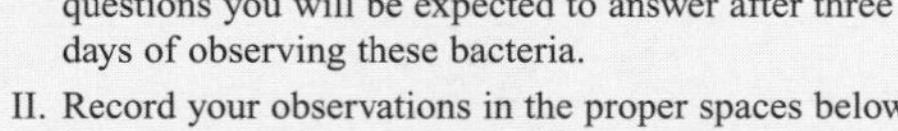

II. Record your observations in the proper spaces below. (Be sure you observe thoroughly enough to answer questions later.)

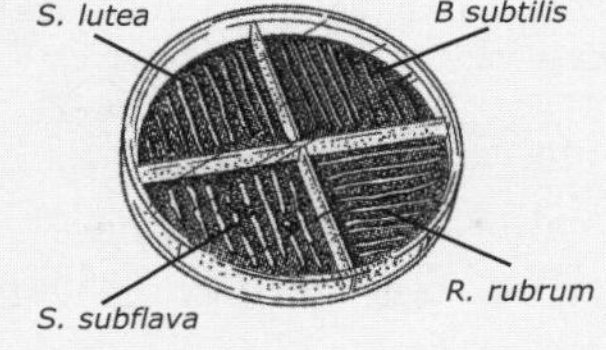

10a.4 ________________
Bacteria on a petri dish

In Incubator

	24 hours	48 hours	72 hours
B. subtilis			
R. rubrum			
S. lutea			
S. subflava			

In Classroom

	24 hours	48 hours	72 hours
B. subtilis			
R. rubrum			
S. lutea			
S. subflava			

Have the students begin their observations as soon as they enter class. Begin your lecture a few minutes late on the days of observations.

If you miss an observation, obtain data from someone else in your class. You must put the person's name with the data you obtain from him, or using the information will be considered plagiarism.

III. Answer the following questions.

- Which bacterium grows the fastest in the incubator? Answers will vary.

  In the classroom? Answers will vary.

  If different bacteria grow best in each of these circumstances, account for this difference. If there is a difference, one bacterium must have had more nearly optimal conditions in one environment and another in the other environment.

- Were there any noticeable differences in other species of bacteria grown under the different sets of conditions? ☐ yes ☐ no What were they? Answers will vary.

  Why would you expect differences? Different species of bacteria grow at different rates.

- Were there any noticeable similarities in growth rates in the various species of bacteria?

  ☐ yes ☐ no What were they? Answers will vary.

  Why would you expect some species of bacteria to grow at the same rate as others? Answers may vary. Some species of bacteria normally live in similar conditions and have similar growth rates when kept in similar environments.

- All these bacteria were grown on nutrient agar. Could the difference in growth rates have anything to do with the medium? ☒ yes ☐ no

  Would it be possible for the slowest-growing bacteria in this experiment to grow faster on some other medium? ☒ yes ☐ no Explain your answer. Since different bacteria require different nutrients, the medium can affect growth rate.

- In our growth rates experiment, there are too many variables to make any definite conclusions about why there was a difference in the bacterial growth rates. What could be done to correct this problem? Light the incubator or keep the room temperature culture dish in the dark.

- We have considered temperature, food, and light as possible reasons that some bacteria grow faster than others. Name two other conditions that could affect the growth rate of bacteria.

  1. moisture
  2. pH; other answers—water availability, oxygen concentration, presence of growth factors, etc.

- Is it possible that even if each bacterium were given optimal conditions for growth, the growth rates would still differ? ☒ yes ☐ no Explain. Optimal conditions for some bacteria may result in a lower metabolic rate than for others. Thus optimal conditions may result in a different growth rate for different species.

Name________________________

Date______________ Hour________

10b
Bacteria and Antibiotics

Materials
- petri dish
- nutrient agar
- a nutrient broth culture of *Bacillus cereus*
- antibiotic disks
- forceps

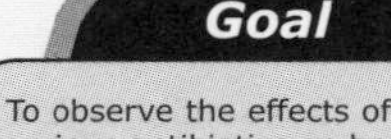
Goal

- To observe the effects of various antibiotics on bacteria

In this laboratory exercise a nonpathogenic species of bacteria will be exposed to several different antibiotics. Not all antibiotics are equally effective against all bacteria. Tests using antibiotic sensitivity disks are sometimes performed to reveal which antibiotic to use in fighting a particular species of bacteria. You will be able to judge the effectiveness of the different antibiotics by observing the growth of the bacteria around the antibiotic.

The species of bacteria used in this lab is nonpathogenic. The teacher will set up the culture as a demonstration. ***Under no circumstance should you open any bacterial culture in the laboratory without the presence and supervision of the instructor.*** *You can easily make your observations for this laboratory exercise through the clear lid of the culture container.*

I. Your instructor will prepare a *sensitivity test plate.*
- A few drops of a well-mixed broth culture of *Bacillus cereus* will be poured into a sterile petri dish containing nutrient agar.
- The dish will be tilted back and forth until the entire agar surface has come in contact with the broth. This will make an even culture of *B. cereus.*
- Forceps will be used to place four different-colored paper disks, each containing a different antibiotic, on the moist surface of the nutrient agar and then they will be tapped lightly.

II. You will be asked to answer the questions in Part III. Read them now. Then record your observations in such a way that you will be able to answer the questions from them.

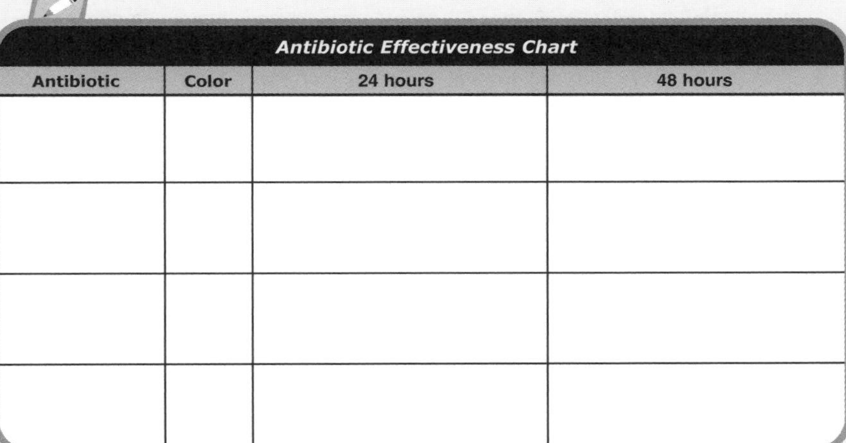
Antibiotic Effectiveness Chart

Antibiotic	Color	24 hours	48 hours

Carolina Biological Supply offers various media in sealed, sterilized petri dishes. Upon request, they will also supply *Bacillus cereus* in a nutrient broth culture rather than on a culture slant (their normal method).

A nutrient broth capable of growing *B. cereus* and many other bacteria can be made by boiling 3.0 g of beef extract and 5.0 g of peptone in one liter of distilled water until dissolved. Fill a test tube about half full of the broth and plug the tube with a cotton stopper. Stand the test tube in a jar or beaker and sterilize it. Permit the broth to cool thoroughly before inoculating it.

Antibiotic sensitivity disks usually come in a set. Students enjoy choosing the antibiotics to be tested. List the possible choices and the colors of the antibiotic disks on the chalkboard and have the students choose the four that will be used for the class demonstration. Most often they will choose one that they have heard of or possibly taken themselves.

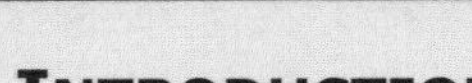

Introduction

This exercise can easily be done with Exercise 10a.

Required / Extra / Omit

The entire exercise must be done, or it should be omitted.

III. Answer the following questions.

- Which antibiotic most effectively prevents growth of *B. cereus?* Answers may vary.

  Least effective? Answers may vary.

- Do your experimental results indicate how effective these antibiotics would be against other bacteria? ☐ yes ☒ no Explain: Different bacteria have different characteristics and different metabolisms. That a particular bacterium is affected by a specific antibiotic does not mean that the antibiotic will be effective against other bacteria.

- What clinical advantage might be gained by preparing an antibiotic sensitivity test plate of an unknown throat bacterium suspected of causing sore throats? The experimenter could identify the antibiotic most effective against the bacterium and thus could control it.

- Pharmaceutical companies are constantly developing new antibiotics because the existing ones seem to lose their effectiveness over a period of time. From a genetic standpoint, explain why this occurs. Like all organisms, bacteria have genes that determine their makeup and functioning. Because these genes allow some variation, effective antibiotics may kill many but not all of the bacteria of a particular species. Those that are somehow able to resist the drug will increase in number by passing on their traits to future generations.

Name________________________________

Date____________________ Hour__________

11 Protista

Materials

- microscope
- glass slides
- coverslips
- living cultures of amoebas, paramecia, euglenas, *Spirogyra*, and *Protococcus*
- preserved slides of amoebas, paramecia, euglenas, *Plasmodium*, desmids, diatoms, *Protococcus*, *Spirogyra*, *Spirogyra* in conjugation, dinoflagellates, and as many other different protozoans and algae as possible
- dropping pipets
- hand lens
- glycerin or methyl cellulose
- carmine powder
- cotton fibers
- toothpicks
- forceps
- scissors
- preserved specimens of *Protococcus*, *Chondrus*, *Fucus*, *Corallina*, and kelp
- pond water
- reference books for algae and protozoans

Goals

- To observe living protozoans
- To note the differences and similarities among various protozoans and the various protozoan phyla
- To observe algae specimens and note the differences among them
- To understand the classification of algae
- To understand the importance of the algae as a group
- To identify examples of the kingdom Protista

Protozoans were at one time classified in the kingdom Animalia (and thus are often discussed in zoology books) in a separate phylum called "Protozoa." In the modern five- or six-kingdom systems, these tiny organisms are placed in the kingdom Protista, and several of the designations that were once classes in the phylum Protozoa became phyla in the kingdom Protista (p. 298 and Appendix B). In the six-kingdom system, Protozoa is a subkingdom containing four phyla that are motile and are (or may be) heterotrophic.

The term algae *refers to five phyla also in the kingdom Protista and one group of organisms in the kingdom Eubacteria (p. 265). This lab deals only with the algae of the kingdom Protista. They are often separated from the more animal-like protozoans into subkingdom Protophyta.*

This laboratory exercise is designed to acquaint you with the major phyla of Protista. When possible, living specimens have been chosen to demonstrate the major characteristics of the phyla. Searching for, chasing, observing, drawing, and labeling living protozoans is interesting, fun, and profitable. The algae subkingdom is fascinating also, with its complexity and other evidences of design. To complete parts of this laboratory exercise, you may need to consult additional references such as a dictionary, encyclopedia, or perhaps a botany or microbiology text.

When working on this lab, keep in mind that you are responsible for each example you observe. You should know its common name (often a part of its scientific name and thus italicized) and to what phylum it belongs, and you should be able to recognize it. When you are asked to observe a specimen but not required to draw it, make mental notes at least. In order to avoid confusion regarding the phylum to which an organism belongs, it is wise to complete all the exercises for one phylum before doing another. You do not need to do the phyla in sequence.

Remember when working with this lab that a preserved slide *is a microscope slide that has a specimen mounted on it, and a* preserved specimen, *or* mounted specimen, *is a specimen in a jar or in plastic, not designed to be used on the microscope.*

INTRODUCTION

The viewing of Protistans can be one of the most interesting and exciting laboratory experiences of the year if you have good laboratory cultures. Students enjoy observing these tiny creatures. The exercise gives clear directions, and the students should have the skills necessary to accomplish most of the work on their own. However, they will probably have trouble locating the various organisms, so be prepared to spend a lot of time saying, "No, that isn't an amoeba" and "Yes, that is one; now draw it."

Since some students are easily confused by the terms in the algae half of the lab, they should complete the Algae Classification and Vocabulary Study sections (pp. L83–L84) before they begin their laboratory work.

Observing Pond Water (p. L90) is an interesting activity for students who have some proficiency with a microscope. After the directed activities, this open-ended activity can be welcome, and it can also be used to show the wide variety of organisms that were not covered in the structured activities.

Observing Pond Water can be done in a matter of a few minutes, or it can take hours, depending upon both how suitable your pond water is and how thoroughly you expect your students to search for organisms in it.

Most suppliers will ship living specimens so that they arrive just prior to a particular date. Protozoan and algae cultures need to be fresh.

You should have on hand preserved slides of all the living organisms you plan to use. Despite a good supplier and careful shipping procedures, occasionally a sour culture will arrive. There is little that can be done about it, especially in time for your class. If it happens often, change suppliers.

Probably the easiest culture to keep alive and the organism that students locate most quickly (because of its abundance) is the euglena. However, because of its small size and euglenoid movement (which is almost impossible to stop), it is difficult to see the internal structures. If a student becomes frustrated trying to find the amoeba or slow down the paramecium, suggest that he try observing the euglena and then come back to the amoeba and paramecium.

Plastic mounts of the various preserved algae are best. However, suppliers tend to give only small sections of a specimen. For example, the large size of *Fucus* is difficult to appreciate by observing only a two-inch segment. Therefore, in addition to the small plastic mounts, try to collect large specimens from the beach and keep the specimens in F.A.A. (See note F, p. A19.)

Pond water containing organisms may be difficult to obtain at the time of year you need it. Unboiled pond water, even though it has been obtained from a cold pond, should produce organisms if it is kept warm for a few days. (See instructions in Laboratory Exercise 19 for making a microcosm.)

One of the problems is keeping the pond water in adequate light without getting it too warm. If placed in direct sunlight in a window, a container of pond water can easily get so warm that most organisms will be destroyed. Artificial light is probably the best. Try to keep the water temperature between 65° and 75°F.

When collecting pond water, get a scoop of the water near the edge of the pond, and add to it a small scoop of the sediment (mud) from near the edge of the pond. If possible, get some submerged vegetation and add it to your culture. This will insure your getting as wide a sample of organisms as possible. It will look very cloudy at first, but it will settle. Even water that is quite dark with sediment can be used for microscopic work.

Stress that the students will be better able to accomplish what they need to do if they come to class prepared. Doing the Preliminary Work will help them learn about the organisms they are looking for in the laboratory. Studying the directions for handling live specimens will also be helpful.

Preliminary Work

R E O

Use information from your text to fill in these comparison charts of four phyla of the kingdom Protista, using the amoeba, paramecium, euglena, and *Spirogyra* as representative members. After each phylum, place an *X* in the boxes that are under column headings that describe that phylum.

	Comparison of Basic Characteristics							Comparison of Reproductive Processes		
	Heterotrophic	Autotrophic	Unicellular	Multicellular	Colonial	Freshwater	Saltwater	Binary fission or mitosis	Cyst formation	Conjugation
Phylum Sarcodina (amoeba)	X		X			X	X	X	X	
Phylum Ciliophora (paramecium)	X		X			X	(X)	X		X
Phylum Euglenophyta (euglena)	X	X	X			X	(X)	X		
Phylum Chlorophyta (*Spirogyra*)		X		X		X				X

	Comparison of Body Structures										
	Flagella	Cilia	Pseudopods	Contractile vacuole	Food vacuole	Single nucleus	Micro- and macronuclei	Ectoplasm & endoplasm	Pellicle	Gullet	Eyespot
Phylum Sarcodina (amoeba)			X	X	X	X		X			
Phylum Ciliophora (paramecium)		X		X	X		X	X	X	X	
Phylum Euglenophyta (euglena)	X			X	(X)	X		X	X	X	X
Phylum Chlorophyta (*Spirogyra*)						X					

Parentheses indicate answers that are correct but that not all students will find.

The answers given to the students in this chart are answers not given in the text.

Cysts are formed by members of phyla Ciliophora and Euglenophyta but not by members in the particular genera that are being discussed.

Various books are available for identification of pond-water organisms. Some of these books are highly technical; others are not. Some are well illustrated, and others are not. Several recommended books are listed in the box following the notes for this chapter.

Required / Extra / Omit

It is suggested that you require students to observe living amoebae and paramecia. Use the Other Sarcodines and Other Ciliates sections for extra credit.

You may find it best to omit observing the phylum Sporozoa slides, but do ask the students to do the recommended study of the life cycle in the text.

Depending on the paramecia you have, the experiment with carmine powder (which is sometimes difficult to obtain) often requires a considerable amount of time. It may be wise to omit this section and to have the students answer the question from text research.

Select carefully those algae that you want your students to be accountable for and then have them do the sections of the laboratory exercise that deal with those algae. It is recommended that you at least have them deal with the following: *Euglena*, *Spirogyra*, desmids, diatoms, *Fucus*, and the dinoflagellates. The specimens to add next are *Protococcus* and kelp. Just because you are making your students accountable for a specimen, however, does not mean that you must have them do all of the activities presented in the exercise.

Although it is often fascinating, you may wish to use the pond water section as an extra-credit section, especially if you are trying to fit this exercise into two days.

Protozoans

How to Handle Live Protozoan Cultures Properly

- Live cultures of the various protozoans are not "pure"; that is, there are other organisms in the culture. Do not be surprised if you see some unidentifiable organisms on your slide. Do not spend much time with these other organisms.
- Cultures sometimes turn "sour"; that is, the cultured organisms die.
  - If this happens, or if for some reason living cultures are not available to you, examine a preserved slide of the organism.
  - If you use a preserved slide, answer questions dealing with live observation according to your research in the text.
- Care for the cultures properly.
  - Keep the lids on the culture dishes. (Lids, however, should not be screwed on tightly.)
  - Use each pipet for only one culture dish. Do not mix the pipets. Contaminating one culture with another often leads to souring.
  - Do not take the cultures to your desk.
  - Keep slides and coverslips clean and free of soap film.

Phylum Sarcodina

The phylum Sarcodina contains those unicellular organisms that move using pseudopods. We will examine the amoeba *(Amoeba proteus* or a similar species) as an example. Actually, there is considerable diversity among members of this phylum, but the typical amoeba clearly shows the major phylum characteristics.

The Amoeba

R E O

I. Prepare and observe a wet mount of living amoebas by following these instructions.
- Obtain an amoeba and prepare a wet mount from its culture.
  - Amoebas usually stay close to the bottom of the culture or crawl on some object.
  - Amoebas can be drawn into a dropping pipet.
    - Squeeze the bulb of a dropping pipet in the air.
    - Place the pipet directly above the place where the amoeba should be.
    - Release the bulb to suck up *one drop.*
    - Put the entire drop on the slide.
  - Wait a minute before placing the coverslip on top of the amoeba culture on your slide. This allows the amoeba to attach to the slide and begin to move.
- Scan the entire slide on low power.
  - Scan from right to left; then move the slide a little lower and scan left to right. Repeat until you have scanned the entire slide.
  - Anything that moves faster than a snail's pace is not an amoeba.
- Be sure the culture medium does not evaporate. Using the pipets from the amoeba culture, add more medium to the edge of the coverslip as necessary.
- Observe the movements of the amoeba for a while on both high and low power.
- Observe the amoebas that other students have found and let them observe yours.

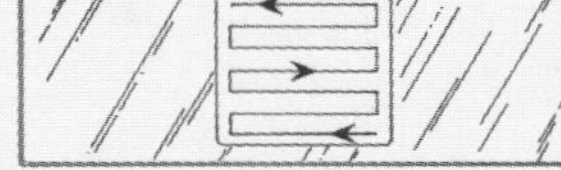

11.1 How to scan a microscope slide

Scheduling Laboratory Activities

It may take up to three days for students to complete all of the activities in this lab, especially if they have not done any of the advance preparation. Decide how much time you have and then assign the required sections accordingly. See the Required/Extra/Omit section for priority suggestions. Of course, availability of cultures, slides, and specimens will also limit your choices. If you have two days to spend, the protozoans could be done the first day and the algae on the second.

If students are required to do the sections Other Sarcodines or Other Ciliates, or if you are permitting them to do these sections as extra credit, direct them toward those organisms for which you have preserved slides.

- Carefully observe the cellular structures of the amoeba. Try to locate all the structures listed in the Comparison of Body Structures chart on page L78.
- You may see an amoeba engulfing food or dividing. If your amoeba appears to be doing either, inform your instructor so that you can share it with the class.

R E O

II. Answer the following questions about amoebas.

- Whether or not your amoeba engulfed any food particles while you observed it, describe the process of obtaining food and describe how the food is digested. The amoeba engulfs food by phagocytosis, the surrounding of food particles by pseudopods. Digestion takes place inside the food vacuole.
- As you observed the amoeba on your slide, what type of locomotion (movement) did the amoeba use? It moved by pseudopods.

  Describe the locomotion. Descriptions may vary.
- What type of cytoplasm fills the pseudopods? At first, pseudopods are formed as ectoplasm flows into the area; later, endoplasm also moves into them.
- Is more than one pseudopod present at one time? ☒ yes ☐ no

  If so, does more than one grow at a time? ☒ yes ☐ no If so, in what circumstances? during phagocytosis
- Amoebas can respond to several types of stimuli. Describe the taxes of the amoeba. You may need to research in your text for a complete answer. Amoebas generally adhere to objects they contact but retreat if touched. They move away from saltiness and toward food.

R E O

III. Draw an amoeba in Area A.

- Draw one of the live amoebas you observed under the microscope.
- Label the drawing as completely as you can.

A

R E O

Other Sarcodines

I. Choose one of the following sarcodines, research it, and prepare a brief report about it (at least a half page, no more than a full page). Tell how it is similar to the amoeba and how it differs from it. (You will need to use reference books other than the text.)

- *Arcella*
- *Difflugia*
- *Actinosphaerium*
- *Actinophrys*
- *Globigerina*
- *Entamoeba coli*

II. If preserved slides are available, make a specimen drawing to illustrate your report.

III. Prepare a schematic diagram to illustrate your report.

Name____________________________

Phylum Ciliophora

The phylum Ciliophora contains many diverse organisms unified by the fact that they all possess cilia. Some, like the paramecium, which will serve as our typical organism for the phylum, have cilia covering their entire body. Others, like the *Vorticella,* have only a band of cilia. Some ciliates are found in sewage, some only in acidic water, some in clean ponds, and others in our bodies.

The Paramecium

I. Study a wet mount of living paramecia.
- Prepare a wet mount from the paramecium culture. Paramecia may be found throughout the culture.
- Scan the entire slide.
  - Paramecia move rapidly and will need to be chased across the slide.
  - The box below contains three methods you can use to slow down or stop your paramecium. Use the method your instructor designates.

Methods of Slowing Protozoan Movement

Coverslip Pressure

1. As the culture medium evaporates, the coverslip will press on the organism and slow its movement.
2. A paper towel on the edge of the coverslip can be used to speed the process. Your lab partner can draw off small portions of water while you chase the organism.
3. Do not permit the medium to evaporate completely. Replenish it by placing a drop of medium beside the coverslip and letting some of it seep under the coverslip.

Cotton Fibers

1. Before you place the coverslip on the medium, you can place a small quantity of cotton fibers on the medium.
2. These serve as obstacles, blocking the path of protozoans and thus localizing their activities.

Thicker Medium

1. Special media (glycerine, methyl cellulose, or commercially prepared products) can be used to slow protozoans.
2. Because these media are thicker than water, the protozoans must move more slowly through them.

- Be careful not to confuse other protozoans in the culture with paramecia. A paramecium looks like the slipper-shaped illustration in your text (p. 300) and is easy to recognize.
- Observe the paramecia on both high and low powers. Observe the paramecia that other students have found and let them observe yours.
- Carefully observe the cellular structures of the paramecium. Try to locate all the structures belonging to the paramecium discussed in the Comparison of Body Structures chart on page L78.
- Sometimes paramecia can be seen during fission or conjugation. If a paramecium appears to be doing either function, inform your instructor so that you can share the observation with the class.

The best method of slowing paramecia for this exercise is to use cotton. Show the students how much cotton is enough, or they will use too much. Although the other methods are acceptable, they do not create such excitement; they may also take too long or may kill the specimen. (Amoebae do not need to be slowed down, and euglenas can be seen adequately without the slowing process.)

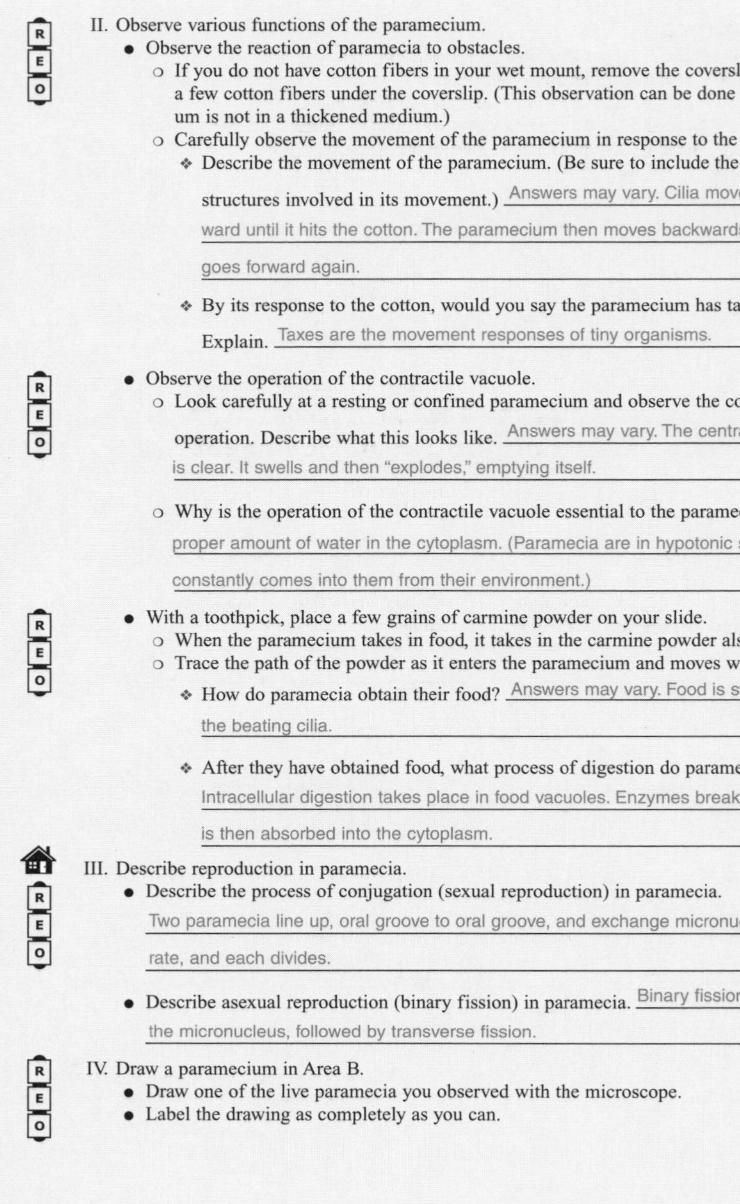

II. Observe various functions of the paramecium.

- Observe the reaction of paramecia to obstacles.
  - If you do not have cotton fibers in your wet mount, remove the coverslip carefully and place a few cotton fibers under the coverslip. (This observation can be done only if the paramecium is not in a thickened medium.)
  - Carefully observe the movement of the paramecium in response to the cotton fibers.
    - Describe the movement of the paramecium. (Be sure to include the names of the cellular structures involved in its movement.) Answers may vary. Cilia move the paramecium forward until it hits the cotton. The paramecium then moves backwards, turns slightly, and goes forward again.
    - By its response to the cotton, would you say the paramecium has taxes? ☒ yes ☐ no
      Explain. Taxes are the movement responses of tiny organisms.
- Observe the operation of the contractile vacuole.
  - Look carefully at a resting or confined paramecium and observe the contractile vacuole in operation. Describe what this looks like. Answers may vary. The central part of the structure is clear. It swells and then "explodes," emptying itself.
  - Why is the operation of the contractile vacuole essential to the paramecium? It maintains the proper amount of water in the cytoplasm. (Paramecia are in hypotonic solutions, and water constantly comes into them from their environment.)
- With a toothpick, place a few grains of carmine powder on your slide.
  - When the paramecium takes in food, it takes in the carmine powder also.
  - Trace the path of the powder as it enters the paramecium and moves within it.
    - How do paramecia obtain their food? Answers may vary. Food is swept into the gullet by the beating cilia.
    - After they have obtained food, what process of digestion do paramecia use? Explain. Intracellular digestion takes place in food vacuoles. Enzymes break down the food, which is then absorbed into the cytoplasm.

III. Describe reproduction in paramecia.

- Describe the process of conjugation (sexual reproduction) in paramecia. Two paramecia line up, oral groove to oral groove, and exchange micronuclei. They then separate, and each divides.
- Describe asexual reproduction (binary fission) in paramecia. Binary fission is mitotic division of the micronucleus, followed by transverse fission.

IV. Draw a paramecium in Area B.

- Draw one of the live paramecia you observed with the microscope.
- Label the drawing as completely as you can.

Name________________________________

Other Ciliates

I. Choose one of the following ciliates, research it, and prepare a brief report about it (at least a half page, no more than a full page). Tell how it is similar to the paramecium and how it differs from it. (You will need to use reference books other than your text.)
- *Prorodon*
- *Stentor*
- *Colpoda*
- *Halteria*
- *Tetrahymena*
- *Vorticella*

II. If preserved slides are available, make a specimen drawing to illustrate your report.

III. Prepare a schematic diagram to illustrate your report.

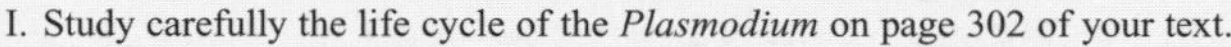

Phylum Sporozoa

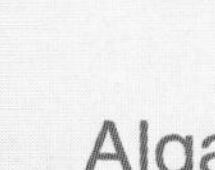

The phylum Sporozoa contains organisms that, as adults, lack methods of movement. (Frequently, stages in their cycle may have pseudopods or other forms of movement.) They also form spores at some stage in their life cycles. They are all parasitic and often have complex life cycles. The *Plasmodium,* which is responsible for malaria, will be the organism we study as an example of this phylum.

I. Study carefully the life cycle of the *Plasmodium* on page 302 of your text.

II. Observe a preserved slide of the various stages of the *Plasmodium* life cycle.

Algae

I. Algae Classification
- One of the major differences among the algal phyla is the color pigments found with the chlorophyll that often give the algae found in nature slightly different colors.
- At one time algae were classified in the kingdom Plantae. Give two reasons that this would have been the logical classification for most algae.

  1. They are photosynthetic (autotrophic).
  2. They have cell walls.
- Under the present system of classification, one group of algae is placed in the kingdom Eubacteria. What characteristics place blue-green algae in this kingdom? They lack an organized nucleus and membrane-bound organelles.
- All of the algal phyla other than the blue-green algae are classified in the kingdom Protista. Give at least one reason that the algae in the kingdom Protista should not be classified as plants. The algae lack tissues.

II. Vocabulary Study

- What are phytoplankton? floating algae used as food for other organisms
- The body of an alga that is not differentiated into leaves, roots, and stems (the vegetative body of an alga) is called the thallus.
- What is a holdfast? a cell (or structure) that anchors a thallus
- What are sessile algae? algae that are attached to something
- Long, chainlike colonies of algae are called filaments.
- What is a pyrenoid, and what does it do? It is a cellular structure in algae that helps to store starch.
- The splitting of an algal colony to form two colonies is called fragmentation.
- Identical gametes that unite to form a zygote are called isogametes.
- What are heterogametes? gametes that are different (usually ovum and sperm)
- What is conjugation? exchange of genetic material between cells
- A spore formed by the union of gametes is called a(n) zygospore.
- What is a zoospore? a motile spore

Phylum Euglenophyta

The flagellates are unusual because many of them are heterotrophic and classified as Protozoans in the phylum Zoomastigina. Others are photosynthetic and are placed with the algae in Euglenophyta, as is our typical organism, the euglena. The euglena is a small organism compared to the amoeba and the paramecium we have previously studied, but the euglena is easier to find on a slide because most laboratory cultures of euglena are more densely populated.

The Euglena

I. Observe a wet mount of living euglenas.

- Prepare a wet mount from a euglena culture. Euglenas will be found throughout the entire culture.
- Scan the slide. Euglenas can move rapidly but usually will not leave the microscope field very rapidly. Occasionally it will be necessary to use coverslip pressure or a thicker medium to slow their movement.
- Observe the euglenas on both high and low powers. Observe the euglenas that other students have found and let them observe yours.
- Carefully observe the cellular structures of the euglena. Try to locate the structures belonging to the euglena discussed in the Comparison of Body Structures chart on page L78.

II. Answer the following questions concerning euglenas.

- Describe the two types of movement euglenas can have.
  1. flagellar movement—movement through the water by whipping their flagella
  2. euglenoid movement—a type of "wiggling" or wormlike contraction and extension
- Were you able to observe these two types of movement? ☐ yes ☐ no usually yes

  What did you note about the way your euglena moved? Answers may vary.
- Explain how euglenas can make their own food. They contain chlorophyll and can carry on photosynthesis to make sugar.

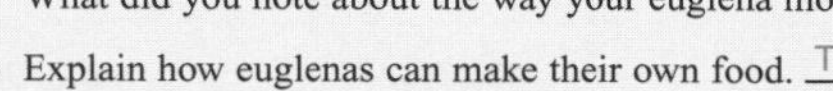

Name

- Explain how euglenas obtain food (other than by manufacturing it). They can absorb food. (Food is not taken in by the gullet.)
- What type of asexual reproduction do euglenas have? binary fission
- What type of sexual reproduction? none

III. Draw a euglena in Area C.
- Draw one of the live euglenas you observed under the microscope.
- Label the drawing as completely as you can.

Phylum Chlorophyta

Chlorophyta, the green algae, is a large phylum. It contains many varied species. Some are tiny, microscopic spheres; others have unusual geometric shapes. Some of these unicellular algae float; others have flagella and swim toward the light. A few even thrive in snowdrifts in the spring. The larger, filament-forming varieties are the usual components of "pond scum," the mat of green, slimy threads that forms on the top of many nutrient-rich water supplies. Microscopic observations of these organisms reveal fascinating structures.

Protococcus (Pleurococcus)

I. *Protococcus* is unusual because it frequently lives on tree bark or on the surface of moist soil. Observe a mounted specimen of *Protococcus*.

II. Observe *Protococcus* through a microscope.
- If a living culture is available, prepare a wet mount of the culture and observe it on high and low powers.
- If a living culture is not available, observe a preserved slide of the organism.

III. In Area D draw three or four cells of this alga, labeling cell walls, chloroplasts, and any other cellular structures you find.

Protococcus is a tiny alga. Students will probably need to use high power to find it.

Tell the students that they may not be able to see simultaneously in a single microscope field all the structures they need to draw. For example, when they look at *Spirogyra* in conjugation, the area that has the zygotes may not have a normal cell nearby. Therefore, they must move their slide to find what they need to know.

Desmid

I. Observe a preserved slide of desmids.

II. In Area E draw the outlines of five different shapes of desmids found on the slide.

III. Give one structural difference between desmids and diatoms. Diatoms have silica in their cell walls. Diatoms and desmids store materials in different forms.

Spirogyra

I. Observe *Spirogyra* through a microscope.
- If a living culture is available, prepare a wet mount.
  - Place a drop of culture medium on a slide.
  - Using forceps and scissors, cut a few short strands of *Spirogyra* and place them on the slide.
  - Be careful to observe cells that are not crushed or broken.
- If a living culture is not available, use a preserved slide.

II. In Area F make a specimen drawing of a normal filament of *Spirogyra*.
- The filament should be three to five cells long.
- Draw the filament, showing how the cells are joined.
- Label the following if possible: sheath, cytoplasm, chloroplast, pyrenoid, and nucleus.

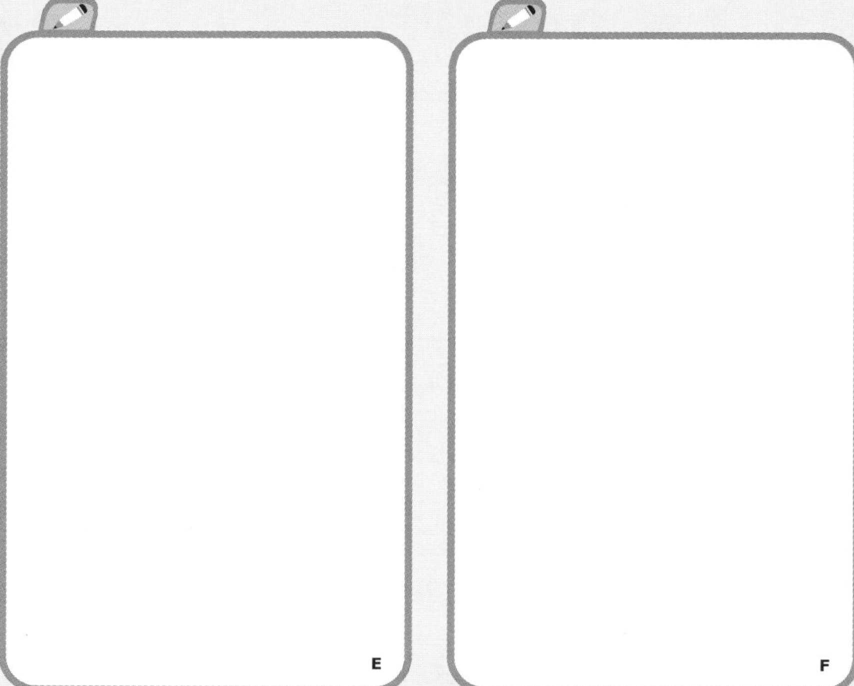

Name______________________________

R E O

III. Observe a preserved slide of *Spirogyra* in conjugation.

- In Area G make a specimen drawing of *Spirogyra* in conjugation.
- Label all the following parts and stages: conjugation tube, zygote, zygospore, empty cell, filament, and normal cell.

Phylum Bacillariophyta

The phylum Bacillariophyta contains the diatoms. These tiny but often intricately patterned organisms are sometimes called "glass boxes" because of their shapes and because they have silica in their cell walls.

R E O

Diatoms

I. Scan the preserved slides of diatoms and observe the various shapes.

II. In Area H draw the outlines of five differing diatoms.

III. Diatoms have been used for many different purposes because of their hard, silica-containing cell walls. List four uses of diatom cell walls.

1. insulating furnaces and boilers
2. silver polish
3. toothpaste
4. glass

G

H

Phylum Phaeophyta

Although the phylum Phaeophyta is one of the smallest phyla in number of species, the sizes of its individual organisms more than make up for their small number. Some of the larger brown algae may have colonies more than 30 m (100 ft) long. Some areas of the ocean are almost overrun with "algae forests" made up of members of this phylum. Although these appear to be plants with large leaves and stems, they actually lack true tissues and are colonies.

R E O

Fucus

I. Observe the mounted specimen of *Fucus*.

II. Identify the receptacle and the air bladder, describing the differences between them.

	Receptacle	Air bladder
Size	usually larger	usually smaller
Shape	usually oval	usually round
Location on thallus	the ends of the thallus	within the thallus
Function	sexual reproduction	keeps the thallus afloat

R E O

Kelp

I. Observe the mounted specimen of kelp.

II. Research kelp in other sources and write a brief statement describing its appearance, use, and importance to man. Identify your sources. Use your own paper.

Phylum Rhodophyta

Members of phylum Rhodophyta, the red algae, are multicellular and red. Most members of the phylum are marine organisms. The red algae are similar to the brown algae except for the foods they store and the pigments they contain.

R E O

Chondrus (Irish moss)

I. Observe the preserved specimen of this marine alga in the laboratory.

II. This alga is economically important. Research to find out what substance is derived from this alga and how it is used. Agar is extracted from this alga. Agar is used as a solidifying agent and a filler in various foods (ice cream, pudding, candy) and is also used in bacterial cultures.

R E O

Corallina

I. This marine alga is important in reef formation. It extracts calcium-containing substances from seawater and deposits them in its cell walls.

II. Observe the preserved specimen of this marine alga in the laboratory.

Name________________________

Phylum Dinoflagellata

The dinoflagellates are often called the "fire algae" because of the reddish to yellowish color these organisms can give to water. Although many of these are harmless, some cause extensive damage.

I. Some members of this phylum have bioluminescent properties. This explains a common phenomenon that startles many when they first see it. What is this phenomenon? The phenomenon is the sea glowing at night.

What are bioluminescent properties? properties enabling organisms to release light

II. Example: Dinoflagellates

- *Karenia* is a marine genus, some species of which cause the red tides of Florida. Research red tides and tell how an alga that is usually considered food can kill large quantities of fish.
  Answers will vary. Some sources indicate that the depletion of oxygen by the decay of dying dinoflagellates causes the fish kills. Other sources indicate that the kills are the result of some poison released by the dinoflagellates.
- *Peridinium*, a common freshwater genus, is illustrated in Figure 11.2.
  - Using the information in your textbook, label the following structures on the diagram: flagella, grooves, and cellulose plates.
  - Observe a preserved slide of freshwater dinoflagellates.
    - Were you able to find *Peridinium*? ☐ yes ☐ no Answers may vary.
    - Describe two other dinoflagellates you may have seen.

1. Answers will vary.
2. ________________________

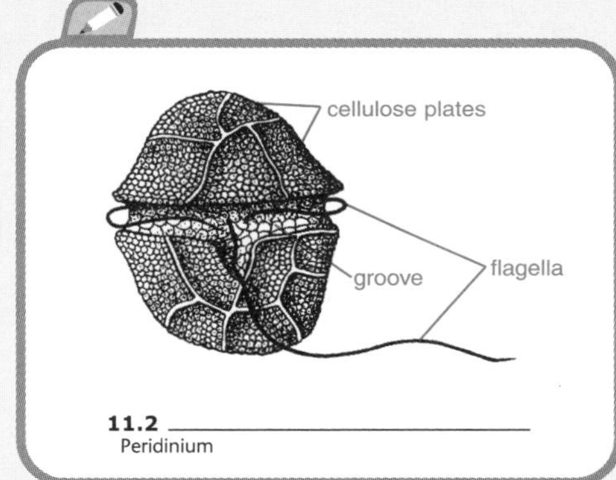

11.2 ________________________
Peridinium

When doing the pond-water section, you may find it profitable to have students compile a class list of organisms rather than independent lists. Use a large classroom chart (possibly a bulletin board or two) on which the first student to identify an organism gets to make the entry (and sign his name). Provide a place to attach a drawing, a description of the organism, and the place in the culture it was found (top, middle, bottom). Then leave a place for others to indicate that they also found that organism. You may want to divide the class into groups, having some use water from the bottom and others from the top.

You may wish to have your students find and describe (draw) a specific number of organisms rather than as many as they can.

Observing Pond Water

Although many other organisms are found as plankton, most easily recognizable plankton belong to the kingdom Protista. Observing pond water can be interesting and profitable. You can often see familiar organisms that you have studied as well as unfamiliar examples of phyla that you have studied.

R E O

I. Observe pond water from the laboratory culture through a microscope.
- Make a wet mount of the material at the bottom of the culture.
- Make another wet mount of the material near the surface of the culture.
- Why is it advisable to take samples from both areas? Different organisms live in different areas.
- Various keys and other reference books are available in the classroom for you to use in identification of the organisms you find.

II. List each organism that you observe under the appropriate heading below.
- Organisms studied (Give name and phylum.) Answers will vary.
- Organisms not studied but recognized (Describe and, if possible, give the names and phyla of the organisms.) Answers will vary.
- Organisms not recognized (Describe.) Answers will vary.

R E O

III. In Area I draw several of the organisms that you found in pond water but had not studied.
- Try to find out the names of what you have and the groups to which they belong.
- Label each of your drawings as completely as possible.

Reference Works for Studying Pond Water

Curtis, Helena. *The Marvelous Animals: An Introduction to the Protozoa*. Bantam Doubleday Dell Publishing, 1982.

Jahn, Theodore, et al. *How to Know the Protozoa*. New York: McGraw-Hill, 1978.

Poindexter, J. S. *Microbiology: An Introduction to the Protists*. New York: The Macmillan Co., 1971.

Prescott, G. W., et al. *How to Know the Freshwater Algae*. New York: McGraw-Hill, 1978.

Rainis, Kenneth G. and Bruce J. Russell. *Guide to Microlife*. New York: Orchard Books, 1996.

In addition to these books, there are many websites that provide clear and colorful photomicrographs of these organisms. Just do a search using the genus name.

Name____________________

Date__________ Hour______

12 Fungi and Lichens

Materials

- microscope
- hand lens
- living cultures of *Rhizopus nigricans*, *Penicillium notatum*, and yeast
- preserved slides of *Rhizopus nigricans*, *R. nigricans* forming zygotes, *Penicillium*, *Aspergillus*, *Coprinus*, c.s. and l.s., and lichen, c.s.
- preserved specimens of puffballs, mushrooms, bracket fungi, and lichens
- methylene blue
- glass slides
- coverslips
- dropping pipets
- immersion oil

Goals

- To observe fungi specimens
- To note the differences between types of fungi
- To note the differences between fungi and other organisms
- To understand how the fungi are classified
- To observe and classify lichen specimens

The smallest kingdom, Fungi, may seem mysterious and irrelevant since we seldom see them unless they have large fruiting structures. Although many are secluded in dark, musty corners or grow on dead organisms, the fungi are still important organisms. They are responsible for most of the decomposition of dead organisms. Imagine the mess we would be in without that service. Also, without fungi and the enzymes they produce, we would not have bread, many cheeses, and mushrooms. That would pretty much wipe out pizza!

Occasionally you will have to research in other books for answers as you are working on this exercise. The fungi were once considered plants; therefore, most general botany texts have chapters covering the fungi.

Technically, lichens are not placed in a phylum or any classification in the biological taxonomic system. Lichens are duo-organisms consisting of an alga and a fungus living together in a close relationship.

Preliminary Work

R E O

I. Answer the following questions about fungi classification and characteristics.

- What is the primary reason fungi are not classified as algae? Fungi do not contain chlorophyll and are therefore heterotrophic.
- What is the primary reason fungi are not classified as plants? They lack tissues. Students may also suggest a lack of chlorophyll, but some plants also lack chlorophyll.
- Give two examples demonstrating how fungi are destructive.
  1. Any two: They destroy or harm beneficial plants and crops; they spoil food;
  2. they cause diseases.
- Give two functions of fungi that benefit man.
  1. Any two: They leaven breads; they serve as food (as in mushrooms or cheese);
  2. they produce antibiotics; they decompose other organisms.

R E O

II. Answer the following questions about fungal vocabulary.

- What is mycology? the study of fungi
- What are hyphae? filaments that make up a fungus

To obtain a yeast culture, put a tablespoon of sugar in a pint jar full of warm water, add about half a packet of baker's dry active yeast, and leave the jar overnight in a warm area. On the day of the exercise, put a drop of the culture on a slide and then place a drop of dilute methylene blue on the drop of culture. Complete the process by putting a coverslip on the slide and setting up a microscope for oil-immersion viewing. Tell the students to observe it as soon as possible.

Cultures of bread mold (*Rhizopus*) can sometimes be found in even the best-kept kitchen. They will serve well for this exercise.

Cultures of *Penicillium* can sometimes be found growing on citrus fruits. They make a good additional example.

Collections of mushrooms, puffballs, and bracket fungi can be made and preserved by drying the specimens or putting them in special solutions for future use. (See note F on p. A19.)

A quick source of fresh mushrooms is your local grocery. Purchase the largest ones available. (Mushrooms are said to lose their flavor and spoil faster as they grow larger. Therefore, food stores usually stock small, button-stage mushrooms.)

In many areas lichen specimens can easily be collected fresh. Often, however, coming up with some of the more unusual types can be difficult. When you find a lichen and can collect a specimen, do so. Most of them dry nicely and can be kept for years.

INTRODUCTION

In the main part of this exercise, the students observe the various fungi they are studying. They frequently have problems with vocabulary in this chapter, so encourage them to complete the Preliminary Work section carefully (pp. L91–L92) before they attempt the rest of the exercise and to refer to it when necessary. The end of this laboratory exercise involves a common but often overlooked group of duo-organisms (the lichens). The exercise is designed to have students view and study these organisms in order to become familiar with them.

Required / Extra / Omit

It is suggested that all students complete the Preliminary Work section to review fungi classification, characteristics, and vocabulary. All they will need for this is their textbooks.

Zygomycota—It is suggested that you have moldy bread (or purchase a laboratory culture of *Rhizopus*) for your students to observe and that you have them do all of the *Rhizopus* exercises. The Other Examples section would be best used as extra credit.

Ascomycota—You may wish to omit a few of these examples. It is suggested that you have the students do the work on *Penicillium* and yeast. The Imperfect Fungi section involves simple research (any good encyclopedia will have this information) and should not be too much of a burden. The *Aspergillus* and Other Examples sections may be best used as extra credit.

Basidiomycota—You may wish to omit a few of these examples. Most of them, however, involve mere observation of a specimen and some research (usually in the text) to answer questions. The exercise does not involve a great deal of laboratory time or equipment. The first thing to omit is the Other Examples section. Puffballs and Bracket (Shelf) Fungi should probably be the next to be omitted (or changed to extra credit), followed by specific examples of mushrooms. The textbook does not have a

- What are aerial hyphae that produce new filaments called? stolons
- What are mycelia? masses of intertwined hyphae
- What are rhizoids? hyphae embedded in the material on which the fungus is growing
- What part of the fungus both produces and disperses spores? the fruiting body
- What are haustoria? hyphae of parasitic fungi that enter the host's cells to obtain nutrition
- What is a sporangiophore? a sporophore that produces spores in an enclosure
- When spores are not in an enclosure and are formed by repeated divisions, what is the spore-producing structure called? conidiophore
- What is an ascus? a sac containing sexually produced spores
- What is a basidium? a club-shaped structure that produces spores
- What are basidiospores? four sexually produced spores on a basidium

Phylum Zygomycota

The phylum Zygomycota contains the organisms we normally think of as fungi. These organisms are usually sessile, produce spores, and resemble algae in structure. These fungi bear asexually produced spores in the sporangia. Sexual reproduction takes place when specialized hyphae unite. Examples of this phylum are common and abundant; they are found under almost every step you take.

Rhizopus nigricans

R E O

I. *Rhizopus nigricans* is a black-colored mold that often grows on bread.

II. Using the stereomicroscope or a hand lens, observe cultures of *R. nigricans.*

- Describe what you see, including any fungal structures you can identify. Answers may vary. Students should see hyphae, sporangia, and other structures under adequate magnification. Students should note hyphae around the outer edge of the culture and spore-producing structures toward the center.
- *R. nigricans* produces hyphae that are clear or white. What causes its dark appearance? It is a result of the colored sporangia and spores.

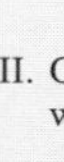

R E O

III. Observe a preserved slide of *R. nigricans*, w.m., on high power.
- Make a drawing in Area A that includes sporangiophores, sporangia, hyphae, mycelia, stolons, and rhizoids.
- Label these structures on your drawing.

Some students find the preserved slides of some fungi difficult to identify and label. A preserved slide of *Rhizopus,* for example, does not look like the textbook diagram. The hyphae are tangled, broken, and not neatly arranged. A word of warning will help the students.

diagram to support the wheat rust life cycle (Figure 12.3), but the boxed text (p. 328) should allow students to find most of the parts, especially the four types of spores.

You might want to have students identify lichen groups as a demonstration, giving them immediate feedback regarding their correctness, and then formulate a description of the lichens as a group rather than as individuals.

The observation of a cross section of a lichen can be done with a microscope attached to a monitor, thus eliminating the need to draw it. Or you may wish to have a group of students draw a lichen structure by viewing the monitor while other students examine the lichen specimens.

Name________________________________

IV. *R. nigricans* reproduces sexually by forming zygotes by conjugation.
- Observe a preserved slide of *R. nigricans* with zygotes.
- In Area B draw a zygote with two parent hyphae.
- What is the difference between a zygote and a zygospore?

In *R. nigricans*, zygotes become zygospores by forming tough protective coats.

B

Other Examples of Phylum Zygomycota

Choose any example of class Phycomycetes not previously used in this exercise. Some examples you might like to choose from are *Pilobolus* (cap-thrower fungi) and *Glomus*.

I. Observe laboratory specimens or preserved slides of your example, if possible.

II. Consult at least one other text for information about your specimen.

III. Make a drawing of your example (specimen drawing if possible, schematic drawing if necessary) and label it completely.

IV. Write a description of the structure, habitat, and economic significance of your specimen.

Phylum Ascomycota

The second phylum we will study is Ascomycota. Often these organisms appear very similar to the zygomycotes, but they differ in their spore-forming structures. Some of the ascomycotes, however, have varied and unusual structures.

Penicillium

I. *Penicillium* is a common mold of fruits and is the original source of the antibiotic penicillin.

II. Using the stereomicroscope or a hand lens, observe the laboratory culture of *Penicillium notatum.*

Describe what you see, including any fungal structures you can identify. Answers may vary. Students should see white hyphae growing around the blue-green spore-covered area.

III. Observe a preserved slide of *Penicillium.*
- Look for conidia and conidiophores.
- On the next page are diagrams of conidia and conidiophores. Which one exhibits the structures found in *Penicillium*? ☒ Diagram 12.1 ☐ Diagram 12.2
- Label the diagram appropriately.

Students are asked to determine whether Diagram 12.1 or 12.2 is *Penicillium* (12.1) by comparing them to a preserved slide. They are then asked to label the diagram. The other diagram (12.2) is *Aspergillus,* another fungus that they are asked to observe (p. L94). You may want them to label both diagrams. Tell them that one is *Penicillium* and the other *Aspergillus.*

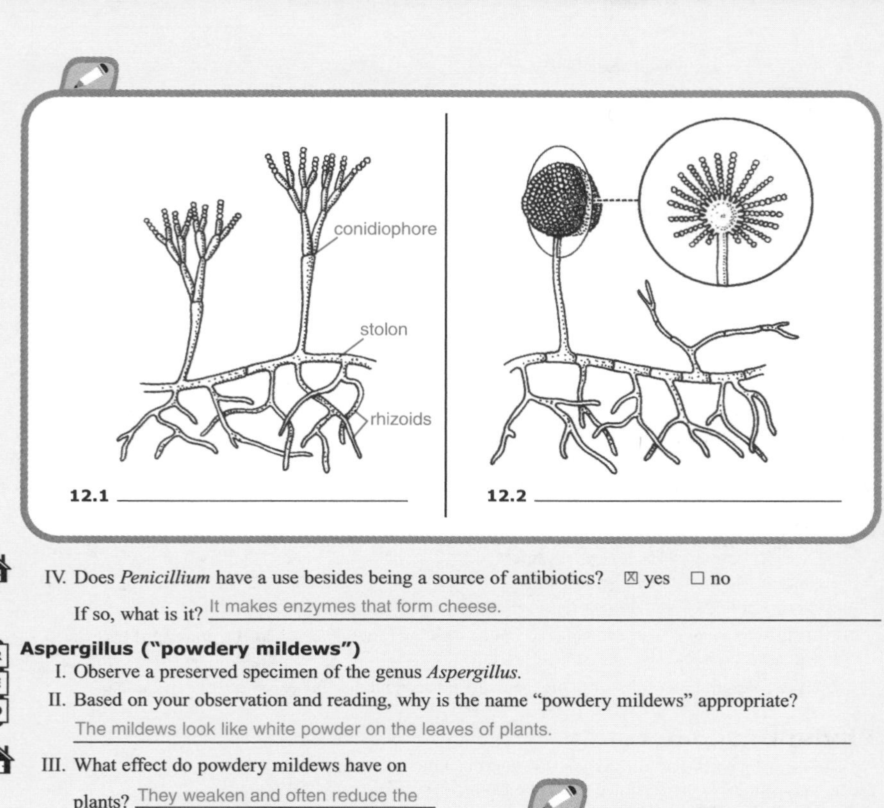

IV. Does *Penicillium* have a use besides being a source of antibiotics? ☒ yes ☐ no

If so, what is it? It makes enzymes that form cheese.

Aspergillus ("powdery mildews")

I. Observe a preserved specimen of the genus *Aspergillus.*

II. Based on your observation and reading, why is the name "powdery mildews" appropriate?

The mildews look like white powder on the leaves of plants.

III. What effect do powdery mildews have on plants? They weaken and often reduce the size of a plant.

Yeasts

I. A drop of yeast culture will be mixed with a stain (methylene blue) and placed on a slide for you to observe. The slide will be set up for oil-immersion viewing (1000×).

- Draw a few yeast cells in Area C. If possible, include some that are budding. Label your drawing as completely as you can.
- Smell the yeast culture and determine whether you detect an alcohol odor. What chemical process does this odor indicate? fermentation, anaerobic respiration

C

L94 Lab 12

Name______________________

II. What are some ways yeasts profit man? They manufacture B vitamins, leaven bread, and cause fermentation, which produces alcohol.

The Imperfect Fungi

One group in the phylum Ascomycota is not known to reproduce sexually. They are few in number, and, except those that are parasitic to man, they have only minor importance.

I. Example: ***Athlete's foot***
Find information about the athlete's foot fungus. Describe the fungus itself. Then describe the common disease it causes, how the disease is spread, how it can be prevented, and how it can be cured.
Answers may vary. Athlete's foot is a small fungus causing dry, red, itchy, scaly skin between the toes; it is spread by contact; it can be prevented by avoidance of contaminated skin or surface; it can be killed by applying various chemicals.

II. Example: ***Ringworm***
Find information about the ringworm fungus. Describe the fungus itself. Then describe the common disease it causes, how the disease is spread, how it can be prevented, and how it can be cured.
Answers may vary. Ringworm is a small ring of hyphae under the skin; it is spread by contact; it can be prevented by avoidance of contaminated skin or surface; it may be treated with various chemical ointments.

Other Examples of Phylum Ascomycota

Choose any example of class Ascomycetes not previously covered in this exercise. Some examples you might like to choose from are *Neurospora*, *Taphrina*, *Morchella* (morel), cup fungi, and *Peziza*.

I. Observe laboratory specimens of your examples, if possible.
II. Consult at least one other text for information about your specimen.
III. Draw your example (specimen drawing if possible, schematic drawing if necessary) and label the drawing completely.
IV. Write a brief description of the structure, habitat, and economic significance of your specimen.

Phylum Basidiomycota

The basidiomycotes are a widely varied group of fungi. They range from those having extremely large vegetative and fruiting bodies to others that have very small ones. Some are harmful parasites; others are saprophytes. Some contain deadly poisons; others are prized as food. A number have several hosts during their intricate life cycles.

Rusts and Smuts

I. The rusts and smuts are usually parasitic fungi with many hosts. Many of them are parasites on food crops and can be extremely harmful.
II. *Puccinia* is the genus that contains many rusts, including the common wheat rust. Compare the life cycle given in other books with the life cycle in Diagram 12.3. Fill in as many labels on the diagram as you can.

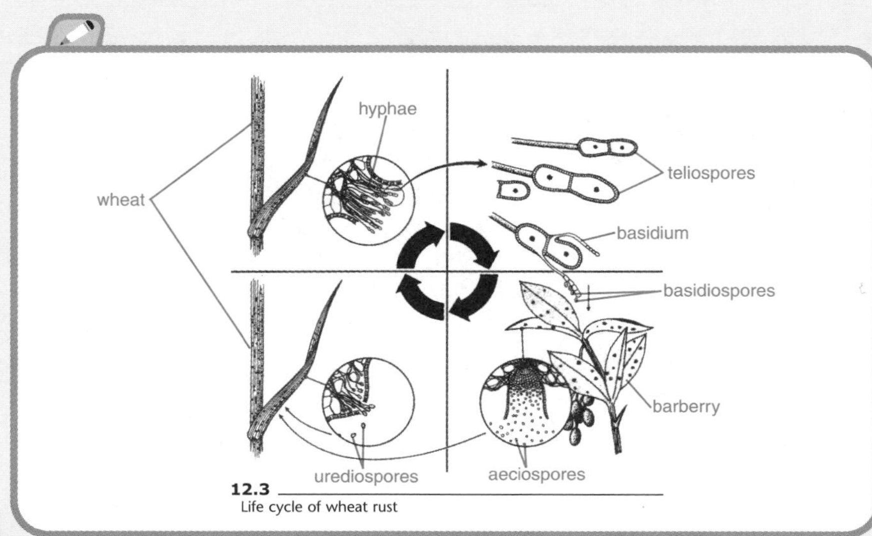

12.3
Life cycle of wheat rust

Puffballs

Observe preserved and dried specimens of puffballs.

I. Where are the basidia and basidiospores (*spores)* located on the puffballs? inside the protective membrane; within the puffball

II. How are the spores released? When the puffball is disturbed, it breaks open and the spores are released.

Bracket (Shelf) Fungi

Observe preserved specimens of bracket, or shelf, fungi and note differences and similarities among the various species.

I. Where are the basidia and basidiospores located on the shelf fungi? On the underside there are tiny pores; the basidia are within these pores.

II. How are spores released from these fungi? They fall out of the pores.

Mushrooms

I. Observe preserved specimens of mushrooms.
- Note the cap, gills, stipe, and hyphae of the various species.
- Note the different colors, sizes, and textures of the various species.

II. Label as many structures as you can in Diagram 12.4.

III. Observe the preserved slide of *Coprinus*, c.s. (Be sure to use the cross section of the cap.)
- Find the gills and locate the basidia and basidiospores.
- In Area D, make a drawing that includes a section of a gill with basidia and basidiospores.
- Label the drawing as completely as possible.

Name________________

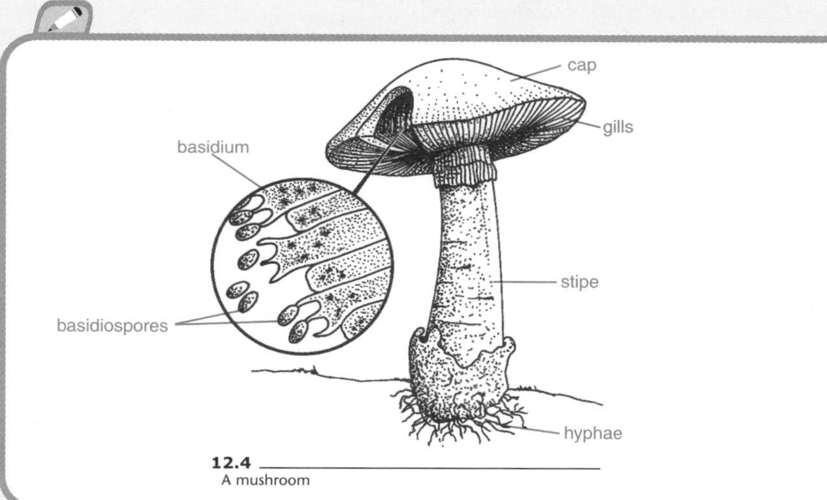

12.4 ________________
A mushroom

IV. Choose any two specific mushrooms and research them in other texts. Briefly describe them, telling their habitat, importance, and a couple of unusual facts.

- Name of mushroom Answers will vary.

  Description Answers will vary.

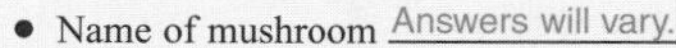

D

- Name of mushroom Answers will vary.

  Description Answers will vary.

Other Examples of Phylum Basidiomycota

Choose any example of class Basidiomycetes not previously covered in this exercise. Some examples you might like to choose from are earthstars, stinkhorns, apple cedar rust, and corn smut.

I. Observe laboratory specimens of your examples, if possible.

II. Consult at least one other text for information about your specimen.

III. Draw your example (specimen drawing if possible, schematic drawing if necessary) and label it completely.

IV. Write a brief description of the structures, habitat, and economic significance of your specimen.

The Lichens

Know the names (common names if possible) of the lichen specimens you use. Often they can be identified with field guides or websites that specialize in nonflowering plants (ferns, mosses, etc.). Often these sources will tell you some interesting facts about the lichen (uses, harm it may do, who eats it, etc.). This kind of information scattered through the lichen activity will make the study of these often overlooked organisms far more interesting.

Lichens are not fungi, but they do contain fungi. Actually, they are a symbiotic set of organisms, living together as one for the benefit of both.

I. What two organisms are always found in a lichen? Trace the organisms to phylum and class if possible.

1. Fungus, phylum Ascomycota (rarely, Basidiomycota)
2. Alga, phylum Chlorophyta or Cyanophyta

II. Your instructor will supply you with several different lichen specimens labeled by letters. There will be at least one of each of the three types of lichens. Identify the type of each specimen and describe it in the chart below.

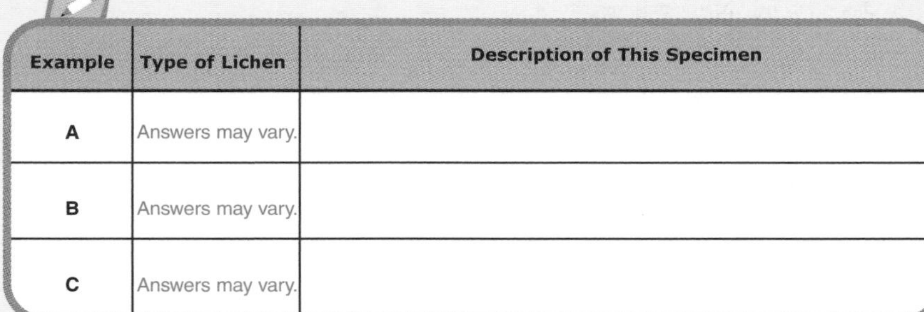

Example	Type of Lichen	Description of This Specimen
A	Answers may vary.	
B	Answers may vary.	
C	Answers may vary.	

You may have to give the students some help in determining what are algae and what are fungi on the microscope slide.

III. Observe a slide of a lichen, c.s., stained to show the alga in one color and the fungus in another.
- In Area E draw a section showing the alga and fungus.
- Label the structures you are able to identify.

Name________________________________

Date________________ Hour__________

13a Plant Identification

Materials

- live and preserved plant specimens

Goals

- To learn major classifications in the plant kingdom
- To recognize various plant characteristics in specimens

It is one thing to see plant characteristics in photographs or drawings, but it is quite another to recognize those characteristics in actual specimens. In this laboratory exercise you will list characteristics you would look for when identifying the major plant groups. You will then use this list to identify as many specimens as possible. It is not important that you know the names of any of these specimens. Your job is merely to assign them to the correct phylum or class. A thoroughly accurate list will allow you to identify more specimens and to do so more efficiently. The more specimens you correctly identify, the better your grade will be.

Preliminary Work

I. Fill in the Plant Classifications Chart on page L101.
- List characteristics for each classification, using characteristics that you can distinguish by sight. (For example, "Has cell walls made of cellulose" would be a poor characteristic to list since you cannot tell this by looking at a specimen.)
- Try to list characteristics that apply only to a particular taxonomic group. ("Has chlorophyll" would be a poor characteristic to list since nearly all plants have chlorophyll.)
- As you identify the specimens in class, you will be permitted to refer to the Plant Classifications Chart only. Put on it all the information you will need.
- You may not list names of plants on your Plant Classifications Chart.

II. Make sketches of the types of leaf venations on page L102. You may draw variations of the venation to help you as you fill in the Specimen Chart. (Remember, you can put no names of plants on your Plant Classifications Chart.)

In-Class Procedures

I. Various specimens will be present in the lab. Some will be fresh; others preserved. Some will be entire plants, while others will be pieces of a plant.
- Each specimen will be numbered, and you will be asked to identify it on the Specimen Chart.
- You must list your reasons for each identification by listing the letters for the appropriate characteristics from your Plant Classifications Chart. (See Sample Specimen Chart.)
- If the specimen has leaves, you must list the type of leaf venation it has in order to get credit for that specimen.
- If the specimen has needles or scales, you must write *needles* or *scales* in the venation section of the Specimen Chart to get credit for that specimen.
- Some of the specimens will have their common and/or scientific names on them. If they are not labeled, you do not need to list their names on the Specimen Chart.

II. This exercise is limited to class time.

A trip through your yard, the school yard, and the yards of two or three friends should supply a number of good, fresh specimens. Even in the winter, some useful specimens of persistent foliage and conifers can be found.

Keep this exercise in mind when selecting your classroom plants. The unusual leaf venations of some house plants are very useful. A fern or two would also be helpful.

A friend with a green thumb and a sunny window may allow you to borrow some house plants for this exercise. Select interesting plants that have distinguishing characteristics.

Consider having a carrot, a pine cone, a fibrous root system, a simple flower without leaves (gladiolus is suitable and is available at a florist), and a stalk of celery (minus its leaves) that is standing in a glass of water with food coloring. These specimens can be identified by observing structures other than leaves.

After obtaining as many fresh plant specimens as possible, try to balance the number of different classifications among them. You will no doubt have more dicots than anything else, but try to vary the types of venation. Then go to your preserved specimens and your herbarium (see note I on p. A20) to find the venations and classifications you are missing.

Plastic mounted specimens of *Marchantia* moss, lycopodiums, and some other hard-to-find plants are recommended. Mosses collected in the woods may be used for this exercise. Often they dry nicely and can be reused year after year.

Introduction

This exercise is designed to help students learn the major classifications of the plant kingdom and to recognize certain characteristics of plant specimens. Some students quickly understand this exercise and do extremely well, while others seem never to grasp the concept and thus do poorly. The basic difference is in the students' attitudes and preparation. To improve their attitudes toward the exercise, approach it as a challenge and an interesting, different experience. To increase their interest, you may want to tell them that they are finally going to be able to do what they have so often wanted to do—use their notes while taking a quiz.

In some respects this laboratory exercise is similar to Lab 9. You will place specimens throughout the classroom for the students to identify individually. However, unlike Lab 9, in which the students used a key to identify each organism, this exercise requires them to use lists of characteristics to identify the classification of a specimen as precisely as possible. Here the emphasis is on the classification groups and their distinguishing characteristics, not on the method used to identify the specimens or on the specimens themselves.

Required / Extra / Omit

This exercise must be done in its entirety or not at all. You may reduce the amount of class time needed by decreasing the number of specimens.

Some teachers with slower classes may prefer to do the exercise orally, with the entire class working on the same specimen at the same time.

Have a few specimens in class the day before the exercise is to be done. Show a specimen and have the students enter its name on the Sample Specimen Chart as number 4. Ask them for the classification. (They may need to look it up.) Ask them why they classified it as they did. Explain that the reasons they are giving should be indicative of the type of characteristics they should list on their Plant Classifications charts before they come to class. Ask for the venation and have them write it in the proper space. Repeat the procedure with several specimens.

Sample Specimen Chart

	Name	Classification	Reasons for identification	Venation
1	Sugar Maple	Dicot	A, C, D	S. Pal
2	Iris	Monocot	A, E	Parl.
3	White Pine	Conif.	E	needles
4				
5				
6				
7				
8				
9				
10				
11				
12				

Note: These letters are for example only and are not intended as accurate answers.

Name ______________________________

Plant Classifications Chart

I. Phylum Bryophyta† (*Bryo*) ‡

A. Lacks vascular tissue; most living specimens about one inch high

B. Answers may vary. Characteristics students may list from the text may not be exclusive but

C. should be effective for "usual identification."

D. ______________________________

E. ______________________________

II. Phylum Lycophyta† (*Lyc*) ‡

A. ______________________________

B. ______________________________

C. ______________________________

D. ______________________________

E. ______________________________

III. Phylum Pteridophyta† (*Pter*) ‡

A. ______________________________

B. ______________________________

C. ______________________________

D. ______________________________

E. ______________________________

IV. Phylum Coniferophyta† (*Conif*) ‡

A. ______________________________

B. ______________________________

C. ______________________________

D. ______________________________

E. ______________________________

V. Phylum Anthophyta

- Class Monocotyledoneae† (*Monocot*) ‡

A. Leaf venation: parallel

B. ______________________________

C. ______________________________

D. ______________________________

E. ______________________________

- Class Dicotyledoneae† (*Dicot*) ‡

A. Leaf venation: pinnate or palmate

B. ______________________________

C. ______________________________

D. ______________________________

E. ______________________________

†Use only these levels of classification when identifying the specimens.
‡The abbreviations in parentheses may be used when filling in the Specimen Chart.

Inform students of the differences between monocots and dicots, using Table 13A.3 on page 343 of the text. Tell them that they may see merely parts of plants on the exercise and that they will need to be able to classify them, even though they may not be able to give the venation.

Students occasionally have problems knowing what is a leaflet and what is a leaf. The key is knowing the difference between a stem and a petiole. If there is doubt, they should look for a stipule, which is found only at the base of a petiole. Thus everything beyond the stipule is a single leaf. Sessile leaves or leaves without petioles may present problems for some students. Stress that you are not trying to trick them.

§ It is suggested that you draw a couple of modifications of the leaves (heavily lobed, etc.) above so that you can more easily recognize them. When identifying succulent leaves, you may have to make an educated guess. Succulent leaves are often very thick, and the venation does not show.

\# Use the abbreviations in parentheses as you fill in the Specimen Chart.

L102 *Lab 13a*

Name________________________________

Specimen Chart

	Name	Classification	Reasons for identification	Venation
1				
2				
3				
4				
5				
6				
7				
8				
9				
10				
11				
12				
13				
14				
15				
16				
17				
18				
19				
20				
21				
22				
23				
24				
25				
26				
27				
28				
29				
30				
31				
32				
33				
34				
35				

Tell the students that although monocots and dicots can be distinguished by leaf venation, ferns also have venation and can occasionally be confused with the angiosperms. Tell them that you will not try to trick them and that any fern included among the other plants will have distinctive fern characteristics that can be used to identify it. The venation of ferns, however, should be listed in the proper column.

Explain to the students that in this exercise, needles and scales are considered leaves, and each is considered a type of venation that must be indicated in the proper column.

Tell the students who have problems with a particular specimen to go on to the next one. For them, the object is to get as many right as they can.

Tell the students that names (either common or scientific) are given for some specimens. They should copy these in the spaces provided.

Tell the students that they must fill in the spaces for classification, reasons for identification, and venation in order to receive full credit for their answer. Inform them whether you will give partial credit.

When grading, check to see that students have written good reasons for each classification on the Plant Classifications Chart (p. L101). For each specimen they should have given a reason or two in the spaces provided on the Specimen Chart. Checking each entry in the Reasons for Identification column is time consuming and unnecessary (if the student has good reasons listed on the Plant Classifications Chart). You may generally assume that if a student correctly identified a plant, he used the proper reasoning. When you hand the exercise back, tell the students that you checked the classification and the venation columns, assuming that if they answered those correctly, they probably had the reasons for identification correct also.

Grading should be similar to that suggested for Lab 9 (see p. L67). However, because the numbers are already included on the Specimen Chart, students will fill in the proper classification for each numbered plant in the corresponding space (i.e., plant specimen 9 is classified on line 9 of the chart). Although the students may start with different specimens, all the answers will appear in the same order on each student's paper.

	Name	Classification	Reasons for identification	Venation
36				
37				
38				
39				
40				
41				
42				
43				
44				
45				
46				
47				
48				
49				
50				
51				
52				
53				
54				
55				
56				
57				
58				
59				
60				
61				
62				
63				
64				
65				
66				
67				
68				
69				
70				
71				
72				

Name________________________________
Date__________________ Hour__________

13b
Plant Organs

Materials

- microscope
- stereomicroscope or hand lens
- preserved slides of leaf, c.s.; *Ranunculus* young root, c.s.; *Ranunculus* stem, c.s.; *Zea* stem, c.s.
- fresh lettuce, spinach, or geranium leaves
- glass slides
- coverslips
- dormant twigs
- plants rooting in water
- leaf with epidermal hairs
- scalpel
- collection of leaves
- forceps

Goals

- To observe some of the plant organs and tissues
- To understand the anatomy and physiology of plant leaves and stems

Plants have their own ways of handling the basic functions necessary for survival. Observing some of their special structures will help you understand the functions of leaves, roots, and stems.

Leaves

Plant leaves are usually the major photosynthetic organs of the plant. Foliage leaves, which are the type you will work with in this exercise, display the typical characteristics of leaves. We will note some of the varieties of foliage leaves and then observe their specialized design for carrying on photosynthesis.

R E O

Gross Structure

I. Study leaf venations.

- Make a collection of leaves typical of the various types of leaf venations.
- Press and mount your leaves on paper, one type per page. You may have several specimens with the same type of leaf venation on the same page.
- On each page write the common names of the specimens you have collected and the names of several other plants with the same type of leaf venation.
- You should have examples of the following types if possible:
  - parallel
  - simple pinnate, pinnately compound, bipinnately compound
  - simple palmate, palmately compound
  - scales
  - needles
  - modified leaves such as bracts and thorns

R E O

II. Study leaf margins.

- Make a collection of leaves with different margins and shapes.
- Press and mount your leaves on paper, one type of leaf margin or leaf shape per page. You may have several specimens with the same type of margin or shape on the same page.
- On each page write the common names of the specimens you have collected and list the names of several other plants with the same type of leaf margin or leaf shape.
- You should have examples of at least the following margins:
  - entire
  - undulate
  - dentate
  - any two others

It is essential that you collect twigs about three feet long with visible bud scale scars and an apical bud at the tip. If too much secondary growth has taken place, the bud scale scars will not be visible.

A few weeks in advance, put a section of a houseplant in water to root it. African violet leaves and most vines root well. Such cuttings can be used in this exercise and also make good illustrations when you are discussing asexual reproduction in plants.

A leaf with epidermal hairs can be found on many house plants, such as the African violet, gloxinia, piggyback plant, and strawberry begonia.

If you are going to require the leaf collections, you may want to give instructions on pressing and mounting leaves. (See note I on p. A20.) If the students are doing them for extra credit, you may want to have the students notify you before they start so that you can give them special instructions. Depending on which region you live in, bear in mind that leaves may be somewhat limited outdoors and set your expectations accordingly.

Introduction

In this exercise the students are to observe structures that they have seen most of their lives. The knowledge they acquire during this study of plants should cause these familiar plant parts to become considerably more interesting to them.

Required / Extra / Omit

Leaf collections (pp. L105–L106) should be graded as extra credit. If you are following the suggested sequence and rate of teaching the text, this exercise should fall around Christmastime. Consider permitting the students to do these collections over Christmas vacation. If your semester ends sometime after the break, some of them may recognize that their biology grade is in jeopardy and may use this opportunity to improve it.

The sections on root gross structure and terminal bud dissection (pp. L107 and L109) are good sections to consider for extra credit.

Consider having students observe both a *Ranunculus* and a *Zea* stem but draw only one.

- You should include at least the following shapes:
  - linear
  - cordate
  - deltoid
  - lobed
  - circular
  - at least one other

Microstructures

R E O

I. Draw a cross section of a leaf from a preserved slide in Area A.

- Draw five to fifteen cells of each type of tissue (for example, five to fifteen upper epidermal cells, five to fifteen palisade mesophyll cells adjacent to the epidermal cells). Continue until you have a section of the leaf from top to bottom, including the vein. Include guard cells and stomata if possible.
- Include a vein (not the large vein in the middle of the leaf). Try to find a vein cut in cross section, not one that has been cut longitudinally.
- Be careful not to draw a torn segment of leaf.
- Label all parts.

A

Some students have difficulty obtaining the leaf epidermis for making the wet mount. Practice tearing leaves in advance and then demonstrate how to rip the leaf so that a section of epidermis is revealed. Tell the students that they need a piece of the lower epidermis. A small section of the leaf (remaining attached to the epidermis) can help to keep the epidermis flat while they are making the wet mount. The coverslip, however, should not teeter-totter on top of the leaf section. Remind the students that they must observe a section of epidermis (which lacks chloroplasts), not a section of leaf.

R E O

II. Study and draw a wet mount of a leaf epidermis.

- Using your forceps or your fingers, carefully peel a piece of epidermis from a geranium, spinach, or lettuce leaf.
- Make a wet mount of this tissue and observe the epidermis using a microscope.
- What is the position of the guard cells? ☐ open ☐ closed Answers may vary.
  What does this tell you about the photosynthetic activity of the leaf at the time you took off the epidermis? Open—photosynthesis was being carried on; closed—photosynthesis was not actively taking place.
- What is the approximate ratio of guard cells to epidermal cells in this epidermis specimen? 1:10
- Would you expect this ratio to be different in other plants? ☒ yes ☐ no

- Why or why not? Other plants carry on photosynthesis at different rates and therefore need more or fewer stomata.
- In Area B draw a section of epidermal tissue, including two stomata with guard cells and several epidermal cells. Label your drawing completely.

III. Observe a leaf with epidermal hairs under a stereomicroscope or a hand lens. Observe the area near the margin of the leaf. Describe what you see. Answers may vary. There are tiny translucent projections along the edge of the leaf.

Roots

Roots anchor plants, help them absorb water and dissolved substances, and provide storage. In this section you will observe the structures of roots that do all these functions. Carefully note which structure of the root accomplishes each function.

Gross Structure

R E O

On your own paper, draw schematic diagrams of a taproot system and a fibrous root system. On both root system drawings, label primary and secondary roots.

Microstructure

R E O

I. Observe the preserved slide of a young *Ranunculus* root, c.s. Follow these instructions.
- Scan the entire slide.
- In Area C draw a wedge-shaped section of the root (triangular, touching both the center of the root and the outside; see Diagram 13b.1 on the next page).
- You may need to move the slide while you make this drawing because what you are drawing is probably larger than the field of view of the microscope.
- Include all the tissues found in the root. Label all the parts.

An alternative method for viewing stomata is to make a mold of the leaf epidermis. Simply spread a very thin layer of clear fingernail polish in a small area on the underside of a leaf, wait about ten minutes for it to dry, and then press a piece of clear cellophane (transparent) tape over it. (The more common invisible tape does not work well.) After peeling the tape off, place the tape on a slide, sticky side up, and view on medium power. You may need to reduce the light intensity using the diaphragm, but the guard cells and other epidermal cells should be clearly visible. You will not need to use water or a coverslip for this method.

Students frequently have difficulty making pie-shaped diagrams. A word of explanation with regard to Diagram 13b.1 may be necessary.

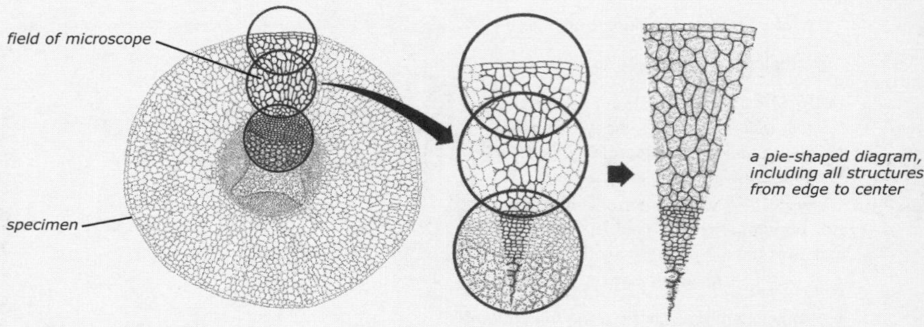

13b.1 ______
Drawing a pie-shaped section

R E O

II. With a hand lens, observe the root hairs on the maturation region of a root growing in water. (A rooting stem or a seedling may be used.)

- What is the function of the root hairs? water absorption
- Which root areas have root hairs? the elongation and maturation regions
- Why are root hairs found only in certain areas? Answers may vary. Root hairs can be only at the tips because once secondary growth starts, the epidermis that produces the root hairs is destroyed.
- What other observation did you make about root hairs? Answers may vary. The length and velvety appearance of the root hairs may be noted.

Stems

Although some plants (such as cactus) have stems that are the primary photosynthetic structures and even the storage organs of the plant, in this section we will observe stems that use typical structures to accomplish the usual function of manufacturing and displaying leaves.

Gross Structure

R E O

I. Observe a dormant twig section. Answer the following questions:

- My twig number is Answers will vary.
- How many years old is the twig? ______
  How do you know? by counting the areas between the bud scale scars
- Was the rate of growth the same each year?
  ☐ yes ☐ no How do you know?
  The distance between the bud scale scars is equal and indicates an even rate of growth, **or** the distance is unequal and indicates varying amounts of growth.
- What is the leaf arrangement of this plant?
  ☐ opposite ☐ alternate ☐ whorled
- How many nodes were produced during the most recent growing season (last summer)?
  Answers may vary.

R E O

II. Using a scalpel, make a longitudinal section of an apical (terminal) bud.

- Do not use the apical bud of any of the twigs used earlier.
- In Area D draw the dissected apical bud and label all the parts you observed.

Students should determine the age of the twig by counting each bud scale scar and the area for the apical bud—not by counting annual rings. For example, the twig in the diagram on page 356 of the text is three years old. By using a twig that has been broken off a tree or one that has its larger end damaged, you can discourage the students from counting annual rings without telling them how to determine the age of the twig.

When you ask the students if the *Ranunculus* and *Zea* are typical of their classes, you assume that they know what is typical of a dicot and a monocot. The information is in their text (p. 359), but they may need to look hard to find it since it is in an illustration.

Microstructure

I. Observe a preserved slide of a *Ranunculus* stem, c.s.

- Scan the entire slide.
- In Area E make a drawing of a pie-shaped section of the stem (triangular, touching both the center of the stem and the outside; see Diagram 13b.1). You may need to move the slide while you make the drawing because what you are drawing is probably larger than the field of view of the microscope.
- Label all the parts.
- *Ranunculus* is a dicot. Is the *Ranunculus* stem typical of this class? ☒ yes ☐ no

II. Observe the preserved slide of a cross section of a *Zea* (corn) stem.

- Follow the directions given above to make a drawing of the stem in Area F.
- *Zea* is a monocot. Is the *Zea* stem typical of this class? ☒ yes ☐ no

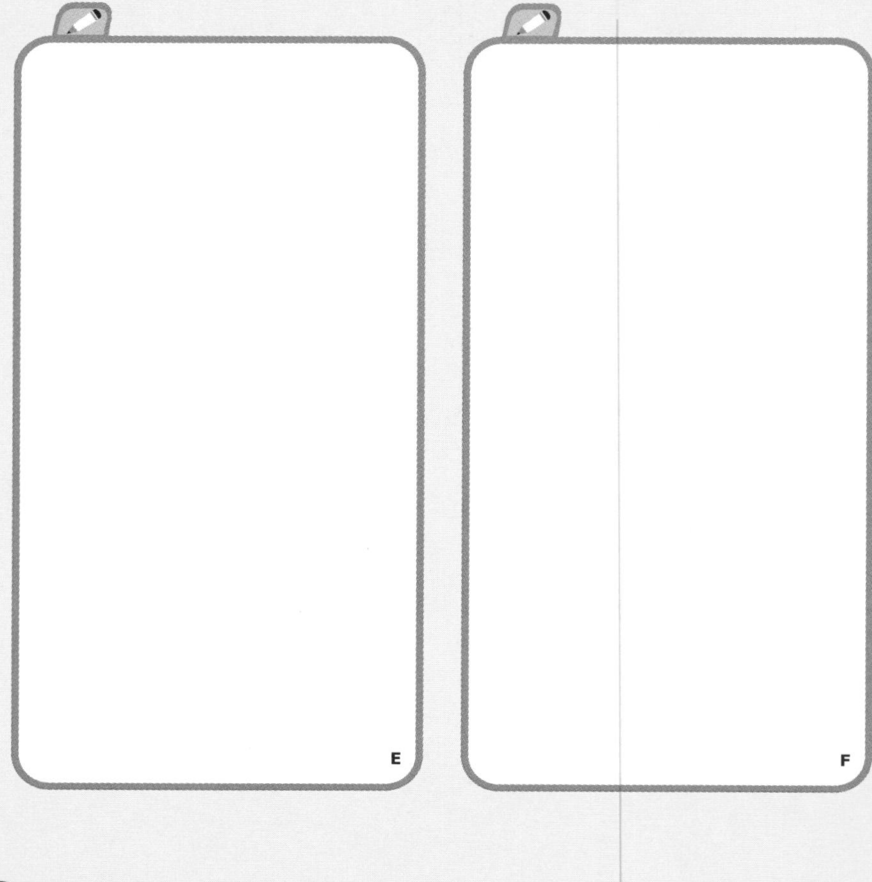

Name__________________________

Date________________ Hour________

14 Flowers, Fruits, and Seeds

Materials

- fresh flower specimens (gladioli)
- fresh fruit specimens (including at least a pome, drupe, true berry, modified berry, and a pod)
- scalpel
- large kitchen knife
- single-edged razor blade
- seeds

Goals

- To observe the structures of a typical flower and to learn the structures of various flowers
- To observe various kinds of fruits and learn their parts
- To observe and learn the structures of a typical seed

The sexual reproductive parts of angiosperms are found in structures called flowers. There are many types of flowers, but they all have certain characteristics in common. Note these characteristics as you study the flowers and their products, the fruits and the seeds.

Flowers

Not all flowers are variations of the rose, lily, or daisy. Many flowers lack showy petals and many have very unusual structures, but most of them share the same basic floral parts.

I. Observe and label the diagrams of various flowers in Diagram 14.1 on pages L112–13.

- On each diagrammed flower, label as many of the following structures as you can: pistil, stigma, style, ovary, ovule, stamen, anther, filament, pollen, petals, sepals, and receptacle. *(NOTE:* Not all of these are visible in all the flowers illustrated. Use your knowledge of these structures to assign the labels.)
- By the names of the various flowers in Diagram 14.1, indicate whether the flower
  - is complete or incomplete.
  - is male, female, or both.
  - has a superior ovary or an inferior ovary.
  - contains a single ovule or multiple ovules.
  - is from a monocot or a dicot.

II. Dissect a flower.

- Using your scalpel, carefully dissect a live flower to see the various internal structures. The best method of dissection is to slice through the ovary area from the top down, as seen on the drawings on the following two pages. Examine with a hand lens if necessary.
- In Area A draw a longitudinal section of your flower. Label all parts.
- Indicate whether your flower is complete or incomplete; is male, female, or both; has a superior or inferior ovary; contains a single ovule or multiple ovules; is a composite flower or not a composite flower; and comes from a monocot or dicot plant. Answers will vary.

Introduction

In this exercise students are to observe flowers, fruits, and seeds that they have seen most of their lives but with which they probably have not become familiar. This exercise is designed to help them gain an appreciation for and an understanding of these plant parts.

Required / Extra / Omit

The labeling of the flower diagrams is an assignment that can be done as homework since it does not require laboratory equipment. This assignment can be used to help teach or reinforce the various floral structures and the flower types.

The dissection of a flower is a good section to require. If you can obtain a supply of different flowers, this section can be exceptionally profitable.

The fruit dissection is difficult and time consuming for most students. Consider making this an extra-credit section or doing it as a demonstration.

The seed dissection can be difficult or easy, depending upon the seeds you choose. You may want to consider making this an extra-credit section or doing it as a demonstration.

Flower dissection should be of a simple flower. Since one stalk supplies several flowers, gladioli obtained from a local florist work well. Roses are also good but are considerably more expensive. Mums, daisies, and carnations are poor choices because they are complex, and the flower parts are tiny, despite the large blooms. When at the florist's (or in that section of a large grocery store), look for some other flowers that can be dissected. Lilies, tulips, daffodils, azaleas, snapdragons, and several others are good choices and are often available.

If you are doing the fruit dissection in class, consider bringing paper plates and clean kitchen utensils for the dissections. Eating the fruits when you are finished adds interest and entertainment. You might make this part of a class Christmas party if this is done at the proper season.

Besides the usual apple, tomato, orange, pear, banana, grape, cantaloupe, cucumber, squash, plum, peach, and watermelon, try to obtain unusual fruits. Snow peas, okra, corn on the cob, kiwi fruit, star fruit, tomatillos, pomegranates, avocados, papayas, figs, dates, strawberries, green peppers, cranberries, raspberries, and pineapples are all interesting and are often available in a form usable for this lab. Some other fruits common on a grocer's shelf include peanuts (in the shell), unpitted olives, pickles (whole), and dried star anise (in Mexican food section). Have fun.

A good number of seeds for dissection will become available as you dissect fruits. Watermelons, pumpkins, squash, green peppers, apples, pears, oranges, cantaloupes, peanuts, peaches, cherries, grapes, and tomatoes all yield dissectible seeds.

Seeds found on a grocer's shelves that are suitable for dissection include pecans, walnuts, pistachios, peanuts, chestnuts, dried beans (a bag of mixed beans will provide variety), peas, corn (popcorn), sunflower seeds (whole), pumpkin seeds, and coconuts. Many of the larger flower or vegetable seeds available at a nursery can also be used. Although difficult, consider marigolds and zinnias. During the proper season collect milkweed pods, poppy pods, acorns, maple seeds, pecans or other nuts with the ovary wall, and other fruits and seeds; dry them or preserve them (see note F, p. A19).

Explain to the students that not all the flowers illustrated in the diagrams have all the possible parts. Tell them to study pages 385–88 of their text for more information. They are to fill in the diagram as completely as possible. Do not expect the students to have all of the labels that are given in the teacher's edition. Grade this section according to the labels you would expect them to have.

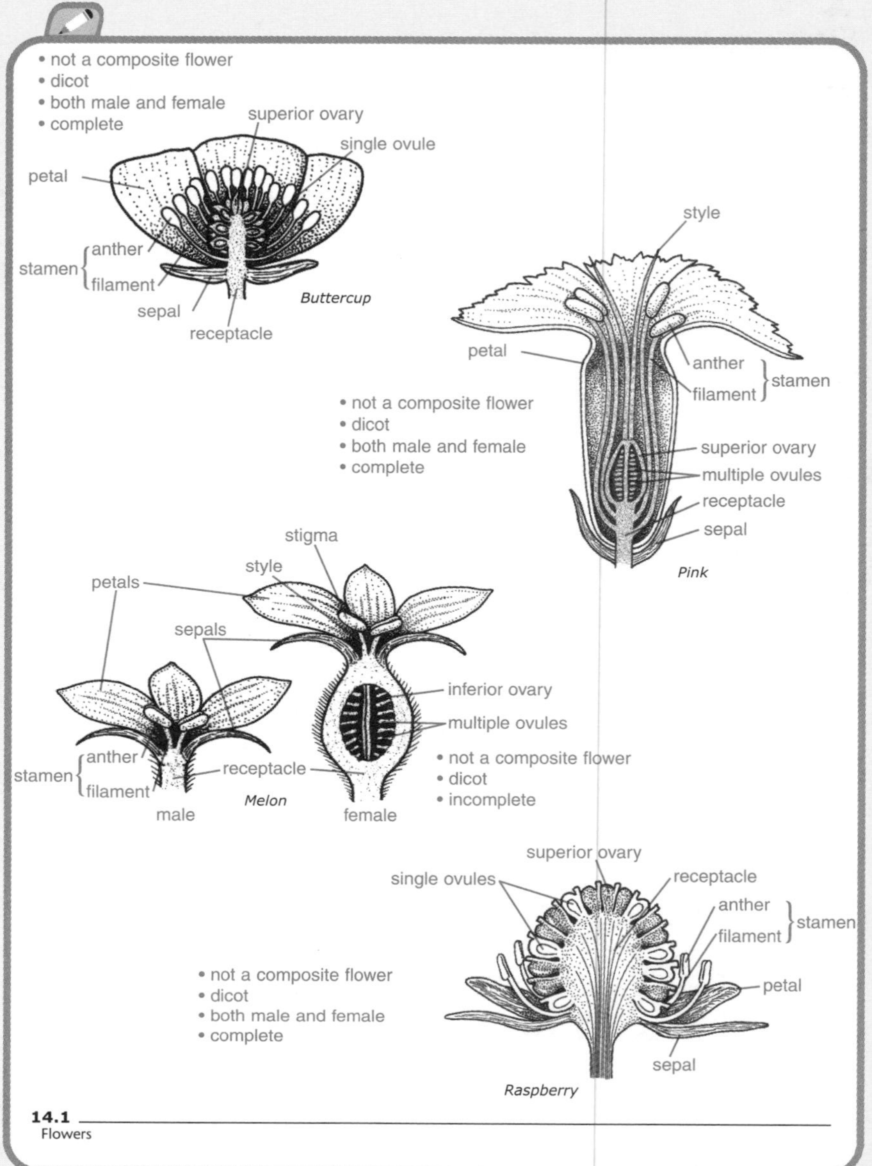

Name________________________

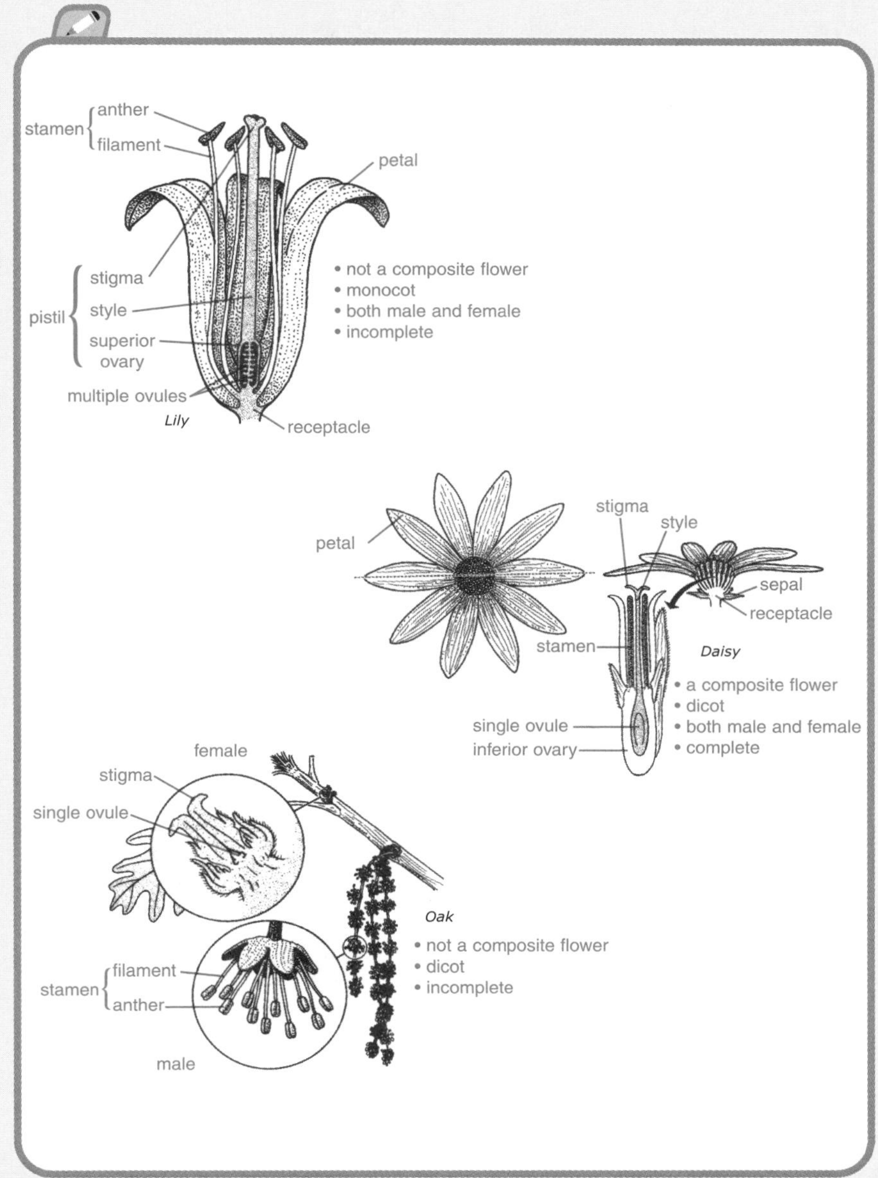
stamen
anther
filament
petal
pistil
stigma
style
superior ovary
multiple ovules
Lily
receptacle
• not a composite flower
• monocot
• both male and female
• incomplete
petal
stigma
style
sepal
receptacle
stamen
Daisy
• a composite flower
• dicot
• both male and female
• complete
single ovule
inferior ovary
female
stigma
single ovule
Oak
• not a composite flower
• dicot
• incomplete
stamen
filament
anther
male

Information about fruits is available on page 391 of the text, but for most students, fruit dissection will require a bit of help from you or from reference books. Such books, however, often use scientific terms beyond the students' understanding at this point. Be prepared to help.

The fruit dissection makes an excellent demonstration. The fruits can then be placed on a table or side counter where the students can identify the kind of fruit and make the drawings while they are doing the flower dissections.

You may want to consider giving a different fruit to each laboratory group. After students have dissected the fruit, identified its kind, and labeled the parts, you may want to have each group share its experiences with the class.

Fruits

A fruit is a ripened ovary. Although many fruits are like the familiar apple and orange, many are quite different. Fruits have been classified into groups based on the different ways their structures develop.

I. Using a scalpel and/or knife, dissect the examples of fruits found in the lab. (Your teacher may assign a different fruit to each laboratory group to dissect, or the fruits may already be dissected for you.)

II. Use the Key to Common Fruit Types (p. L115) to identify the type of each of the fruit specimens.

Fruit Types

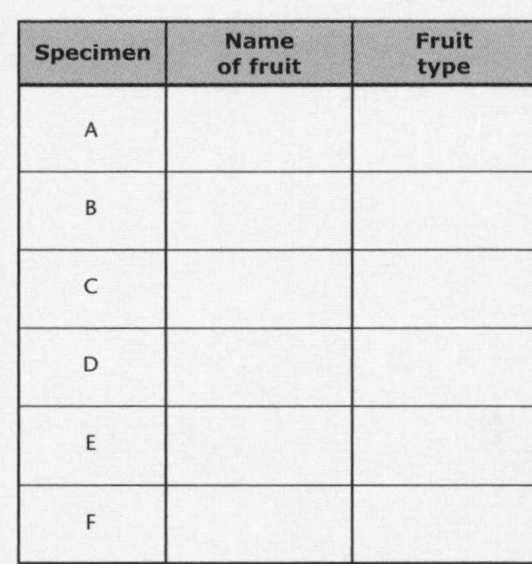

Specimen	Name of fruit	Fruit type
A		
B		
C		
D		
E		
F		

Specimen	Name of fruit	Fruit type
G		
H		
I		
J		
K		
L		

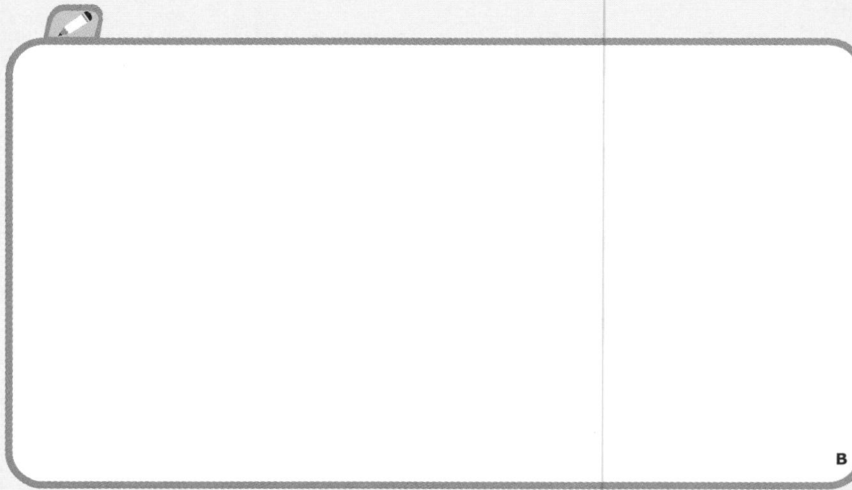

III. In Area B draw longitudinal section views of the fruits your teacher selects and label the parts indicated by the fruit type. Research may be necessary.

- Pome: Label receptacle, ovary, remains of flower parts, pedicel, ovary wall, and seeds.
- Drupe: Label pedicel, remains of flower parts, ovary (outer layer and inner layer), and seed.
- True Berry: Label pedicel, remains of flower parts, skin, ovary, section of fruit, and seeds.
- Pod: Label pedicel, remains of flower parts, ovary, and seeds.
- Modified Berry: Label pedicel, remains of flower parts, skin, ovary, section of fruit, and seeds.

A Key to Common Fruit Types

1. Single ovary that may have one or more chambers for ovules, usually without other floral parts .... (Simple Fruit) **3**
   Collection of ovaries, usually with other floral parts .... (Compound Fruit) **2**

Compound Fruits

2. Several separate ovaries of a single flower that ripen individually, usually on an enlarged receptacle .... **Aggregate Fruit**
   Several ovaries from separate flowers that ripen fused together, usually on an enlarged receptacle .... **Multiple Fruit**

Simple Fruits

3. Fruit dry at maturity .... (Dry Fruit) **4**
   Fruit fleshy at maturity .... (Fleshy Fruit) **10**

Dry Simple Fruits

4. Fruit open when ripe **5**
   Fruit closed when ripe **7**
5. Ovary wall thin. Single-chambered ovary with many seeds. Opens along one or two sides when ripe **6**
   Ovary wall thin. Multiple-chambered ovary, each chamber with many seeds. Opens when ripe .... **Capsule**
6. Opens along one side .... **Follicle**
   Opens along two sides .... **Pod**
7. Fruit with thin wing formed by ovary wall .... **Samara**
   Fruit without wing **8**
8. Thick, hard, woody ovary wall enclosing a single seed .... **Nut**
   Thin ovary wall **9**
9. Ovary wall fastened to a single seed .... **Grain**
   Ovary wall separated from a single seed .... **Achene**

Fleshy Simple Fruits

10. Fleshy portion develops from receptacle enlargement. Ovary forms leathery core with seeds .... **Pome**
    Ovary fleshy **11**
11. Ovary two-layered, outer layer fleshy, inner layer forming hard, woody stone or pit, usually enclosing one seed .... **Drupe**
    Entire ovary fleshy **12**
12. Thin-skinned fruit with divided ovary, usually with each section containing seeds .... **True Berry**
    Thick, tough-skinned fruit with divided ovary, usually with each section containing seeds .... **Modified Berry**

The seed observation and dissection can be done as a demonstration, but doing it as a group project is recommended. Each group should contain two to four students. They should be given about half a dozen specimens of the seed they are to dissect. Thus, if a mistake is made, they can use another seed. Carefully select the seeds for variety and difficulty.

It is recommended that you have the students start with their seed observation and dissection and complete this section before going on. Have each group place its dissected seed(s) and a sample drawing in a particular place in the classroom. Then while they are doing other parts of the laboratory exercise, have them observe the displayed dissections. During the last few minutes of class, congratulate those who had difficult seeds but did good dissections and observations and ask the class whether there were corrections they thought should be made. Make appropriate comments.

Another method of doing seed dissection is to select a few different seeds (three to six) and give each student (or laboratory group) a set of seeds. Have them dissect and draw each of the seeds. You will need to have extra seeds available, since seeds are often damaged the first time or two a dissection is attempted.

Try the various seed dissections before you ask students to do them. Give special instructions when needed. Tools such as nutcrackers and even saws may be needed for some seeds. Dried beans can be soaked in water overnight to make them easier to open.

Seeds

The three basic parts of a seed are the embryo plant, stored food, and a seed coat. The diversity of these structures found in different plants, however, is almost as wide as the diversity found in the floral parts and fruit types.

R E O

I. Observe the seed(s) found in the lab. (Your teacher may assign a different seed to each laboratory group, or he may give each group a few seeds to observe and dissect.)
- Use a hand lens to observe the exterior structures of the seed(s).
- Seek to identify the following structures:
  - The *hilum* (point where the seed was attached to the ovary).
  - The *micropyle* (point where the pollen tube entered the ovule).
- In Area C draw the seed you observed, labeling as many parts as you can.

R E O

II. Dissect the seed(s) supplied by your instructor.
- You will need to use a sharp scalpel or a single-edged razor blade to dissect most seeds.
  - If your dissection instrument is dull, you will damage the structures.
  - The size or hardness of some seeds makes using a sharp instrument dangerous.
    - ❖ If possible, hold the seed with forceps or other instruments when you are attempting to cut it open.
    - ❖ If your seed is very hard (a nut or a pit) you may need to use special instruments to open it. Your teacher will give you special instructions.
- Often a single, well-placed cut will reveal all of the structures listed below. Some seeds, however, will require additional cuts. Some seeds (such as nuts) must be taken apart in pieces to reveal all of the structures.
- Once you have dissected the seed, seek to find the following parts:
  - The embryo plant, composed of the epicotyl, hypocotyl, and radicle
  - The cotyledon(s)
  - The endosperm
- Is the seed you dissected a monocot or a dicot? ☐ monocot ☐ dicot
- In Area D draw the seed you dissected, labeling as many parts as you can.
  - You may need to draw both halves of your dissected seed in order to get all of the parts in your drawing.
  - You may need to reconstruct some of your dissected seed in order to draw it.

R E O

III. After everyone is finished, observe their dissected seeds and their drawings.

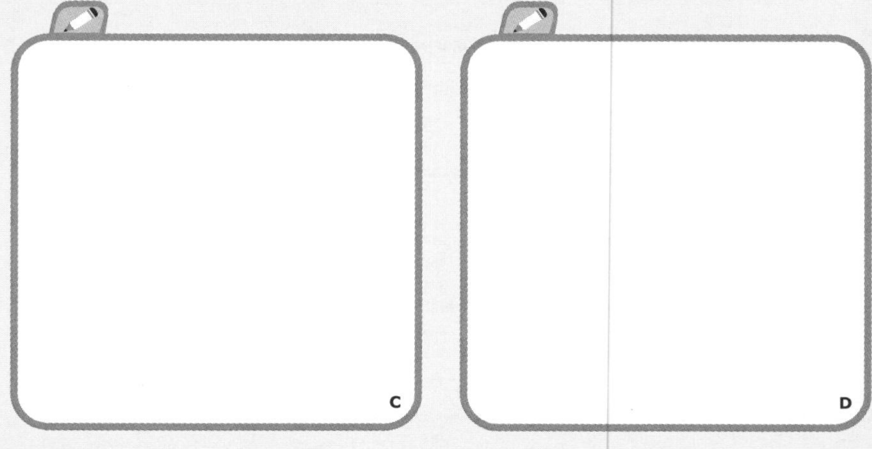

Laboratory Exercises

Contents

Name__________________________

Date______________ Hour________

15a Porifera

Materials

- preserved slides of *Grantia*, c.s. and l.s., and *Grantia* spicules
- preserved specimens of various sponges
- dissection kit
- hand lens
- microscope
- glass slides
- coverslips

Goals

- To observe typical sponges
- To draw conclusions regarding the structure and unique specializations of sponges

You will study these unusual animals in phylum Porifera by observing preserved specimens. Before you begin, read carefully the Life Processes Chart for Grantia. *You are responsible for knowing the structures and functions of each organism covered in the laboratory exercises as an example of the particular phylum you are studying.*

Grantia

R E O

I. Study the picture of *Grantia* in your text on page 449.

II. Without using the microscope, observe a cross section and a longitudinal section of *Grantia* found on a preserved slide. Measure the height and width of these sections of *Grantia*:

______ mm high by ______ mm wide.

III. Scan both the c.s. and the l.s. of a *Grantia* preserved slide under a microscope.

- How is the sponge structure of *Grantia* classified? ☒ simple ☐ complex

  Why? There is only one central chamber.

- After studying your text and a preserved slide prepared for observing spicules, describe the spicules of a *Grantia*.

R E O

IV. In Area A draw a portion of a *Grantia* cross section by following these directions:

- Include sections of both cell layers and the mesenchyme.
- Label as many different structures as you can see.

A

Introduction

In part, this exercise is an introduction to the method of study that will be used in the laboratory exercises of the animal kingdom. This exercise involves microscopic observation of a simple sponge and observation of a bath sponge specimen, activities easily omitted in a survey biology course. The exercise, however, is designed more to introduce students to the terms and procedures of laboratory exercises used in the next four chapters.

Also in this exercise the Life Processes Chart method of study is introduced. The Life Processes Chart for the sponge is completed for the student as an example. See the box on page L120 for an explanation of the Life Processes Charts.

Required / Extra / Omit

It is suggested that you require the observations of *Grantia.* The observation of the spicules (III) is sometimes difficult and, depending on your specimen, sometimes requires oil-immersion power (unless the resolution of your microscopes is exceptionally good). Thus the section may need to be omitted.

The bath sponge section can be difficult if your specimen is not typical. If you have a mounted specimen of a complete bath sponge (with its cells and mesenchyme) to compare with the spongin fibers, the answers are clear and obvious. It may be better to cover this material in lecture and show the spongin fibers as a visual aid. Having the students make wet mounts of small amounts of the spongin fibers is profitable.

Be sure the amount of spongin fibers used to make the wet mount is minute. Large amounts make it difficult for the student to see anything of value.

Bath Sponge

R E O

I. Observe a preserved specimen of a bath sponge.

- What structures are you able to see? various chambers, oscula, canals
- Classify the structure of a bath sponge: ☐ simple ☒ complex

  Why? It has many chambers and is large.

R E O

II. Observe the spongin network of a bath sponge.

- Use a hand lens to observe the spongin fiber network of a bath sponge.
  - Observe sections of a dry bath sponge and of a wet bath sponge.
  - What differences are you able to observe? The fibers of the wet bath sponge should appear the same size as the dry bath sponge, but there should be more space between them.

R E O

- Make a wet mount of the spongin fibers of a bath sponge.
  - Use a very small piece of sponge.
  - Describe what you see. a twisted, branching network of golden brown fibers
  - Draw in Area B several of the spongin fibers as seen on low power of your microscope.

Life Processes Charts

The nine basic life processes that all animals accomplish are described on pages 444–45 of your text. As you read about and study the various animal phyla, you will learn about the methods and structures they use to accomplish these life functions. To help you associate the different organisms with their structures and methods and to make sure that you have grasped all the information you need to know, you will fill in Life Processes Charts for the representative animals of several phyla.

Unless you are told otherwise, you will find in your text most of the information you need to fill in these charts. When you finish them, they will serve as excellent study guides, and they will reveal how carefully you have read.

On pages L121–22 a Life Processes Chart has been completed for the sponge *Grantia*. Because *Grantia* is a simple organism, not all the spaces on the chart have been used. The entry in the column labeled Notes describes, defines, or explains the entry in the Structure column. The lack of special structures for a particular function *does not* indicate that an organism does not accomplish that function. You should explain in the Notes column the way it accomplishes that function. Normally, the first time you use a term in a Life Processes Chart, you should define it in the Notes column.

Scheduling Laboratory Exercises

Laboratory Exercises 15a through 15d can be combined in various ways. Often it is wise to omit laboratory-related sections of an exercise and to keep the pencil work (such as Life Processes Charts or comparisons between phyla) when you combine the exercise with one in which you have a laboratory-related section such as microscopic observations, living observations, or dissections. This helps to keep a balance. With some of the laboratory exercises, one must wait for results (for example, it takes the hydra a few minutes to recover from being jabbed with a probe). While the student waits, some pencil work, even if it is from another exercise, will be a wise use of time.

The possible combinations of the exercises are almost endless and should reflect your goals in teaching this chapter. One should not do a section just because equipment is available or omit a section just because it will involve much class time. Have your students do laboratory exercises that will help them accomplish your educational goals. From the suggested laboratory activities, choose the ones you want the students to do and either omit the rest or offer them as extra credit.

Name

Life Processes Chart

Organism Sponge (*Grantia*)

Phylum Porifera Class Genus *Grantia*

Structure	Notes
Movement *(structures responsible for movement; types of movement)*	
No Structures	Sessile; it does move its environment (water) into incurrent pores and out the excurrent pore (osculum). (See Collar cells under Nutrition below.)
Body covering *(what covers the body; how it protects the animal)*	
Epidermis	One cell layer thick. (Some sponges, such as *Grantia*, have spicules that stick through the epidermis for protection.)
Support *(structures responsible for support; what they are made of)*	
Spicules	Made of lime; help to support. (NOTE: Spicules of other sponges are made of silica and spongin.)
	Much support comes from fullness caused by mesenchyme filling between cell layers.
Nutrition *(structures of digestion; methods of ingestion; types of food; assimilation)*	
Collar cells	Food is carried in by currents made by collar cells, engulfed by collar cells, and digested in vacuoles of the collar cells.
	Nondigestible material is egested.
	Food: algae, protozoans, bacteria, etc.
Respiration *(structures used in gas exchange for respiration)*	
No structures	Gases are exchanged between cells and water environment.

Life Processes Charts

The Life Processes Charts, introduced in this exercise, may require some explanation. Spend time in class going over the sample Life Processes Chart. (This is a good method of teaching the structures of a sponge as well as the techniques for completing Life Processes Charts.) Emphasize to the students that Life Processes Charts are a good method of study. Organizing on paper the way various organisms accomplish the life processes makes studying each organism considerably easier.

If the students know that they are going to be doing a Life Processes Chart on a particular organism before they read the material in their text about the organism's phylum, they will be able to look for pertinent information in their reading. While you are discussing an organism for which the students are expected to do a Life Processes Chart, point out concepts that may be difficult for them to grasp. You should not go over each point, however. Students should be able to glean most of the material from the text.

Students frequently have difficulty with the support category, asking such questions as "Is a clam's shell for support or body covering?" Stress to them that it is not really important which category they place structures such as the shell in, provided it is included in one of the possible places and cross-referenced in the others.

In the exercises that follow, Life Processes Charts are called for in Exercises 15b (hydra), 15c (planarian and *Ascaris*), 16a (crayfish), 16b (grasshopper), and 17a (yellow perch). A completed Life Processes Chart for each of these has been included in the Appendix. You may consider assigning Life Processes Charts for the earthworm, clam, snail, starfish, spider, frog (unless you plan to do the Laboratory Final Examination), and bird.

There are eight blank Life Processes Charts at the end of the text for the students to use, and there is one for use on the overhead projector included in the Visual Packet.

Structure	Notes
Circulation *(structures responsible for internal movement of substances)*	
Amoebocytes	Cells in the mesenchyme; in larger sponges these cells transport substances.
	Most circulation takes place by diffusion.
Excretion *(structures for the collection and elimination of soluble wastes)*	
No structures	Wastes are released by diffusion.
Responses *(structures for receiving stimuli and for responses; level of responses)*	
No structures	Osculum sometimes can be closed in response to substances in water.
	Collar cells can change their rate of flagellar movement.
Reproduction—Asexual *(structures for and types of asexual reproduction)*	
Gemmules	Some freshwater sponges produce gemmules to survive unfavorable conditions.
Budding	Most sponges reproduce by buds and regenerate by fragmentation.
Reproduction—Sexual *(structures for sexual reproduction)*	
Testes	Eggs and sperm are produced by one sponge or by separate sponges.
Ovaries	

Other Notes *(habitat; size range; unusual examples; etc.)*

Most are marine; some, freshwater.

Many are small; a few, large.

Simple sponges usually have only one cavity; complex sponges may have thick walls and many cavities.

Bath sponges have a spongin network of fibers.

They are asymmetrical or radially symmetrical.

Name______________________________

Date____________________ Hour__________

15b Cnidaria

Materials

- preserved slides of plain and budding hydra, a cross section of a hydra, hydra with ovaries, and hydra with testes
- preserved specimens of coral and jellyfish
- living cultures of hydra and brine shrimp or *Daphnia*
- spring water
- dissection kit
- hand lens
- microscope
- dilute acetic acid (vinegar)
- culture dishes
- pipet
- glass slides
- concavity slides
- coverslips

Goals

- To observe typical cnidarians
- To draw some conclusions regarding the structure and unique specializations of cnidarians
- To compare sponges and cnidarians

Although many widely varying animals belong in the phylum Cnidaria, they all have body forms and responses similar to the hydra. Therefore, you will study the hydra in detail as a representative cnidarian and then observe other examples.

Class Hydrozoa: The Hydra

R E O

I. Study the life processes of the hydra and prepare a Life Processes Chart for the hydra.

II. Draw the hydra.

R E O

- In Area A, make an outline drawing of an entire hydra with bud from a preserved slide. Use only low power.
  - The entire hydra will not fit into the microscope field. You will need to move the slide several times as you draw.
  - Label as many structures as you can find. (Carefully look for reproductive structures.)

R E O

- Using high power, draw a portion of hydra wall, c.s., in Area B.
  - This drawing should include internal structures and should not be just an outline.
  - Label as many of the cellular structures of the hydra as you can.

R E O

- In Area C, using low power, prepare an outline drawing of an entire hydra with ovaries and testes. Label the ovaries and testes.

If tap water is used for the hydra, the water must be treated with chemicals used in freshwater aquariums (Start Right by Jungle is recommended). This will remove excess chlorine and other chemicals that harm the hydra. Spring water, boiled pond water, or water from a freshwater aquarium may also be used.

The hydra is the most perishable of the living organisms needed for the next few exercises. The other organisms should keep well. If you order all these organisms at the same time, you can save postage.

The hydra is a bit finicky. The wrong water, wrong temperature, or dissolved materials in the water can render even healthy hydrae unresponsive. To get the best possible results, supply the hydrae with quiet, stable conditions before the students begin. Thus the disturbance of getting set up for the exercise will not greatly affect the hydrae, and they will become relaxed again more quickly. However, you should be prepared to tell the students that the hydrae are not cooperating and that the students should do the best they can to answer the questions.

Students frequently need to be reminded to follow the directions in the laboratory exercise concerning the drawings. They are asked to draw only the outline of the hydra and its buds. When drawing the cross section, however, they should include internal details.

Introduction

Observations of a living hydra help to make the entire phylum Cnidaria more understandable. Jellyfish, coral, the Portuguese man-of-war, and the other interesting and significant organisms in this phylum become clearer as soon as a student encounters and understands the simple hydra.

Also in this exercise the students are asked to do their first Life Processes Chart. (See box, p. L120.) This Life Processes Chart is relatively simple and virtually all of the material is available in the chapter.

Some teachers find it helpful to combine Exercises 15a and 15b into a single day's laboratory work or to combine Exercise 15b with other exercises in this chapter. (See box on p. 120.)

Required / Extra / Omit

It is recommended that your students do the hydra Life Processes Chart (I), the outline drawing of the hydra (II), and the observations of a living hydra (III).

The coral and jellyfish observations can be beneficial but are not essential.

You may wish to offer the drawing of a portion of the hydra wall, c.s., done under high power and the drawings of the hydra with ovaries and testes under low power as extra credit.

See page A21 for a completed Life Processes Chart for the hydra.

Hydra testes have a small projection on the end; ovaries are usually round. If students do the section in which they draw these, they will need to research in other texts to learn how to tell the differences between a hydra's ovaries and testes.

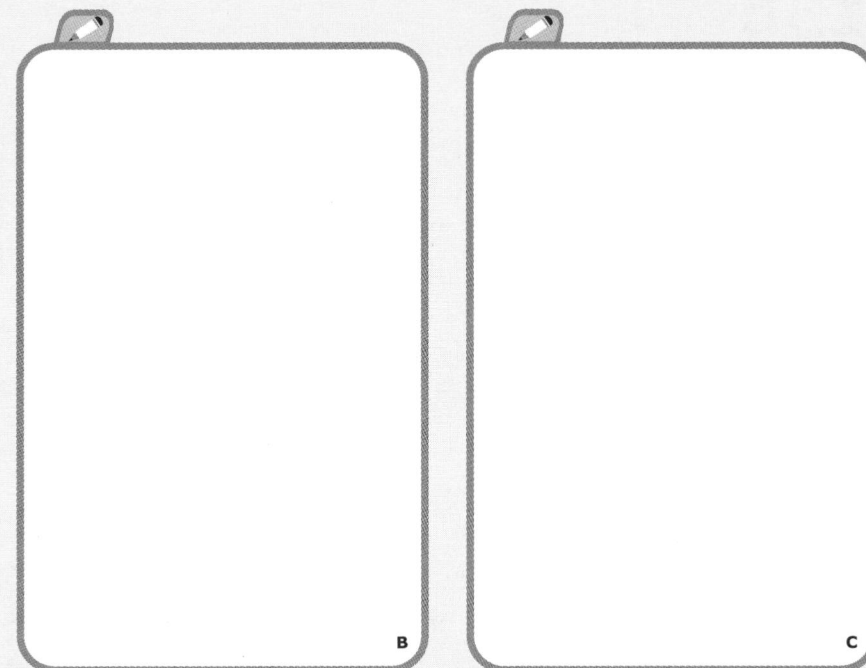

Quickly flush the hydra from the dropping pipet into the culture dish. If it becomes attached to the inside of the pipet, it is usually damaged by the repeated flushing necessary to get it out of the pipet.

R E O

III. Observe a living hydra.

- To obtain a living hydra for observation, do the following:
  - Fill a clean culture dish with spring water (or treated, "aged," or pond water).
  - Using a dropping pipet, follow these instructions to obtain a specimen from the culture.
    - Flush a stream of water from the pipet onto the hydra you have selected in order to dislodge the specimen.
    - Draw the dislodged hydra into your pipet and flush it onto the culture dish.
- Observe your living hydra and the hydras of other students in your class. Identify as many different forms of locomotion, or movement, as you can. Describe as many forms as you observe. Movement of tentacles is usually seen. Somersaulting occasionally occurs. Floating may also be seen.

R E O

- Study the nerves and the responses of the hydra.
  - The hydra's nervous system consists of a nerve net. From the information in your text (and possibly other research), describe a nerve net. Answers may vary. A nerve net is a network made up of nerve cells in the mesoglea. It lacks a brain (or ganglia).

- Observe the responses of the hydra.
  - Very gently swirl the water around the hydra. What is its reaction? Answers may vary. Usually a body contraction
  - After the hydra has recovered from the above experiment (which may take several minutes), touch your probe as gently as possible to its base. What is its reaction? Answers may vary. Often a body contraction
  - After the hydra has recovered from the above experiment, touch your probe as gently as possible to one of its tentacles. What is its reaction? Answers may vary. Usually a body contraction
  - After the hydra has recovered from the above experiment, arrange your probe so that the hydra will touch the probe of its own power. What is its reaction? Answers may vary. Usually a movement of tentacles toward the probe

R E O

- Observe the feeding process of the hydra.
  - Using a dropping pipet, place a few living *Daphnia* or brine shrimp in your culture dish near the hydra. Be careful not to add the food so rapidly that you disturb the hydra.
  - Using a hand lens, watch carefully the actions of your hydra. Note especially any activity in the mouth region.
  - From your observations, describe the feeding process of the hydra. Tentacles touch food and then move it toward the mouth, which opens to receive the food.
  - Describe digestion in a hydra by answering the following questions:
    - In what structure of the hydra does extracellular digestion take place? gastrovascular cavity
    - What cells provide the enzymes for this digestion? the gland cells of the endoderm
    - What happens to the partially digested food? It is engulfed by cells.
    - What happens to the substances that cannot be digested? They are egested through the mouth.

R E O

- List typical food for a hydra. *Daphnia* and other small arthropods
- Observe the reaction of the hydra to acid.
  - Carefully remove your hydra and set it in a large drop of spring water placed on a concavity slide.
  - Place a coverslip over the slide and observe the hydra (or sections of it) with a microscope.
  - After it has recovered from the transfer and you have been able to focus on cells of its tentacles, place a small drop of the dilute acetic acid on the edge of the coverslip.
  - Watch the hydra carefully. For the best results, one partner should put the acetic acid on the slide while the other partner observes the reaction through the microscope.

The living hydrae will require rest time between experiments. During this time the students should be doing their microscope work.

Students frequently become frustrated while trying to get the hydra to eat. You cannot force-feed a hydra. It must take the food on its own initiative. Simply keep the food within tentacle distance without disturbing the hydra. Sometimes energetic food will disturb it. Damaging but not completely killing the food with the probe will sometimes stimulate the hydra to eat.

○ What did you observe as the acid reached the hydra? The hydra coiled up and released its nematocysts in response to the acid.

- Draw conclusions from your observations of the movement, feeding, and reactions of the hydra.
  ○ How specialized to different stimuli are the responses of the hydra? In other words, is the hydra able to respond differently to various kinds of stimuli?
  ☐ yes ☐ no Answers may vary. The hydra appears to have two types of reactions.
  ○ Explain your answer. One reaction is recoiling from stimuli; the other is going after the stimulus to feed on it.
- To remove your hydra, flush the slide with spring water while holding it over a separate culture container for "used" hydra. Do not return the hydra to its original culture.

Class Anthozoa: The Coral

I. Observe the preserved coral specimens in the classroom. What structure are you actually observing? the skeleton or the case that the coral has secreted

II. Compare a living coral organism and a hydra. They are very similar except that the coral organism secretes a stone skeleton and lives in colonies.

Class Scyphozoa: The Jellyfish

I. Observe and describe the preserved jellyfish in the classroom. Answers may vary. It is a thin, transparent, bell-shaped organism with tentacles.

II. Compare a jellyfish and a hydra (diagrams may be helpful). Answers may vary. The jellyfish is larger than the hydra and is free-swimming, but both have tentacles, a single opening to the gastrovascular cavity, and a thin, membranous body.

Name________________________________

Date__________________ Hour__________

15c

Worms 1: Platyhelminthes and Nematoda

Materials

- culture of living planarians
- spring water
- culture dish
- dissection kit
- hand lens
- Epsom salts
- glass concavity slides
- preserved slides of beef tapeworm (*Taenia saginata*) scolex, proglottid, and bladders in meat, *Clonorchis sinensis*
- preserved specimens or preserved slides of *Ascaris lumbricoides*, *Necator americanus*, and *Trichinella spiralis*
- illuminator
- microscope

Goals

- To observe planarians and other flatworms
- To draw conclusions about the structure and special characteristics of flatworms
- To compare planarians and various flatworms to previously studied organisms
- To recognize some of the more familiar nematodes that can infect humans

In this laboratory exercise you will observe free-living and parasitic flatworms (phylum Platyhelminthes) and some significant roundworms (phylum Nematoda). Although Annelida may be the most familiar of the worm phyla, these two phyla contain organisms that are far more significant to humans because of the diseases they cause.

Platyhelminthes

Phylum Platyhelminthes contains simple organisms with only three basic cell layers: an epidermis, a gastroderm, and a mesoderm. Various structures develop from these cell layers. Some of these structures correspond to many of the organs and systems in more complex animals. The flatworms exhibit two "ways of life": free-living and parasitic. We shall examine the planarian as an example of the free-living variety.

R E O

Free-Living Flatworms: The Planarian

I. Study the life processes of planarians.

- Read the sections in your text that deal with phylum Platyhelminthes (pp. 456–57, 460).
- Prepare a Life Processes Chart for the planarian.

Laboratory Techniques for Handling Planarians

- Fill a clean culture dish with fresh spring water.
- Move the planarian by following these instructions:
  - Agitate the water around the planarian (make small currents with a dropping pipet) until it floats about in the water.
  - Quickly draw it into a dropping pipet.
  - Quickly put it into the container you have ready. Speed is important; if the planarian uncoils and attaches itself to the side of the pipet, it is often difficult to remove.
- On occasion it will be best to put your planarian on a glass slide in order to restrain it and to view its ventral surface easily. If you use a concavity slide, a coverslip can be placed on it. However, if you use a flat slide, the coverslip will squash the planarian.

R E O

II. Observe the movement of planarians.

- Obtain a planarian by following the instructions in the box.
- Study the two different means by which the planarian moves.

Slides and plastic mounts of the beef tapeworm (*Taenia saginata*) may not be as readily available as those of other tapeworms. You may successfully use slides and mounts of other tapeworms for the scolex and proglottid, but for the bladder stage, a photograph of beef containing bladders is the best substitute.

Introduction

You might want to encourage the students to take their planarians home after the exercise is completed and keep them as pets (provided their parents do not object). They should place a small piece of liver in the planarian's jar for about half an hour every week or so. The water will need to be changed when it becomes cloudy following each feeding. Water taken from a spring, well, or aquarium is best, but tap water that has been left standing for several days can be used. Additional information can be found in books on culturing planarians. Encourage students to consider performing regeneration experiments on their planarians at home. Or you can feed leftover planarians to aquarium fish.

Required / Extra / Omit

Observing a live planarian is a valuable exercise. The students' seeing something that they have only read or heard about helps to cement for them what the creature really is.

A microprojector or microvideo system works well for observing a beef tapeworm, making this section a visual aid to a lecture. You can then use the outline and diagram on pages L129–L130 as a visual for reinforcing knowledge of a beef tapeworm's life cycle.

Hookworms and trichina worms can also be observed with a microprojector or microvideo system. *Ascarids* are best observed as mounted specimens.

You may consider using the tapeworm and human liver fluke sections (pp. L129–L130) as extra credit if time is short.

See page A22 for a completed Life Processes Chart for the planarian and page A23 for a completed Life Processes Chart for *Ascaris*.

Tell the students not to stab the planarian. Because it has no blood, a planarian will not bleed; but because its epidermis is only one cell layer thick, it can easily be damaged.

The experiments with currents around the planarian require a steady current for several minutes. Each lab group will need several dropping pipets. To see the reaction better, place the planarian on a glass plate. Tilt the glass plate and for several minutes slowly pour treated water down its surface. Make sure that a steady stream of water passes over the planarian for the entire time. This makes an effective demonstration.

- ○ Study ciliary movement.
  - ❖ Where are the cilia located on the planarian? the ventral side
  - ❖ After observing the planarian moving by using its cilia, describe this type of movement. It appears to glide along.
- ○ Study muscular movement.
  - ❖ Place a few grains of Epsom salts into the water right next to the planarian. Watch carefully as the Epsom salts begin to dissolve near it.
  - ❖ After you have observed the movement that results, remove and discard the grains of salt and add some fresh spring water to dilute the salt.
  - ❖ Describe muscular movement in comparison to the ciliary movement you have described above. The body twists, frequently raising itself from the surface on which it rests.
  - ❖ Where are the structures for muscular movement located? beneath the epidermis
- ● Briefly compare the structures for movement in the planarian to structures for movement in the hydra. Although the hydra can direct movements of its tentacles and body, many of its movements are all or nothing; the planarian seems to be able to direct all of its movements.

III. Observe the responses of planarians.

R E O

- ● Observe the responses to touch.
  - ○ With a clean probe, touch very lightly the lateral surface of the planarian. What is the response? Answers may vary. Usually it turns away from the side touched.
  - ○ Touch lightly an auricle (side point of the head). What is the response? Answers may vary. Usually it moves away from the side touched.
  - ○ Touch lightly the posterior end. What is the response? Answers may vary. Usually it moves anteriorly.

R E O

- ● Observe the responses to current.
  - ○ Fill a clean pipet with water and slowly force the water out to produce a current.
  - ○ Direct the current to one side of the planarian in the culture dish. (Take about thirty seconds to empty one pipet of water. Have several pipets ready.) What is its response? Answers may vary. It should turn to move toward the current.
  - ○ Direct a current toward the side of the planarian's head. What is its response? Answers may vary. It should turn to move toward the current.
  - ○ Direct a current toward the posterior end, directly behind the planarian. What is its response? Answers may vary. It should turn to move toward the current.

R E O

- ● Compare the degrees of specialization (how specific the organism's responses are) in the planarian and in the hydra. Answers may vary. They are similar, but students should observe that the planarian's responses are more specialized.

R E O

IV. Investigate the ingestion and digestion of planarians.

- ● Place your planarian on a glass slide, using the techniques described in the box (p. L127).
- ● Look for the planarian's feeding structures.

Scheduling Laboratory Exercises

You may wish to combine Laboratory Exercises 15c and 15d into a two-class-period laboratory marathon. You may still need to omit sections of these exercises, depending upon the laboratory skills of your students, their academic level, and their motivation to work.

See the Required / Extra / Omit sections for suggestions regarding what material can be omitted.

You may also wish to combine this exercise with Laboratory Exercise 15a and/or 15b. See box on page 120.

Name______________________________

- Holding the slide above your head, look for the mouth and pharynx of your planarian.
- Describe the mouth's location on the body. The mouth is a hole near the middle of the ventral surface.
- Describe the appearance and the function of the pharynx. It looks like a tube and can protrude out of the mouth. It sucks up food.

- Describe the digestion of planarians.
  - Describe the area within the planarian where digestion begins. Be sure to use the proper name for this structure. The intestine, a cavity inside the worm that has a single opening (mouth), is the place where the digestion of foods begins.
  - After the structure described above completes preliminary digestion, what happens to complete the digestion of the small particles of food? The small particles are engulfed by the cells lining the intestine by the process of phagocytosis. Digestion is completed inside the cells of the gastroderm.

Parasitic Flatworms

There are many different types of parasitic Platyhelminthes. You will study two of the most common human parasites: the beef tapeworm (*Taenia saginata*) and the human liver fluke (*Clonorchis sinensis*). These two pathogenic organisms are examples of different classes in the phylum Platyhelminthes.

REO I. Study the beef tapeworm.
- Using low power, observe preserved slides of the following stages (structures) in the life cycle of the beef tapeworm: scolex, mature proglottid, and bladders in meat.
- Study the life cycle of the beef tapeworm.
  - Carefully study the outline of the beef tapeworm's life cycle given below.
  - From your observations, complete Diagram 15c.1 of the stages of the beef tapeworm's life cycle.
  - Add labeled drawings in the three circles of the diagram.
  - Add the following labels in the places where they belong: *intestine of man, intestine of cow, blood vessel of cow, contaminated meat, adult tapeworm, egg containing six-hooked larva.*

REO

Life Cycle of a Beef Tapeworm

- Eggs of the tapeworm are eaten by the cow.
  - An egg hatches in the intestine as a six-hooked larva.
  - The larva bores through the intestinal wall, enters the bloodstream, and is carried to a muscle.
- The larva burrows into the muscle.
  - In the muscle, the larva becomes a bladderworm (cyst).
  - Inside the bladder is an immature scolex.
- The muscle infected with the bladderworm is eaten by a human.
  - If the meat is not cooked enough or treated to kill the bladderworm, the bladderworm hatches in the human's intestine.
  - The scolex (head) of the tapeworm embeds itself in the lining of the intestine.
- The adult tapeworm lives in the intestine of a human.
  - The scolex produces proglottids (the chain of which may be over 10 ft in length), which contain hundreds of eggs.
  - The ripe proglottids are passed in the feces.
  - Cows graze on grass fertilized with infected feces.

Tell the students that they are to draw the required structures in the three circles in Diagram 15c.1. They should label their drawings.

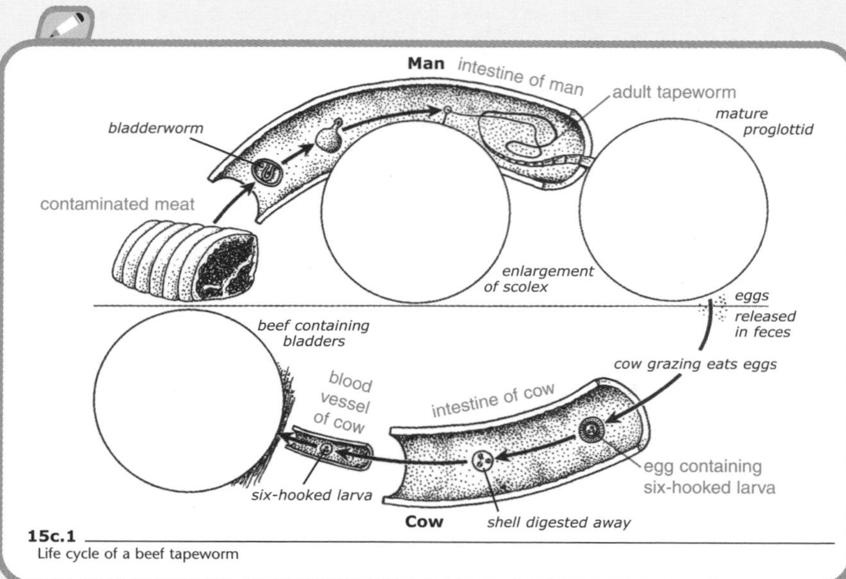

15c.1
Life cycle of a beef tapeworm

II. Observe and describe a preserved specimen of a human liver fluke (*Clonorchis sinensis*).

Answers may vary. Thin, flat, etc. (Size description is based on the particular specimen.)

Nematoda: Roundworms

The roundworms (phylum Nematoda) are surprisingly alike in their body structure but are extremely diverse in their habitats and life cycles. In this laboratory section we will observe some of the organisms that are pathogenic to humans.

I. Prepare a Life Processes Chart for the *Ascaris.*

II. Observe preserved specimens or slides of various roundworms and describe them (color, length, shape, etc.).

- Human *Ascaris* (*Ascaris lumbricoides*) Answers will vary depending on the specimen.
- Hookworms (*Necator americanus*) Answers will vary depending on the specimen.
- Trichina worms (*Trichinella spiralis*) Answers will vary depending on the specimen.

15d
Worms 2: Annelida

Name____________________

Date____________ Hour________

Materials

- dissection kit
- hand lens
- flashlight or illuminator
- living earthworms
- preserved earthworms
- dissection pan
- dissection pins
- plastic bag
- ether
- alcohol

Goals

- To introduce dissection techniques
- To observe the structures of an earthworm
- To compare the earthworm to other organisms

The organisms in phylum Annelida are very diverse. For classroom observation the most common of the annelids is an excellent choice, even though it may not be considered typical of all of the organisms in this phylum.

In this laboratory exercise you are asked to dissect an earthworm. To prepare for the dissection, be sure to read the information in the box below and define the terms indicated. These terms will be commonly used in describing dissection procedures.

Dissection Techniques

General Instructions

These instructions apply to all dissections in these laboratory exercises.

- Read carefully the entire exercise before you begin. This reading can prevent many wrong cuts.
- Reread the directions before you begin to cut.
- Make sure you have identified the correct structures by comparing them to drawings before you cut.
- Handle the specimens delicately. Preserved structures often tear and break easily.

Temporary Storage of a Dissection Animal

- Put your name and lab hour on a plastic bag with a permanent marker.
- Wrap the organism in a very wet paper towel.
- Place the organism and the wet paper towel in the plastic bag. Gently squeeze out most of the air and tie or zip the bag closed.
- Organisms wrapped in this manner may be kept for a few days without great deterioration.

Dissection Vocabulary

R E O

Define the following terms. Be sure you know how they apply to each animal before you begin a dissection. ***The terms* right *and* left *in the instructions refer to the organism's right and left, not yours.***

- Anterior: toward the "front" end
- Posterior: toward the "back" end
- Dorsal: top side, toward the back of the body
- Ventral: bottom side, toward the stomach of the body
- Median: the middle of the organism
- Longitudinal: length of the organism (anterior to posterior)
- Transverse: across the organism
- Lateral: the side
- Cephalic: toward the head
- Caudal: toward the tail

Many preserved earthworms—those that come in plastic bags with most of the air forced out—are poor specimens. The internal structures have been so thoroughly compacted that there is nothing to see inside. You may have to pay a bit more for good earthworms, but the advantages will be obvious during the exercise. (Carolina Biological Supply stocks good earthworms.)

Have each student remove the dissected worm remains from his dissection pan, put them in a paper towel, and dispose of them. The dissection pan should be rinsed in cold water and the excess water shaken into the sink. (Do not rap the pan on the edge of the sink. The wax may break and fall out.) Dissection pans can be left out to air-dry before being put away.

When dissection pans that have wax in them have been used for a while, they can be placed in a warm oven to melt the wax; this process will remove any pinholes and student artwork.

Introduction

This is the first laboratory exercise that includes a dissection. Emphasize to the students that they should carefully study and complete the section on dissection techniques on page L131 before class. You may also want to go over the care and safe handling of dissection materials. A way to make dissections more enjoyable is to have each student name his dissection animal and then write the animal's name, rather than the student's name, on the storage bag. It is suggested, however, that the teacher write the names on the bags to avoid inappropriate or duplicate names.

A Life Processes Chart is not suggested for the earthworm because the dissection instructions have been set up in a form similar to that of the Life Processes Chart. If the laboratory exercise is done properly, students can study from it and will not need to do a Life Processes Chart.

Required / Extra / Omit

The dissection of a preserved earthworm is an excellent way to get started in dissections. It is recommended for all students.

Observing a live earthworm (pp. L135–L136) is valuable, but it may be a bit difficult and may take an undue amount of time if the earthworm does not feel like cooperating. You may wish to use this section as extra credit.

You may want to have only two students do the live earthworm dissection. The remainder of the class should be required to observe the live dissected earthworm.

Scheduling Laboratory Exercises

You may wish to combine this exercise with Laboratory Exercises 15a, 15b, and/or 15c. See boxes on pages 120 and 128.

Students may want to bring a protective garment for this exercise.

A day or two in advance, tell the class that the earthworm dissection is coming up. Explain to the students that once they are in the laboratory, you expect no "yucks," screams, tears, or other immature reactions. If the students know in advance what kind of behavior you expect, they will probably cooperate. Thousands of high-school students successfully dissect earthworms each year without any adverse side effects.

The pans used for the living earthworm observations should be clean. Dissection pans (or 9″ × 13″ baking pans) are recommended.

Earthworm Dissection

R E O

Observing External Structures

I. Examine the surfaces of your specimen carefully. Rub your fingers lightly across its surface. As you touch the skin of the earthworm, you should feel tiny bristles.

- What are these bristles called? setae
- How many are there on each segment? four pairs
- On what area of the body do these bristles appear? lower side of body, near ventral surface
- How do they help in locomotion? The setae anchor segments of the earthworm during movement.

II. Identify the anterior and posterior ends of your specimen.

- Does the earthworm have definite anterior and posterior ends that can be determined by sight?

  ☒ yes ☐ no Explain your answer. The anterior end is closer to the clitellum and has a prostomium.
- Locate the prostomium. What is its function? It is sensory. It also serves as an upper lip that helps to push in food.
- Locate the anus. What is its function? It releases solid wastes from the intestine.

III. Examine the clitellum.

- How many segments are there in the clitellum? six

- What is the function of the clitellum? It functions in reproduction. For students, it distinguishes the anterior end.

IV. Examine other body openings.

- Using a hand lens, try to locate the nephridiopores. How many are there on each segment? two
- Examine segment 14 and locate the female pore through which eggs leave the body. (NOTE: Segments are numbered beginning at the mouth and continuing toward the anus.)
- Locate the male pore in segment 15. Sperm leave the body through this opening.
- Try to locate the openings in the furrows between segments 9 and 10 and segments 10 and 11 through which sperm enter the body. (These are sometimes impossible to locate.)

Opening the Body Cavity

I. Place your specimen in a dissection pan with the dorsal side up.

II. Pin the anterior and posterior ends to the pan, using care not to put the pins through any internal organs.

III. Place your scissors slightly to the left of the mid dorsal line about an inch posterior to the clitellum. Carefully cut through the body wall. Then extend the cut anteriorly to the prostomium. *Be careful not to cut anything but the body wall.*

Name____________________

IV. Separate the edges of the cut and look into the body cavity.
- Observe that the wall is separated from the intestine by a space. What is this space called? body cavity or coelom
- Notice that the space is divided by partitions extending from the body wall to the intestine. What are these partitions called? septa
- Using forceps and probes, carefully break these partitions segment by segment until the internal structures found in the anterior end of the worm are entirely exposed for study.
- To hold the body wall open, pin it to the wax or pad in the dissection pan.

Locating the Earthworm's Muscular Structures

I. Locate the circular and longitudinal muscles in one or two of the segments of your worm. (This is sometimes difficult with small preserved worms.)

II. Suppose that the worm's circular muscles have already contracted and its setae have anchored its anterior end to the soil. In the earthworm's movements, what structures will function next and what movement will result? It will contract its longitudinal muscles, drawing its posterior end toward its anterior.

Locating the Earthworm's Interior Digestive Structures

I. Locate the pharynx, a thick-walled area posterior to the buccal cavity. What is the purpose of the thick walls? help in swallowing

II. Locate the esophagus, which extends from the pharynx to segment 14. What is the function of the esophagus? passes food to the crop

III. Locate the crop, a large thin-walled area posterior to the esophagus. What is the function of this structure? stores food

IV. Locate the gizzard, a thick-walled area posterior to the crop. What is the function of the gizzard? grinds food

V. Locate the intestine, which extends from the gizzard to the anus. What is the function of the intestine? digests and absorbs food

VI. Make an outline drawing of the digestive system of the earthworm using the outline provided in Diagram 15d.1. Be sure to include all the structures listed in the digestive section (above), placing them in the correct body segments.

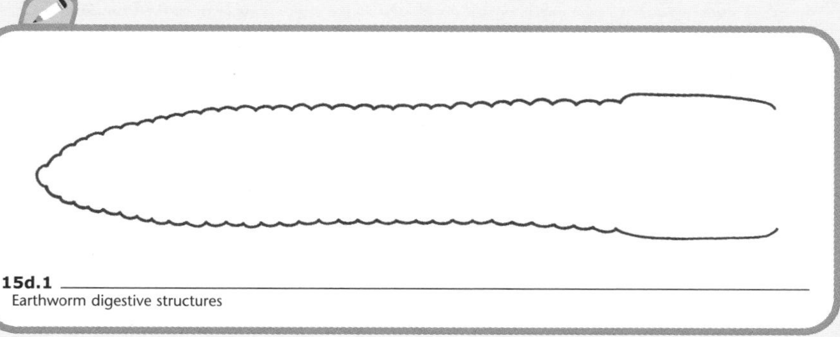

15d.1 ____________________
Earthworm digestive structures

Observing the muscular layers in the body wall of an earthworm can easily be done by viewing a preserved slide of a cross section of an earthworm. Consider setting up a single microscope on a side counter and telling the students to observe the slide of earthworm muscle layers sometime during the class hour.

Locating the Earthworm's Circulatory Structures

R E O

I. Find the dorsal blood vessel on your specimen. It appears as a dark, brownish-colored vessel running along the medial surface of the intestine. In many specimens you can see this structure lying on the intestine.

II. Remove the seminal vesicles by lifting them out from the left side of the body.

III. Look in segment 11 for a pair of stout tubes coming from the dorsal blood vessel and extending ventrally. These "hearts," or aortic arches, are often discolored because they contain blood. What is the function of these structures? They maintain blood pressure and circulate the blood.

IV. Look at each segment from 7 to 11 for the rest of the aortic arches. You will have to remove the septa to see these clearly.

V. Near the posterior section of your cut, use probes to move the intestine to the right and try to find the ventral blood vessel. (This structure is often difficult to locate.) Does it look any different from the dorsal blood vessel? ☒ yes ☐ no

R E O

VI. Make an outline drawing of the circulatory system of the earthworm using the outline provided in Diagram 15d.2.
- Include and label the dorsal blood vessel, the ventral blood vessel, and the aortic arches. Be sure they are in the correct segment.
- Make the drawing as though the worm were being viewed laterally.

15d.2 ______
Earthworm circulatory structures

Locating the Earthworm's Excretory Structures

R E O

Nephridia are located in every segment except for the first three and the last one.

I. Extend the body wall incision posteriorly about two inches.

II. Carefully open the body wall in this area, trying not to tear the septa.

III. Carefully remove the intestine from the area.

IV. Use a hand lens or stereomicroscope to find the nephridia. (In some specimens the nephridia are difficult to find.) To what human organ do the nephridia of the earthworm correspond? kidney

Name____________________________

R E O

Locating the Earthworm's Nervous System

Locating the structures of the nervous system may be difficult, and if you have not been careful in your dissecting, you may have destroyed them. A hand lens may be helpful.

I. In the area of segments 2 and 3, dorsal to the buccal cavity, the "brain," or suprapharyngeal (*supra* "above," and *pharyngeal* "pharynx") ganglia, is located. Try to find the ganglia.

II. Two nerve fibers extend from the suprapharyngeal ganglia, pass around the pharynx, and join below the pharynx at the subpharyngeal (*sub* "below") ganglion. Try to locate the subpharyngeal ganglion.

III. The ventral nerve cord extends from the subpharyngeal ganglion. Remove a part of the intestine from the posterior part of the body and try to locate the nerve cord.

IV. Note the small ganglion present in each segment. Also note the small nerves going from each of these ganglia into the body wall.

V. In Diagram 15d.3, label the suprapharyngeal ganglia, subpharyngeal ganglion, ventral nerve cord, nerve cord ganglia, and nerves to body segments.

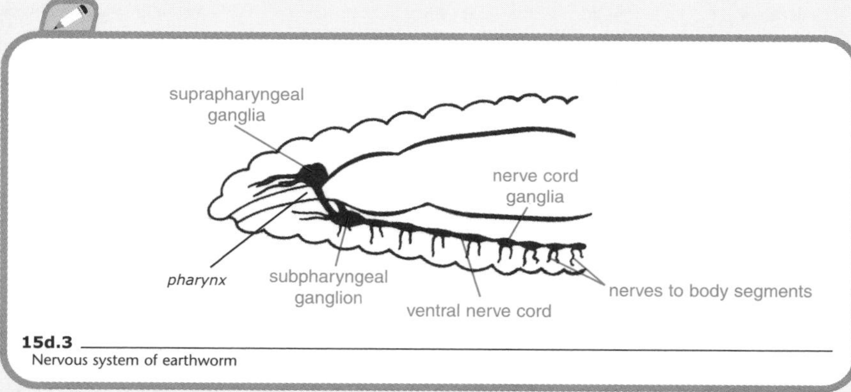

15d.3 ________________________
Nervous system of earthworm

R E O

Locating the Earthworm's Reproductive Structures

I. The parts of the reproductive system are found in the first fifteen segments.

II. Segments 9 to 13 contain pairs of white structures called seminal vesicles. Sperm are stored in these organs.

III. Segments 9 and 10 contain pairs of small white spherical structures called seminal receptacles. These organs receive sperm from other earthworms.

IV. Locate the small ovaries, in which the eggs develop. They are under the seminal vesicles.

Reactions of a Live Earthworm

To see how an earthworm responds to various stimuli, you will need to test a living earthworm. Place a living specimen in a clean dissection pan that has a number of crumpled, wet paper towels in it. Keep the earthworm wet. After you have finished the experiments, return the worm to the laboratory culture.

To anesthetize a live earthworm, place it in a closed jar with a piece of cotton that has been saturated with ether or chloroform. Be sure to remove the earthworm as soon as it appears to be slowing down. Do not wait for it to lie completely still. Too much anesthesia kills the earthworm, and there will be no moving structures inside. Too little anesthesia will cause the earthworm to pull itself apart during the dissection.

Have the students open the body cavity of the live worm the same way they did for the preserved specimen. Pin open the body cavity, but do not remove any structures. The worm is now ready for viewing.

R E O

Testing the Earthworm's Response to Touch

I. Touch the posterior end lightly with a probe. (Do not stab it.)
- Pause until the earthworm is moving slowly.
- Repeat several times.
- What is the worm's reaction? Answers may vary. It should move away, going anteriorly.

II. Do the same to the anterior end. What is its reaction? Answers may vary. It should turn away or retract.

III. As the worm lies on the paper towels, touch its body near the middle as low on its side as you can. What is the reaction? Answers may vary. It should move away from the side touched.

R E O

Testing the Earthworm's Response to Light

I. Remove the towels from the dissection pan, cover the pan, and keep the worm in the dark for several minutes.

II. Peek inside (keeping it as dark as possible) to find the worm's anterior end.

III. Still keeping conditions as dark as possible, shine the flashlight or illuminator on the worm's anterior end. What is its reaction? It moves away from the light.

R E O

Dissection of a Live Earthworm

Under supervision, two students will anesthetize a live earthworm with ether and follow the directions given earlier for opening the body cavity. All students will observe the specimen and then answer the following questions. After the class's observation, the worm will be put to death with alcohol.

I. What moving structures indicate that the earthworm is alive? Aortic arches and muscles may be moving, depending on amount of anesthesia.

II. How do the aortic arches beat? ☐ in unison ☐ in a rhythm ☐ without coordination Answers will vary.

III. Other than movement, what are the major differences between the preserved specimen and the live specimen? Can you explain these differences? Answers will vary, depending on specimen and amount of anesthesia. Blood and color may be different. Usually the preservative causes the differences.

Name____________________

Date____________ Hour________

16a Crustaceans

Materials

- preserved crayfish
- dissection kit
- dissection pan
- culture dish
- preserved slides of crustaceans
- preserved specimens showing crayfish life cycle
- preserved specimens of other crustaceans
- plastic bag

Goals

- To observe arthropod characteristics in the crayfish
- To note the variety of appendages and the specialization of internal parts of a crayfish
- To observe other crustaceans and compare them to the crayfish

You will begin this laboratory exercise by studying crayfish appendages, noting their varied shapes and functions, and then studying the life processes of a crayfish. As you observe other crustaceans or other arthropods, you will find that although their structures vary greatly, the basic body plan is the same in all of them.

External Anatomy of the Crayfish

The Segments of the Exoskeleton

R E O

I. Place your crayfish in a dissection pan and carefully observe the dorsal side of your specimen.
- As you find each of the structures italicized below, label them on Diagram 16a.1. NOTE: You will need to draw in details in order to label all the structures.
- Examine the hard, chitinous *exoskeleton* covering the crayfish and note that the body is divided into two main regions, the *cephalothorax* and the *abdomen.*

II. Examine the cephalothorax, the anterior region of the crayfish.
- Note that the cephalothorax is covered by a single piece of exoskeleton called the carapace.
  - The anterior extension of the *carapace*, which forms a horny beak between the eyes of the crayfish, is called the *rostrum.*
  - Locate the *cervical groove* on the carapace, which marks the division between the *head* and the *thorax.*
- Note the segments of the cephalothorax.
  - There are either thirteen or fourteen segments in the cephalothorax, depending on whether the segment preceding the one bearing the antennules is considered a true segment.
  - On the ventral side these segments are easy to locate if you remember that there is one set of appendages per segment.

III. Examine the abdomen of the crayfish.
- How many segments (not appendages) are there in the abdomen? six
- The last segment is called the *telson.* Label it on Diagram 16a.1.
- Although it is not a segment, locate the anal opening on the ventral side of the abdomen.

The Appendages of the Head

R E O

If possible, continue to label Diagram 16a.1 with the italicized structures discussed in this section.

I. Locate the appendages of sensation.
- What is an appendage? a structure growing from the main part of the body
- Although they do not fit the definition of a true appendage, locate the stalked *compound eyes.*

Medium-sized crayfish (approximately four inches from rostrum to uropods) are acceptable for this exercise. Do not waste money on exceptionally large specimens. Tiny crayfish, however, are almost useless.

Introduction

Those students who feel that they did an exceptional job in dissecting their earthworms may feel a bit slighted because you did not give them grades on their dissection skills. Others may conclude that it does not matter how they dissect as long as they answer the questions correctly. Both views are partly correct and partly wrong.

If you plan to use the frog dissection as a laboratory final examination, as it has been designed, you can correct both attitudes by informing the students that they will be graded on how well they dissect during the Frog Lab. At that time, however, you will offer no assistance on their dissections. At the present, students' dissections are done somewhat for practice, though students are graded on their responses and on their drawings made from the dissected animals. However, the Frog Lab requires neither drawings nor written answers, but since it is a final examination, its value is considerable. The students are graded on how well they dissect and on how much they learn from the exercise. Lab partners should gain experience by taking turns dissecting sections of the crayfish and yellow perch while their dissection ability is not being graded. For the Frog Lab, each student gets his own frog and dissects it on his own. Telling the students what to expect on the Frog Lab should help them to understand the importance of careful dissection now.

See page A24 for a completed Life Processes Chart for the crayfish.

Required / Extra / Omit

It is suggested that the entire crayfish dissection be required.

Some teachers may wish to have students observe preserved crayfish but not dissect them. The external observations, without removing and drawing the mouthparts, can be a valuable exercise that takes only a few minutes and permits the use of the same crayfish for years.

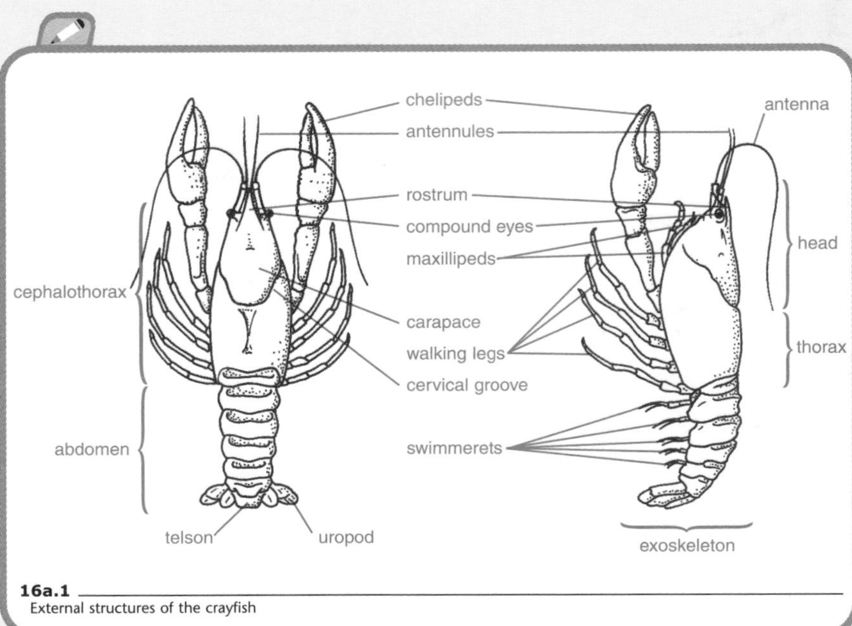

16a.1 External structures of the crayfish

- Locate the most anterior appendages, the *antennules*.
  - How many antennules are there? one pair (looks like two pairs)
  - They are used for balance, taste, and touch.
- Other appendages near the antennules are the long *antennae.*
  - How many of these are there? one pair (two)
  - They are used for taste and touch.

R E O

II. Locate the appendages of the mouth.

- Turn your crayfish ventral side up in the dissection pan and locate all the mouthparts.
- Compare what you find with those drawn in Diagram 16a.2.
- Do not remove them.
  - The one pair of mandibles (or true jaws) is just posterior to the antennae. They are small hard coverings of the mouth that pulverize food.
  - The two pairs of maxillae are just posterior to the mandibles and assist in chewing.
  - The three pairs of *maxillipeds* (or jaw feet) are posterior to the maxillae. (When counting these appendages, do not be fooled by their branched appearance.) Maxillipeds are used to hold food in place.
- Observe mouthpart movement.
  - Human mouthparts move vertically (up and down). In what direction do the mouthparts of a crayfish move? (Note especially the mandibles.) horizontally
  - Does this characteristic reinforce the idea that the mouthparts are appendages?
    ☒ yes ☐ no

The Life Processes Chart should be required. The section on other crustaceans (p. L142) should be for extra credit.

Name

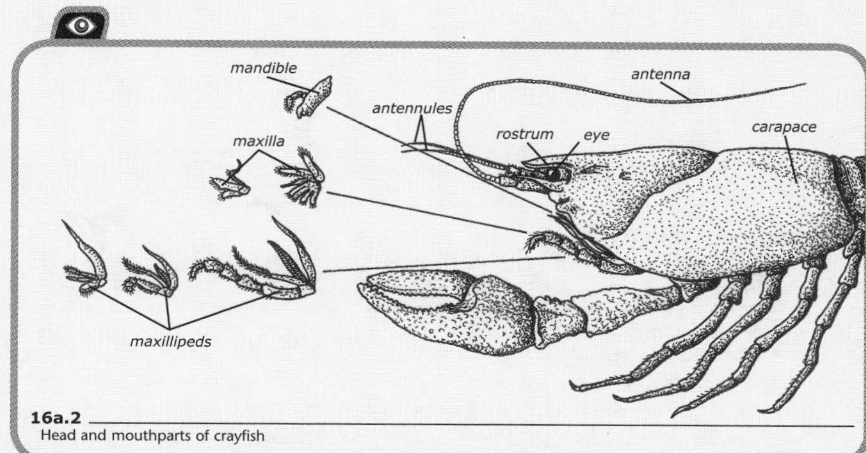

16a.2
Head and mouthparts of crayfish

- Remove the mouthparts, including the maxillipeds, from one side of your crayfish. (You still have the other side of the organism to work with if you are unsuccessful the first time.)
  - Remove the maxillipeds; then locate and remove the other mouthparts.
  - To remove the appendage, grip the base with forceps and pull the entire appendage out.
- In Area A draw all the mouth appendages you have removed from the crayfish.
  - Label the drawing completely.
  - Draw the appendages in the order they were in the crayfish, the most anterior at the left of the drawing and the most posterior at the right.

R E O

The Appendages of the Thorax

As you locate each of the appendages discussed below, label them on Diagram 16a.1.

I. The thoracic appendages move either the organism or the materials around the organism.

How many pairs of appendages does the thorax have? five

Removing mouthparts intact is difficult for some students. If they do not grasp the base of the appendage with either their fingers or their forceps, they will remove only part of the structure. After the three maxillipeds have been removed, the thin maxillae will be exposed. In order to find the bases of these mouthparts, the students should use probes to tease the maxillae. The mandibles are anterior to the maxillae and are tucked behind a swelling in the exoskeleton.

Students often have problems making a proportional drawing of the crayfish mouthparts. Illustrate the meaning of proportional by drawing three items (a cup, a pitcher, and a bathtub, for example) first incorrectly and then correctly on the chalkboard.

II. The most obvious appendages of the thorax are the *chelipeds*. Note the large pincers (the claws), which are used for protection and capturing food.

III. The next four pairs of appendages are *walking legs*. Carefully examine these thoracic appendages.

How do these legs differ from one another? They get longer and thinner toward the posterior.

Do all the walking legs have pincers? If not, which do? The front two often have pincers; the back two frequently do not.

The Appendages of the Abdomen

I. The abdomen has five pairs of appendages called *swimmerets*. Label these on Diagram 16a.1.

II. Carefully examine preserved male and female crayfish.
- In the male, the most anterior swimmerets are enlarged and point anteriorly. In the female, the anterior swimmerets are greatly reduced in size.
- What sex is your crayfish? ☐ male ☐ female

III. The sixth abdominal appendages are called the *uropods*. They grow from the telson. Together these structures form a powerful tail fin. How would the crayfish use this tail fin?

The crayfish bends its abdomen under itself and then extends it, using the tail fin to swim backwards.

Internal Anatomy of the Crayfish

Read all the following directions carefully before starting your dissection. The following procedures must be done in order. You will be expected to know the functions and locations of the organs that have been italicized.

The Body Cavity

I. Place your animal in the dissection pan with its dorsal side up.

II. Carefully insert the point of the scissors under the dorsal surface of the carapace at the posterior edge of the cephalothorax. Cut anteriorly along the midline of the body to the rostrum.

III. Reposition the scissors just behind the eyes and make a transverse cut.

IV. Carefully remove the two pieces of the carapace without disturbing the structures underneath.

The Respiratory Structures

I. Note carefully the exposed gills and study their structure.
- Remove a few gills and place them in a culture dish of water. Observe and describe their structure.

  Answers will vary.
- Carefully remove the rest of the gills.

II. Gills are able to exchange gases only when they are wet. Explain how the crayfish can spend many hours at a time on land. By getting water under its carapace and keeping the gill chamber closed, it can "hold water" in a way similar to the way we "hold our breath."

The Circulatory Structures

I. For easier handling of the animal, remove the legs attached to the thorax.

II. Carefully separate the dorsal tissues in the thorax and locate the middorsal *heart*.
- Locate the main *blood vessels* attached to the heart.
- The crayfish, as well as most other arthropods, has an open circulatory system.

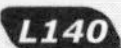

- ○ How does an open circulatory system work? The blood leaves the blood vessels and bathes the organs.
- ○ Does an open circulatory system circulate materials as efficiently as a closed circulatory system? ☐ yes ☒ no Why or why not? because it depends on gravity and a closed circulatory system does not
- ○ Explain why being forced to lie on its back would cause death for a crayfish. The blood would collect around the heart and not drain over the organs.

- Do crayfish have red blood? ☐ yes ☒ no If not, what color is their blood? (Do research to find the answer. Observing a preserved specimen is not sufficient.) Clear or blue

The Reproductive Structures

I. Look between the digestive glands (described in the next section) to find the reproductive structures.
- If your crayfish is a male, look for a small pair of white gonads (*testes*) and coiled ducts.
- If your crayfish is a female, look for a large mass of dark-colored *eggs* (inside the ovaries). (Figure 16A.5 on p. 478 of your text is of a female.)

II. Remove these reproductive structures so that you can see the digestive structures.

The Digestive Structures

I. The two light-colored masses extending along each side of the body cavity beyond the cervical groove are the *digestive glands.* What is their function? They produce digestive enzymes.

II. To expose the *intestine*, insert the point of the scissors underneath the dorsal side of the exoskeleton covering the abdomen. Cut posteriorly to the telson.
- Open the abdominal exoskeleton along the cut. The intestine appears as a tube on the dorsal side of the abdominal muscles.
- Do not confuse the intestine with the dark-colored dorsal blood vessel.

III. Trace the intestine anteriorly to the portion of the cephalothorax where the intestine joins the large thin-walled *stomach.*

The Viscera

I. Remove most of the internal organs (viscera) of the crayfish by following these instructions.
- Just behind the eyes, cut the bands of muscles leading to the stomach. These muscles hold the stomach in place.
- Pull the stomach posteriorly and cut the short esophagus located just below the stomach.

II. Carefully lift out the organs all in one piece. What is attached to the organs that keeps them all together? mesenteries (connective tissues)

The Excretory Structures

I. Clean out the remaining tissue in the head to expose the *green glands* (kidneys) just posterior to and below the antennules. They are soft, small, and only slightly green.

II. If you are careful, you may also be able to find the small saclike bladder, which is connected to the green glands.

The Nervous System

I. At the front of the head cavity, between the eyes, note the brain, a tiny mass of white tissue.

II. Trace the nerves that go from the brain to the antennae and the eyes.

III. Trace the *nerve cord* back from the brain to the abdomen by cutting the hard tissue on the floor of the thorax with the scalpel.
- Spread the abdomen apart and pull out the large muscles. (This is the portion of the shrimp, lobster, and fresh crayfish that we eat.)
- The nerve cord should now be exposed on the ventral side of the abdomen.
- The swollen portions of the nerve cord are called the ganglia.

IV. Why is it an advantage for the crayfish to have its nerve cord on the ventral side rather than on the dorsal side, as it is in humans? Answers may vary. It is closer to the appendages, and it is protected better, especially during molting.

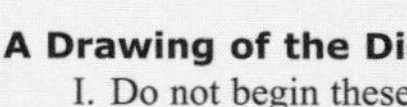

A Drawing of the Dissected Crayfish

I. Do not begin these drawings until after you have completed your dissection.

II. In the crayfish outlines in Area B, draw a dorsal view of the viscera of your specimen. Use different outlines for different body systems so that the organs will not overlap in your drawings (suggested combinations: digestive/excretory, reproductive/circulatory, nervous/respiratory). Label all of the structures that you are able to identify from the dissection instructions.

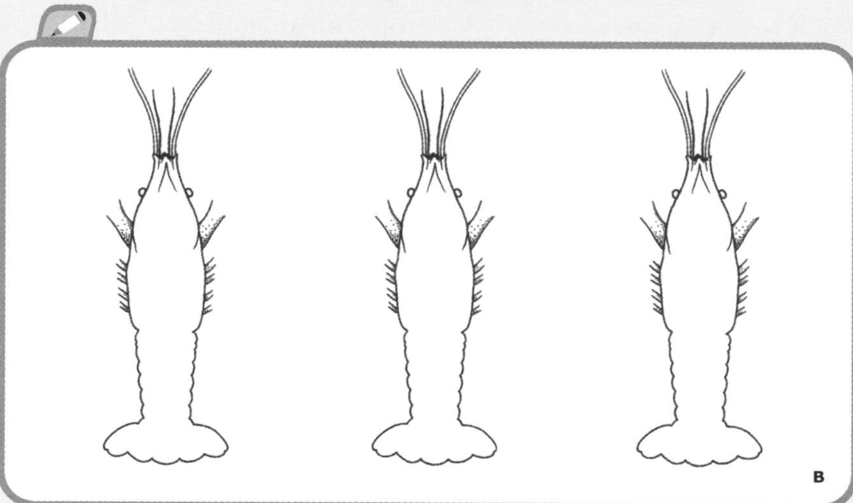

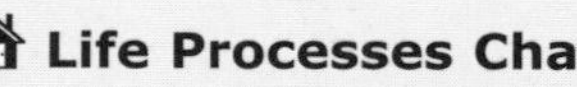

Life Processes Chart: Crayfish

I. Fill out a Life Processes Chart for the crayfish.
- Be careful not to repeat material covered in the anatomy sections of this laboratory exercise.
- Include an extensive Other Notes section in your Life Processes Chart.

II. Add to your Life Processes Chart a final section called Other Crustaceans.
- Choose two of the following: *Cyclops*, ostracod (seed shrimp), *Daphnia*, pill bug, barnacle, fiddler crab, brine shrimp (*Artemia*), blue crab, edible shrimp, lobster.
- Do research in another source about the two crustaceans you choose. Then write one or two paragraphs covering their unusual features, their habitats, and their economic and environmental importance. Observe preserved specimens if available.

L142 Lab 16a

The drawings of the internal systems to be done in Area B should show the structures drawn from the dorsal side. This distinction makes it difficult for the students to copy from the diagram in the text, which shows the lateral view of a crayfish. Some students may try it, so warn them in advance.

Students who have female crayfish and must remove many eggs may wish to draw the reproductive system separately.

Students will require additional instructions in order to do the Life Processes Chart. They should not repeat the information regarding external structures (appendages, mouthparts, exoskeleton, etc.). However, they should include the internal structures of the crayfish. Stress that they should emphasize physiology. For example, movement should be described in terms of the actions of the muscles within the appendages and not by listing the appendages.

Name________________________________

Date____________________ Hour__________

16b
The Grasshopper

Materials
- preserved specimen of lubber grasshopper (*Romalea microptera*)
- dissection kit

Goal

- To observe the major insect characteristics as seen in the grasshopper

The order Orthoptera, the straight-winged insects, includes the grasshopper, cockroach, cricket, and praying mantis. Because of its large size, the lubber grasshopper is often used in the science laboratory. It is native to the states on the Gulf Coast. Its wings are small compared to its body, making the lubber unable to fly.

External Anatomy of the Grasshopper

R E O

I. Examine the preserved specimen, taking care not to dissect or damage the specimen in any way. Locate all the following structures. Use a hand lens if necessary.
- Antennae (Note the segments of the antennae and compare the length of the antennae to the grasshopper's body length.)
- Compound eyes
- Simple eyes
  - The simple eyes are located between the compound eyes.
  - How many simple eyes are there? (Research may be necessary.) three pairs
- Head
- Thorax
- Tympanum—What is the purpose of the tympanum? hearing
- Jumping leg—Identify these parts of the leg, beginning at the base (the part closest to the body) and progressing toward the tip.
  - Trochanter
  - Femur
  - Tibia
  - Tarsus (the foot)—Which section of the leg is the largest? femur
- Forelegs—How do the forelegs and the jumping legs differ?
  - In appearance: The forelegs are shorter and less muscular.
  - In function: The forelegs are used for walking.
- Forewings—The forewings are thick, heavy wings that are not used in flight. What is their purpose? They protect the hind wings.
- Hind wings—You may need to lift the forewings in order to see these structures. Look for the fine veins in the hind wings.
- Abdomen
- Spiracles—Where are the spiracles located? on the abdomen
- Ovipositor—Does your organism have an ovipositor? ☐ yes ☐ no
- What does the answer to this question indicate? the sex of the specimen

II. On Diagram 16b.1, label all the external structures listed above. (NOTE: You will need to draw in details in order to label all the structures.)

When ordering grasshoppers, be sure to order large specimens.

Grasshoppers for this exercise may be reused for several years. Place undamaged specimens in an airtight jar containing the preservative that came with the specimens.

Emphasize that the students are not to dissect the grasshoppers. They are merely to observe their specimens in order to help them label the diagrams on page L144.

Introduction

To most students, insects are fascinating. This laboratory exercise stresses the major insect characteristics as seen in the grasshopper.

See page A25 for a completed Life Processes Chart for the grasshopper.

Required / Extra / Omit

It is suggested that you do this entire exercise or that you not do it at all.

Scheduling Laboratory Activities

Because it should take students only a few minutes to complete the observation of the grasshopper and to do the drawings, you may wish to combine this exercise with 16c.

The parts of a grasshopper's jumping leg are not listed in the text. Either tell the students to look up the answer or inform them that the thick, thighlike portion is the femur and let them figure out the other leg parts. The trochanter is more obvious on specimens than it is on the drawings.

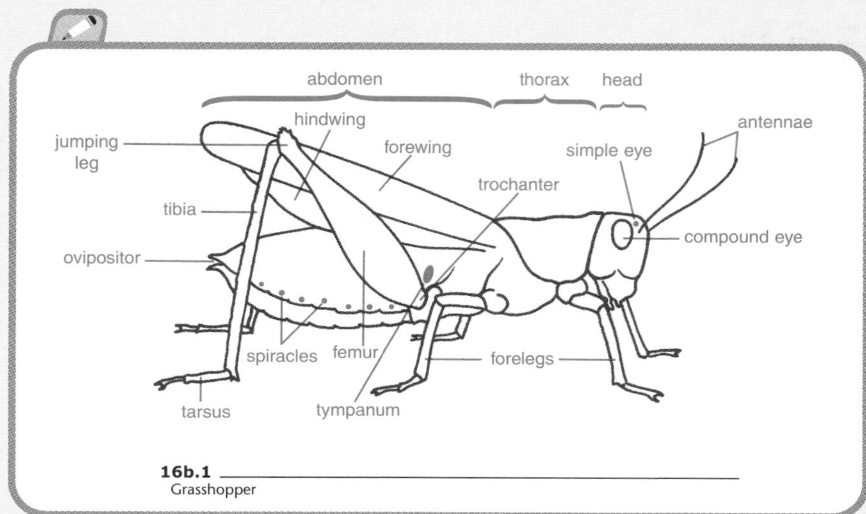

16b.1 ______
Grasshopper

III. On your specimen, locate all the mouthparts listed below.
- Label the mouthparts on Diagram 16b.2.
- In the spaces below, tell how many of each mouthpart the grasshopper has.
  - Labrum: one
  - Mandible (jaw): two
  - Labium: one
  - Labial palp: two
  - Maxilla: two
  - Maxillary palp: two

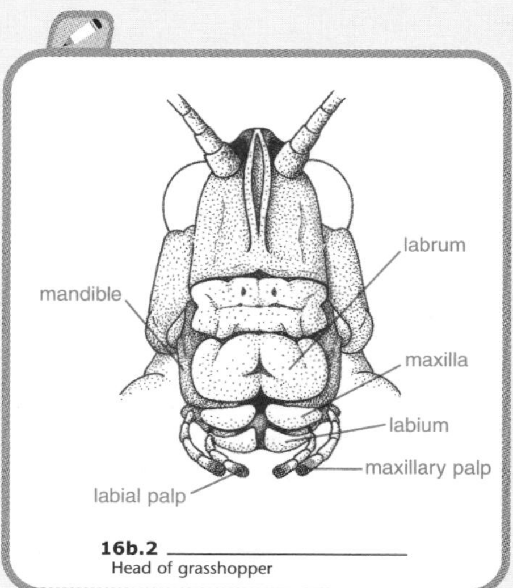

16b.2 ______
Head of grasshopper

Life Processes Chart: Grasshopper

I. Read Section 16B in your text and take notes on the grasshopper and other members of the Class Orthoptera. Do additional research in another text.

II. Fill out a Life Processes Chart and include all the information you learned in this laboratory exercise. Do not copy from the exercise.

Name____________________

Date____________ Hour________

16c
Insect Orders

Materials
- visuals of insects
- live cultures of fruit flies (*Drosophila melanogaster*) and flour beetles (*Tribolium sp.*)

Goals
- To learn about some of the diversity among insects
- To use and enhance research, writing, and oral skills
- To learn how insects affect man
- To learn about some of the techniques man uses to control insects
- To learn about insect metamorphosis

The majority of organisms in the animal kingdom are insects. In class Insecta, there are over thirty orders, representing hundreds of thousands of different species. The population of each species is thousands to billions. In this exercise, we will study the major orders of insects (based on number of species) to survey the insect kingdom.

In many respects, insects compete with man for dominance on the land's surface. In the second part of this exercise, you will observe living insect cultures. Following these observations, you will be given information about the role of insects as pests and how they are controlled. You will draw some conclusions about controlling insects. You will have to reason out these answers from the information given in this laboratory exercise and from the observations you make of the insect cultures.

Reports on Insect Orders

R E O

Written Reports on Insect Orders

I. Prepare a written report on any three of the following insect orders.
- Coleoptera
- Lepidoptera
- Hymenoptera
- Diptera
- Orthoptera
- Odonata

II. Follow these guidelines.
- Each insect order report should be one or two pages in length or the length assigned by your teacher. (One side of a sheet of paper, typed or handwritten, is a page.)
- Much of the information you will need is available from encyclopedias or the Internet.
- Begin your report with a description of the order.
  - Indicate the number of wings.
  - Indicate the type of mouthparts.
  - Indicate the type of metamorphosis.
  - Indicate the type of eyes.
  - Indicate the special characteristics that set this order apart from the others.
  - Do not repeat phylum or class characteristics unless they are greatly modified in the particular order.
- Choose two insects as examples of the order and describe them. Include a description of the following, if applicable, as you describe each example.
  - Habitat
  - Life cycle (if interesting or unusual)
  - Food
  - Economic and personal relationships to man (pet, pest, or harmful insect; diseases carried by it; competition with man for food)
  - Social instincts

Placing a little food coloring in the fruit fly medium as it is being prepared will make observation of the larvae easier.

Sift the culture of flour beetles through a piece of gauze to separate the various stages found in the medium. Place them in a petri dish or culture glass and cover it with a flat piece of clear glass. Place this dish on a dark background for better visibility.

Instructions for culturing fruit flies and flour beetles and methods of obtaining cultures from the wild are given in note E on page A18.

Introduction

In part of this exercise, students are asked to find out about large, well-known insect orders. This research activity should increase their knowledge of insects and improve their research skills at the same time. Another part of this exercise asks students to work in groups to prepare an oral report on an insect order. Again, students will have the opportunity not only to exercise and improve their skills in oral communication and research but also to learn about the diversity of insects.

It is suggested that you present a sample oral report on the order Orthoptera to show the students what you expect of them. Give the various characteristics of the order and present interesting facts about several examples of the order (praying mantises, walking sticks, locusts of the Egyptian plagues, and others). Assign the students the various insect orders several days before the laboratory exercise is due and encourage them to start their research in encyclopedias and other books as soon as possible. Allow time at the end of the next few class hours for students to get together to discuss how they will present their reports.

Tell the students just prior to (or after, if you prefer) their oral presentations that only those orders discussed in the text (Coleoptera, Lepidoptera, Hymenoptera, Diptera, Odonata, and Orthoptera, the one you discussed in class) will be on the test. It is recommended that you not assign any of these orders for oral reports but cover them yourself or have the students do the written reports (p. L145) that cover these orders.

Observing live insects in various stages of metamorphosis and attempting to solve practical problems of insect control can be valuable classroom exercises. Various kinds of insects can be observed in class. Some biological supply companies offer eggs and larvae of butterflies and other insects that can, within a reasonable length of time, be

Tell the students that the visual aids they use for their oral reports must be large enough to be seen from the back of your classroom, where you will be sitting. If they cannot find large photographs in books, they will need to make illustrations that are large enough to be seen clearly from the back of the classroom.

Oral Reports on Insect Orders

The class will be divided into small report groups of two or three students. Each group will be assigned an insect order and will prepare an oral report to present to the class. Your teacher will give you a time limit.

I. Follow the guidelines for the written report, choosing material that will be interesting and valuable to the class.
II. Prepare at least one visual.
III. Choose one or two people to do the speaking.
IV. Practice the presentation. Be sure to time the presentation and to adjust it to fit the criteria given by your teacher.
V. On the day of your report, give your teacher a list of the contributions of each group member.

Insect Metamorphosis and Control

Flour Beetles

The flour beetle (*Tribolium sp.*) is found in stored grains and sometimes in packaged foods such as cake mixes. Often it becomes a serious pest.

I. Observe the living culture of the flour beetle.
- What type of metamorphosis does the flour beetle have? ☒ complete ☐ incomplete
- Name and describe the stages of the beetle's life cycle that you were able to find in the culture.
  Eggs are tiny and probably not visible in the flour medium. Larvae are wormlike. Pupae are generally also wormlike but inactive. Adults have three pairs of legs and look like familiar beetle insects.
- From your observation, to what insect order do flour beetles belong? Coleoptera
- In Area A, draw the various stages of the flour beetle's life cycle that you were able to observe. Draw the stages in proportion and label them.

Review how to make a series of drawings with proportional sizes for the life cycle drawings on pages L146 and L148. (See margin note by drawing area A on p. L139.)

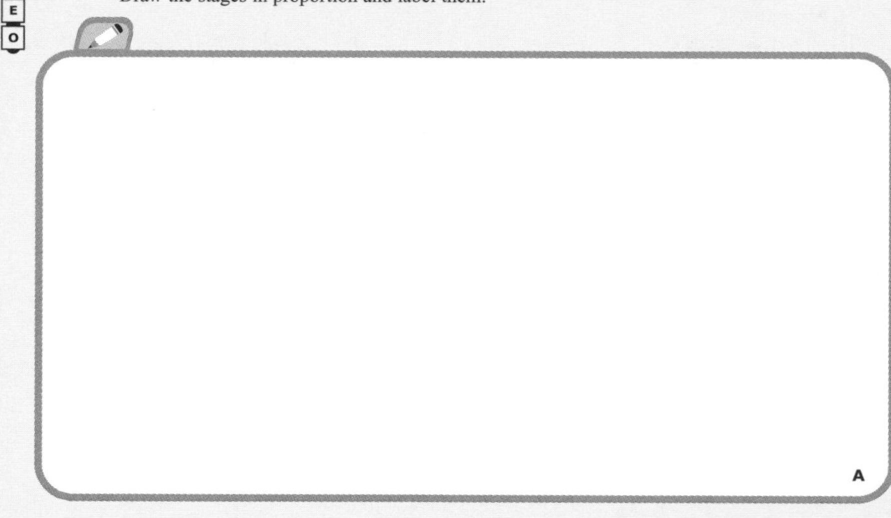

seen to go through metamorphosis. You may wish to have your students observe these.

For this exercise, however, insect pests have been selected for study, and methods of controlling them are discussed.

Required / Extra / Omit

The reports on insect orders come in two parts: a written section and an oral section. You can do either or both. They are designed to complement each other, and their best benefit comes when done together.

You may wish to combine this exercise with the observation of the grasshopper (Exercise 16b).

The written reports on insect orders (p. L145) are designed to familiarize all the students with those orders that are covered in the text. Your decision regarding assigning these reports will depend upon how competent your students are and how thoroughly you cover this material in class lectures.

The section on metamorphosis and control (pp. L146–L148) is a valuable experience for the students. It includes observations of living insect cultures, an activity that exposes the students to stages in an insect's life cycle that are not frequently seen. You may wish to omit the drawings in this section to save time. A thorough class discussion of the life cycles of these insects (preferably with photographs or illustrations) can replace the observations and still enable the students to do the section that requires them to suggest control methods. These sections on insect control could be assigned as homework, providing material for a class discussion the next day.

Name______________________________

R E O

II. An infestation of flour beetles in a large grain elevator could cause thousands of dollars' worth of damage. How would you control these pests?

- At what stage(s) in its life cycle would the flour beetle probably be easiest to control?

  ☐ egg ☒ larva ☐ pupa ☐ adult Why? It cannot get away, and it eats a great deal.

- Would it be advisable to put in the flour beetle's medium (grain) a type of chemical insecticide that has to be eaten by the insects to kill them? ☐ yes ☒ no

  Why or why not? The chemical would remain in the grain, contaminating it.

- Some gases (such as carbon dioxide, carbon disulfide, ammonia, and carbon tetrachloride) can be blown through the medium as fumigants to kill flour beetles. Why would fumigants be a more desirable form of control for flour beetles than a liquid spray or dust insecticide? Give at least two reasons. Answers may vary. The gases would diffuse into the air after killing the insects; sprays and dusts would leave residues. Gases can penetrate the medium to kill the pests, while sprays and dusts would affect only insects on the surface.

- Flour beetles can be killed by keeping them at a temperature of 49 °C for two hours. Which method (fumigation or heat) would be practical for grain storage elevators to use? Which would be practical in the home? Heating a large grain elevator to this temperature would be difficult. Heating a small quantity of a flour product in an oven would be considerably easier than using dangerous fumigants. Therefore, fumigants should be used for grain elevators, and heating for the home.

Fruit Flies and How to Control Them

The fruit fly (*Drosophila sp.*) is often seen buzzing around almost any ripe (or more likely, overripe) fruit that is not being refrigerated. These small flies, although more of a nuisance than actual pests, can be a problem for a fruit transporter.

R E O

I. Observe the living culture of fruit flies.

- What type of metamorphosis does the fruit fly have? ☒ complete ☐ incomplete
- Name and describe the stages of the fruit fly's life cycle you found in the culture.

  Tiny white eggs can be seen in the culture medium (if the medium is stained). White larvae feeding in the medium and tan-colored pupae on the sides of the culture jar can easily be distinguished from the flying adults.

- From your observation, to what insect order do fruit flies belong? Diptera
- In Area B, draw the various stages of the fruit fly's life cycle that you were able to observe. Make sure the stages are drawn in proportion and labeled.

B

R E O

II. Study the control of fruit flies.

- At what stage(s) in its life cycle would the fruit fly probably be easiest to control?

  ☐ egg ☒ larva ☐ pupa ☐ adult Why? It cannot get away, and it eats a great deal.

- Although fruit flies can be killed with heat, the 49 ºC that kills flour beetles only stops the growth of fruit flies; it does not kill them. What drawbacks does control by increased temperature have?

  Fresh fruit must be kept cool or it will spoil.

- Lowered temperatures are more advisable than raised temperatures for controlling fruit flies. What drawbacks might lowering the temperature have? expense and damage to fruit

- Would a liquid spray or dust insecticide be advisable? (Recall your observation of the insect's life cycle and how the various stages feed.) ☐ yes ☒ no Why or why not? Since larvae burrow into the fruit (the medium), a spray or dust insecticide would not be a good control method for them. Adults may be affected, but they can fly away.

- To prevent mold and other problems, producers transport softer fruits (which are preferred by fruit flies) in open boxes or boxes with air holes. These boxes allow an infestation of fruit flies in one area to spread quickly to another. In this situation, what drawbacks do fumigants have as a control method? The fumigants would easily diffuse into the air from the open boxes, thereby losing their effectiveness against the insects.

- After seeing the drawbacks of the methods most frequently used to control pests in foods, give another possible method of fruit fly control. Describe its advantages and disadvantages.

  Answers may vary. Sealed refrigerator trucks or various biological controls (sterile members, pheromones, etc.) seem to be the best answers.

Tell the students that suggesting other possible methods of insect control will require careful thought. They will need to be able to explain why the methods would work.

Name____________________

Date______________ Hour________

17a
Live Bony Fish

Materials
- living fish

Goals
- To observe the motion of fish
- To note specialized structures that equip the fish for its environment
- To observe the external anatomy of the fish

Class Osteichthyes, the bony fish, is the largest vertebrate class. From your observation of living fish, you will see how a fish uses its specialized structures in its environment.

Although there is great similarity among most fish, there is also some surprising diversity. The members of this class demonstrate fragility, as well as brute strength. Their fins often have unusual and intricate designs, and their body shapes take many different forms.

Studying a Living Fish

Observe the movements of fish swimming in an aquarium. Note the different body movements of various fish. Also note the different body and fin structures in each fish. Base your answers for the questions below upon observations of a typical fish (one without major body modifications) found in the aquarium. Remember that you are to observe the natural movements of the fish; do not tap on the glass.

Body Shape

I. Describe the body shape as viewed from the side. Answers may vary. Spindle shaped, pointed anterior, flat posterior

II. Describe the body shape as viewed from the front. Answers may vary. Round with fins up and down, triangular (depends on fish)

III. In what ways is the fish's body ideally suited for its aquatic environment? The streamlined body shape helps the fish move easily through the water.

Movements of the Mouth and Opercula

I. Describe the position of the opercula when the mouth is open. usually closed

II. Describe the position of the opercula when the mouth is closed. usually open

III. Why are these movements in the fish important? They help the fish force water over the gills.

Eyes and Eyelids

I. Are eyelids present? ☐ yes ☒ no

How movable are the eyes in their sockets? Answers may vary. Hardly movable

II. The pupils are large. Why is this important to the fish? Light does not pass through cloudy water easily. Large pupils admit more light than small pupils.

Live Bony Fish L149

Frequently a student has an aquarium at home or knows a friend who has one. He may even go to the local pet shop to view the fish there. As long as he observes fish that are shaped somewhat like the yellow perch, a student can do these observations anywhere.

If you know a good aquarist, you may want to ask him to lend you some good-sized fish for observation in your class. Ask him to set up the equipment in your classroom. Large fish are usually the result of many months or years of care, and their owner will not want to lose them.

If you are going to purchase live fish just for these observations, buy a few ordinary goldfish.

Freshwater aquarium fish recommended for observation include swordtails, barbs, and dwarf gouramis. Fish to avoid for this observation include angelfish (because of fin modifications), bottom-dwelling catfish (because of body-shape modification), zebra fish, neon tetras, and other tiny, fast-moving fish.

Nasco and many other science suppliers sell rubber fish replicas cast from actual fish species. There is a wide range of shapes and fin styles available. A sampling of these would make a good comparative study.

If you have a public aquarium in your area, now would be a great time for a field trip. Most aquarium visits can be completed in three hours or less, even with a presentation or guided tour from the staff.

Doing Exercises 17a and 17b together (see box on page 150) will eliminate the problem of having too many students at a time trying to observe the aquarium. Set a limit on the number of students that can be at the aquarium at one time. Students not at the aquarium can be doing parts of the other exercises.

Introduction

For this exercise students are asked to observe living fish and to prepare a Life Processes Chart for the yellow perch. Although we often see fish swimming in the water, few of us make the necessary observations to understand how they swim. With careful observations a student should be able to learn much about how a fish moves. The questions in this exercise are designed to lead to the proper observations.

See page A26 for a completed Life Processes Chart for the yellow perch.

Required / Extra / Omit

It is suggested that the Life Processes Chart for the yellow perch be required. Be sure to go over the material that should and should not be covered, as explained for the student on page L151. For example, under the movement section of the chart, students should not include the fins of the fish since they are covered in detail in the exercise. However, students should include the muscles of the fish.

The respiration process is covered in the section on external structures in Exercise 17b. If you have your students do this section, you may decide to omit respiration on the Life Processes Chart.

The reports on two interesting fish (p. L151) should be extra credit. Have some exciting, colorful books about fish in the classroom. Tell the students to be sure that they are reporting on members of class Osteichthyes and not on members of some other class (e.g., whales, porpoises, or sharks).

Filling out the Fish Fins chart requires the students to use both the text and their observation of living fish.

Fins

I. Study the fins closely and determine their number, location, and function. Using information from your text and observations of live fish, fill in the Fish Fins chart below.

Answers will vary, depending on the species observed.

Fish Fins

Name of Fin	Number	Location	Function
Pectoral			
Pelvic			
Anterior dorsal			
Posterior dorsal			
Anal			
Caudal			

II. When the fish is not moving, which fins move to keep it in position? usually the pectoral fins, sometimes in coordination with the pelvic fins

III. Observe the fish closely as it rapidly swims forward. What provides the main thrust?

☒ caudal fin and tail region ☐ pectoral fins ☐ pelvic fins

Explain your answer. The main thrust is usually provided by the caudal fin and the muscles just anterior to it.

Scheduling Laboratory Exercises

You may wish to combine Laboratory Exercises 17a and 17b into a two-period laboratory exercise. During the first period the students should be able to do the live fish observations and the external observations of the yellow perch. During the second period students should be able to complete the dissection of the yellow perch. This schedule will fluctuate, depending on when the students are able to get to the aquarium to observe live fish.

Name____________________

Researching the Bony Fish

Unusual Modifications of the Fish's Body and Fin Structure

Read completely the material in your text concerning fish and the yellow perch. Do research to find at least two unusual body and fin modifications found in some fish and the purposes they serve. Do not use illustrations given in the text or in class.

R E O

I. Body modifications

1. Body modification: ____________________

Function: ____________________

2. Body modification: ____________________

Function: ____________________

R E O

II. Fin modifications

1. Fin modification: ____________________

Function: ____________________

2. Fin modification: ____________________

Function: ____________________

R E O

Life Processes Chart: Yellow Perch

I. Do not repeat the material covered in Studying a Living Fish.

II. Do cover the following materials:
- Scales of the fish
- Muscles of the fish
- Internal structures of the fish (Be sure to describe the structure and function of those items italicized in the dissection section of Exercise 17b.)

R E O

Report

I. Choose two other fish that interest you, research them, and write a brief report on each one.

II. These may be saltwater, freshwater, or aquarium fish. Choose an exotic fish and tell what makes it unusual.

III. Each report must be at least one hundred words but not more than two pages.

Name________________

Date__________ Hour________

17b
Dissection of a Bony Fish

Materials

- preserved fish (yellow perch)
- culture dish
- hand lens or stereomicroscope
- dissection pan
- dissection kit
- plastic bag

Goal

- To observe the external and internal anatomy of the fish

Observation of a preserved fish will permit you to see many external structures that are not visible on a live specimen. The internal structures of a fish are typical of vertebrates, and fish dissection can be useful in illustrating and learning these structures.

Medium-sized perch (6 inches long) are large enough for this exercise. Ordering larger perch is a waste of money.

R E O

External Structures of a Yellow Perch

Using a preserved specimen of the yellow perch, examine the structures listed below.

I. Mouth

- Describe the teeth. Small pointed teeth can be felt and seen in the upper and lower jaws.
- Tell why the type and placement of the teeth are important to the feeding habits of the yellow perch. Answers may vary. Teeth are small because perch swallow food whole and chew little. Teeth point inward as a barrier to any food's getting out.
- Examine the tongue. Describe its texture, location, and attachment in the mouth. The tongue is short and rough and is attached to the floor of the mouth.
- Examine the esophageal opening. Insert your probe into it. Explain the need a perch has for a large elastic esophageal opening. A fish usually swallows food whole. It needs to have an elastic esophagus to do so.

The small teeth of the perch are more easily felt than seen.

II. Nostrils

- Where are the nostrils located? They are above the mouth, below and anterior to the eyes.
- Describe the structure of the nostrils. They are small pockets; they have no passages leading into the head.

III. Fins

- Raise the dorsal fins by pulling them forward. The dorsal fins of a yellow perch consist of a spiny and a soft portion.
  - To determine whether a structure in a fin is a ray or a spine, put your finger on the very tip of the structure and then push on it. A spine will not bend; a ray bends.
  - How many spines are there on your specimen's anterior dorsal fin? twelve to fifteen
  - Compare the number you counted with the number of spines on other specimens. Is the number the same? ☐ yes ☐ no Answers will vary.

    If the answer is no, how wide is the variation? Answers will vary.
- Tell whether the other fins on the yellow perch are supported by rays or spines or both. Answers will vary.

Pectoral:	☐ rays	☐ spines	☐ both
Pelvic:	☐ rays	☐ spines	☐ both
Anal:	☐ rays	☐ spines	☐ both
Caudal:	☐ rays	☐ spines	☐ both

Inform the students that the joint at the base of a ray or spine that causes the fin to stand erect or lie next to the fish's body does not demonstrate the type of flexibility that determines whether the structure is a ray or a spine. It is the flexibility of the calcified "rod" that extends from the body to the end of the fin that matters.

Introduction

This is the last dissection the students will do before they do the Frog Lab. If the students have done the other dissections suggested in this text, they should be able to perform these procedures with a minimum of instruction from you. The structures in the fish are relatively obvious and easily identified, and many of them are comparable to human structures. Students should find this dissection relatively simple.

Required / Extra / Omit

It is suggested that the entire exercise be required.

You may wish to omit or make extra credit the drawings of the heart and brain, depending on the amount of class time you have for this exercise.

Blood vessels in the gill arch are difficult to see.

IV. Body covering

- Locate the lateral line. What function does it serve? It detects changes in water pressure or current.
- Carefully examine a scale from the yellow perch with a stereomicroscope or with a hand lens. What structures are you able to observe? growth rings (scale rings)

V. Opercula and gills

- Raise the right operculum and with a probe carefully separate the layers of gills to examine them. How many layers of gills are there? four Is this true of both sides?
  ☒ yes ☐ no
- Insert your probe through the gills and into the mouth cavity. Note where it enters the mouth. Why is the mouth-gill chamber opening necessary? To allow water to pass over the gills, the fish "swallows" the water.
- With scissors, cut the left operculum away and remove one set of gills by cutting the upper and lower attachments of the *gill arch*.
- Rinse the gills and place them in a culture dish filled with water; examine them closely. Examine the feathery *filaments* and the comblike *rakers*.
- Examine the upper and lower ends of the arch and try to find the blood vessels that enter and leave the gill. Why should the gill be so richly supplied with blood? This is the place where the blood exchanges gases.

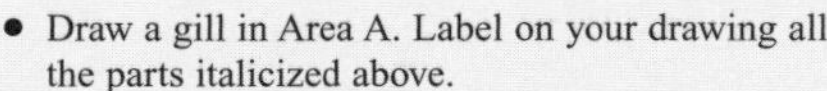

- Draw a gill in Area A. Label on your drawing all the parts italicized above.

R E O

Diagram 17b.1 is an outline of a yellow perch. Draw in the external structures not shown and label as many of the external parts as you can.

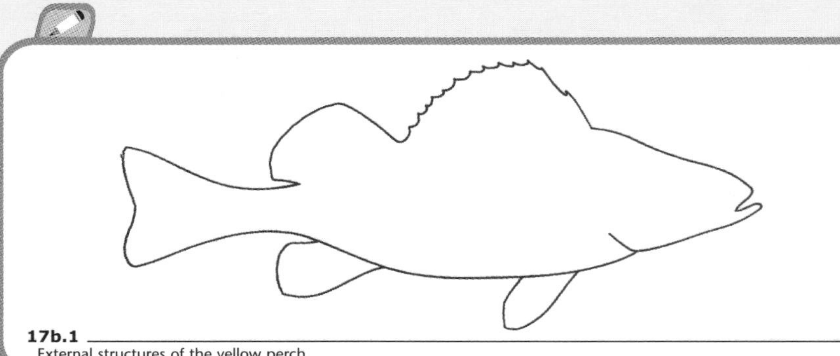

17b.1
External structures of the yellow perch

Internal Structures of a Yellow Perch

R E O

Read the entire section on dissecting the perch before you begin to cut. Note carefully the diagrams you are to draw. You should include all the following italicized terms in your Life Processes Chart of the yellow perch (Exercise 17a). Do the remainder of the exercise in sequence.

I. Open the body cavity.
- Hold your fish with ventral side up, head pointing away from you. Insert your scissors through the body wall in front of (anterior to) the anus; cut along the midline of the body to the area between the gill covers on the lower side of the head.
- Lay your fish on its right side (with the head toward your left). Continue the incision from the point between the gills, around the front of the operculum, to the top of the body cavity. (A good portion of the dorsal side of the fish is a muscle layer. You need cut only to the top of the air bladder.)
- Make another incision close to the anus and cut dorsally to the top of the body cavity.
- With your scalpel, make the remaining incision across the body cavity (just dorsal to the air bladder).
- Remove the side wall of the body. The removal of the wall will reveal the body cavity with the organs in their normal positions.

II. Locate the internal organs.
- The digestive system
  - Locate the beige *liver*. It is in the anterior end of the body cavity. Gently raise the lobes of the liver and find the *gallbladder* (it looks like a very tiny flattened balloon) attached to the lower surface of the liver. Cut the liver free and remove it in one piece, if possible.
  - Locate the short *esophagus* and *stomach*.
  - Locate the *intestine* and follow its loops to the *anus*.
  - Cut the esophagus where it enters the mouth and cut the intestine near the anus.
  - Remove the digestive system without disturbing the other organs and place it beside the fish in the dissection pan.
  - Draw in Area B the digestive system as it lies outside the body cavity. Label all the organs italicized above as well as the *pyloric ceca*.
  - Cut open the stomach. Can you recognize any specific food? ☐ yes ☐ no

    If yes, what? Answers may vary. Insects and worms (parasitic nematodes often found)
- The urogenital system
  - With the alimentary canal removed, you should see the *gonads* and perhaps the *urinary bladder*.
    - ❖ The female perch may have a large yellow orange *ovary* (called a *roe*) containing many eggs. (If your fish was about to lay eggs, you may have already removed this structure in order to see the other organs.) The ovary could also be a small beige drumstick-shaped structure if the fish was not ready to lay eggs.

When scraping the fish's skull to reveal the brain, the students should not scrape toward themselves.

  - ❖ The male perch will have small cream-colored *testes*.
- ❍ Trace the white threadlike ducts coming from the gonads and the small tube from the urinary bladder to the *urogenital opening.*
- ❍ Find the *kidneys*, which usually are dark red strands along the spine.

- The air bladder and the circulatory system
  - ❍ Locate the *air bladder* along the top of the body cavity. It may have broken when you removed the body wall.
  - ❍ On the ventral side of the body cavity, near the opercula, locate the *pericardial cavity*, which contains the *heart.*
    - ❖ The soft upper chamber of the heart is the *atrium.*
    - ❖ Below and anterior to the atrium is the *ventricle.*
    - ❖ A purplish muscular bulb, the *bulbus arteriosus*, gives rise to the *ventral aorta*, which branches to the gills.
  - ❍ Remove the heart and draw it in Area C. Label as many structures as you can.

R E O

- The nervous system
  - ❍ Expose the brain of the fish.
    - ❖ Hold the fish with its dorsal side up and position its head so that it points away from you. Using your scalpel and scissors, cut away the skin from the skull.
    - ❖ Scrape the skull with your scissors to wear away the bone.
    - ❖ When the bone becomes thin, pick away the bone with the forceps to expose the brain.
  - ❍ Locate the *olfactory lobes* in front, the larger lobes of the *cerebrum* behind these, and the very large *optic lobes* posterior to the cerebrum. The *cerebellum* is posterior to the optic lobes, and the *medulla oblongata*, an enlargement of the spinal cord, is posterior to the cerebellum and slightly underneath it.
    - ❖ Considering the size and function of each brain part, in what function should the fish be most adept? sight

      Is the fish most adept at this function? ☐ yes ☒ no

      Explain. Sight is actually limited in fish.
    - ❖ When you consider the size and function of each brain part, in what function should it be least adept? smell, voluntary muscle activity

      Is the fish least adept at this function? ☐ yes ☒ no

      Explain. The sense of smell is one of the fish's keenest senses.

R E O

  - ❍ Draw the nervous system in Area D and label the brain regions and the spinal cord as you found them.

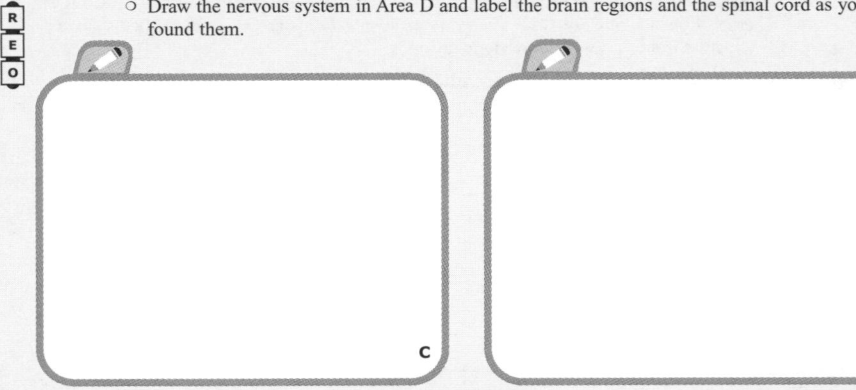

Name________________________________

Date____________________ Hour__________

18a
Birds

Materials
- microscope
- feathers (contour, including body and flight; down)
- preserved slides of feathers (contour and down)
- raw chicken egg
- dissection pan
- dissection kit
- hand lens

Goals
- To learn about the body coverings of birds
- To observe parts of a typical egg
- To learn about local birds

The class Aves contains warm-blooded vertebrates that hatch from eggs—the birds. They are the only animals with feathers. After observing these remarkably strong yet lightweight structures, you will note other structures that equip birds for flight. An examination of a chicken egg will reveal the major components of bird eggs. Then you will be asked to learn about the birds found in your area.

Observing Bird Feathers

R E O

I. Obtain a down feather and contour feathers (include flight feathers and body feathers).
- Examine the feather structures described on page 545 of the text.
- What observations can you make regarding the differences between a body feather and a flight feather? Not only are flight feathers longer, but they are also thicker and considerably stronger than the soft, flexible body feathers.
- Holding a flight feather at the base, use the thumb and forefinger of your other hand to pinch the vane near the top and then slide your fingers down, separating the vane. Next, use the same fingers to smooth the feather back into correct position by rubbing the other direction. What parts of the feather allow it to be repaired? barbs, barbules, and hooks

  What term is used to describe a bird's repairing its feathers using only its beak? preening

R E O

II. Examine a preserved slide of down and contour feathers under a microscope.
- Can you see barbs, barbules, and hooks on the contour feathers? ☒ yes ☐ no
- Can you see all these structures on the down feathers? ☐ yes ☒ no

  Explain why all these structures are or are not necessary. They are not necessary because a down feather does not need a flat vane. Down feathers serve as insulation.

R E O

III. In Area A, draw and label a section of a bird feather as seen through the microscope. Draw a large enough section to show the shaft, barbs, and barbules.

The loose feathers needed for this exercise can be obtained in bulk from most larger craft stores. Even if you can find only feathers that have been dyed, they will work fine. Down feathers can be taken from old down pillows, comforters, and jackets. Feathers may also be available from any of your students who have poultry or pet birds. As a precaution, however, you should disinfect feathers by spraying them with a bathroom-type bactericidal cleaner and rinsing them well with water.

Beware that many migratory songbirds and all birds of prey are federally protected. This means you may not collect or possess their feathers, eggs, or nests without special permits.

Introduction

This laboratory exercise effectively covers two key features of birds—feathers and amniotic eggs. Both are readily available and familiar to students, yet the most familiar things are often the most overlooked. Live birds are fascinating creatures for observation, so if one of your students can bring in the family pet for a day, it should further enhance you students' appreciation for this class of vertebrates.

Required / Extra / Omit

The observation of feathers should be required. This section can be done easily and quickly.

The egg dissection requires little expense, and it is a good tool for determining whether students can follow simple directions. While most if not all students have cracked and eaten eggs, probably few have thought about what each part is for and how a chick is able to grow inside of one. If you plan to do the chick embryology lab later, you may choose to omit this section.

You will probably want to limit the number and lengths of written reports on local birds. Make a list of the birds as a class and then assign a different one to each student for a written report. Afterward, require that they read one another's reports.

Oral reports are recommended if you have a considerable amount of class time available. If the reports are assigned for extra credit, be sure to place a time limit on them so that you can schedule all of them within the class time available for this unit.

When students look for pores in the eggshells, let them know that they are very small. Some chicken eggs may contain as many as ten thousand pores. The air space at the rounded end of the egg is not present until after the egg exits the mother and cools. The cooling of the egg causes the contraction of the liquid contents and consequent separation of the inner membrane from the outer membrane. Eggs fresh from the farm will have a much smaller space than those that have been sitting on a grocer's shelves.

When students are conducting research for their written reports, the Internet may be their best source of information. Most states have wildlife web pages managed by their game departments. Please navigate to the Resources Online section of our website at www.bjup.com to see a list of informative science websites.

The students' written reports on either the birds or mammals (18b) could be compiled into a booklet, duplicated, and distributed to the class. You may even consider having a good student in the class edit the reports. It is suggested that you require all the students to read the booklet. A quiz or several test questions over the contents of the booklet would help make its value apparent to the students.

Dissecting a Bird Egg

R E O

I. Place a raw chicken egg in a dish or dissection pan.

II. Using a probe, carefully break into the larger, more rounded end. Using tweezers, chip away the hard shell to expose this air space.

What separates this air space from the liquid contents of the egg? a membrane

III. Using tweezers, begin to chip away the hard outer shell starting at the air space and continuing along one side.

IV. When you have exposed most of one side—still enclosed by a membrane—use your scissors to cut into the membrane to reveal the contents.

What is the large yellow mass called? the yolk

What is the purpose for this material? food for the developing chick

Can you see an embryo growing here? ☐ yes ☒ no

Why or why not? The egg is not fertile (it came from a chicken farm with only hens).

What is the clear material in the egg called? albumen

In addition to water, what is the primary component of this clear material? protein

V. See if you can identify the thickened, whitish bands connecting the yolk to each end of the egg.

What are these bands called? chalazae

What is their function? to suspend the yolk within the albumen and keep it centered in the egg

What might happen to the developing chick if these bands do not form and function properly?

The bird might develop improperly if it rubs against the inside of the egg. The chalazae can twist, allowing the bird to stay upright in the egg and closest to the incubation heat from the mother.

VI. Examine part of the egg shell with a magnifying glass. You should be able to see tiny pores. Why would these pores be present? to allow oxygen to enter the egg and waste gases like CO_2 to escape

Studying Local Birds

R E O

I. Prepare a list of five birds native to your area.

II. Write a description of each bird.
- Each description should be about one page long.
- Include in each description the following details:
  - Size of bird; coloration; type of beak, wings, legs, and feet
  - Food, feeding time, seasonal changes in diet
  - Preferred nesting sites, description of nest and eggs, number of young, incubation period, time of year the young hatch, amount of parental care, whether young are altricial or precocial
  - Migration—if, where, and when it goes; if nonmigratory, how it survives the winter
  - Population status and protection level if endangered or threatened
  - Ecological significance—whether the bird helps or harms human interests
- Obtain illustrations of each bird if possible and include them with your reports.

Name________________________________

Date____________________ Hour__________

18b
Mammals

Materials
- mammal fur
- an unidentified mammal skull
- a ruler

Goals
- To examine mammal fur and compare it to human hair
- To observe parts of a mammal skull
- To learn about local mammals

Like birds, mammals are endothermic, but they are characterized by fur rather than feathers. They are the animals that have body characteristics and intelligence most like man's. They make a fascinating study. In this lab you will examine different kinds of mammal fur and compare it to your own hair. You will also examine an unidentified mammal skull to learn what its form indicates about its function. Finally, you will do some research to learn about some mammals from your area.

Observing Fur

R E O

I. Use a stereomicroscope or a hand lens to examine guard hair and underhair.

II. Compare fur and hair.
- Prepare a wet mount of a guard hair, an underhair, and a hair from your head.
- What differences do you notice between guard hair, underhair, and human scalp hair?

Answers will vary.

Examining a Skull

R E O

I. Select a skull from those that are available. The letter identifying my skull is ____________.

With a ruler, measure the skull's length and width (at its widest point) to the nearest millimeter and record your findings.

__________ mm in length and __________ mm in width

II. Locate the opening where the spinal cord enters the brain cavity at the back of the skull. Measure the diameter of this opening. __________ mm

III. Examine the skull to find where the ear canals and nostrils enter the skull. Considering the placement and size of these spaces, how important might hearing and smell be to this mammal?

Answers will vary.

IV. Find the eye sockets (orbits).
- Identify the opening at the back of each socket where the nerve bundle connects the eye to the brain.

You can get loose hair from nearly anyone who owns a dog or cat. Hair or hides from native wild species are often available from local taxidermists who often trim fur or even cut off large pieces of hide with attached fur when mounting animals or heads. These hide sections with fur are especially suitable for showing the relationship between the guard hair and the underhair.

Skulls suitable for the observation exercise could be found in nature. Unfortunately, these are often missing teeth and falling apart if they have been exposed to the elements for very long.

A better source for skulls is science and museum supply catalogs. An increasing number of skulls are now available as plastic replicas cast from originals. These replicas have all of the detail needed for this lab exercise, and while they sometimes cost slightly more, they are less likely to break than natural skulls. Please navigate to the Resources Online section of our website at www.bjup.com to see a list of science supply companies. Many suppliers sell a comparative set of several contrasting skulls that would be great for this exercise.

When they are comparing mammal and human hairs under the microscope, students should look especially at the roots and the tips.

The close examination of skulls is fascinating for students and can be an effective teaching tool when the activity is carefully directed. It is even more instructive if students do not know the species represented by the skull. Label each skull with a letter instead of a name and ask students to identify which skull they observed. While students may not be able to get the exact name of the mammal, they should be able to narrow it down to the correct order.

Introduction

Mammals, like birds, are often taken for granted because of our frequent exposure to them. Both the fur and skull observations are simple but valuable because they require students to apply their skills of observation and comparison. By adding a skull or two each year, you can develop a varied collection that will be useful in lecture as well as the lab.

Required / Extra / Omit

The fur observation is simple and should be included.

The skull examination is a valuable exercise linking math and life science. It also gets students to recognize the features that God has designed into His creatures. It can be done as a demonstration by the teacher or with specific students assigned to each question. If skulls are limited, you should suggest that students take turns doing the observations.

Depending on the amount of class time you have for written reports, you may assign some students to birds and some to mammals.

You may want to combine exercises 18a and 18b into one class period. In that case, you could omit some sections or limit the number of reports based on the time and resources available.

- Predators usually have eyes that are directed more toward the front while prey species often have eyes oriented toward the sides. Why might God have made them this way? Eyes directed toward the front enable predators to find prey and accurately judge distances; prey animals have greater field of view (peripheral vision) with eyes on the sides and can see predators more easily.
- Which of these categories would your mammal belong to? Answers may vary.
- Nocturnal species often have eyes that are proportionally larger than diurnal species to allow for better nighttime vision. Do you think your mammal is a nocturnal species?
  ☐ yes ☐ no Answers may vary.

V. Examine the teeth of your mammal skull and record the number of teeth that would fit into each of these three general categories (if some teeth are missing and you see only sockets, try to determine their type based on the teeth that remain).

____ incisors ____ canines ____ molars

- After washing your hands, count the teeth in your own mouth and record the numbers here.

____ incisors ____ canines ____ molars

- Based on the number, size, and arrangement of the teeth on the skull, would you say this mammal is an herbivore, carnivore, or omnivore? Answers may vary.

Studying Local Mammals

R E O

I. Prepare a list of five mammals native to your area.
  - Be specific. (The term *mouse* is not specific enough. *Field mouse* and *deer mouse* are specific enough for this exercise.)
  - Try to list animals from five different orders.

II. Write a brief description of each mammal.
  - Each description should be about one page long.
  - Include in each description the following details:
    - Type of teeth, food, feeding time, seasonal changes in diet
    - Preferred home sites, type of home built, number of young, time of year young are born, time it takes young to mature
    - What the animal does during the various seasons
    - Ecological significance, whether the mammal helps or harms human interests
  - Obtain illustrations of each mammal if possible and include them with your reports.

Name________________________

Date________________ Hour__________

19
Succession and Pollution

Materials

- sterile (boiled) pond or spring water
- dried plant material from a pond
- small all-glass aquariums or large (quart) jars with lids
- microscopes
- dropping pipets
- slides
- coverslips
- fertilizer
- algae cultures
- protozoan cultures
- baking soda
- vinegar
- powdered lime
- Hydrion (pH) test papers
- hydrochloric acid

Goals

- To observe succession in a microcosm
- To observe the effects of various pollutants upon succession

Succession is the predictable change of a biotic community over a period of time. Succession progresses through a series of stages to the climax stage for that particular area. In this exercise you will set up an ecosystem in a jar. A small artificial environment is sometimes called a microcosm. A microcosm will progress through various stages and, if permitted to continue long enough, will conclude in a climax. Unless the microcosm is managed by human intervention in the later stages of succession, the artificiality will result in the death (one form of climax) of all the organisms. Lack of space and lack of a wide enough variety of populations in the microcosm prevent the complete cycling of the various substances that exist in natural ecosystems.

Natural succession of an area can, however, be altered by intervention. In the second part of this laboratory exercise, several microcosms will be set up, different factors introduced, and the successions taking place in the microcosms compared.

Setting Up an Aquatic Microcosm

- Clean a one-gallon glass aquarium or a jar with a lid. Use salt as a cleansing agent to make sure there is no soap film.
- Fill the container half-full of sterile (boiled) pond or spring water.
- Place a handful of dried grass, leaves, or other plant material obtained from the edge of a pond into the water.
- Cover the container (a piece of glass placed over the opening is good) and set it in a well-lighted area (but not in direct sunlight).

R E O Observing Succession in an Aquatic Microcosm

I. After the aquatic microcosm has been set up for two or three days, make the following observations and record the data you obtain on a classroom chart like the one illustrated on page L163.
- Record statistics about the microcosm.
  - Do not disturb the microcosm as you make these observations.
  - Record the temperature (without stirring the microcosm).
  - Place a drop of the microcosm on a Hydrion test paper. Record the pH.
  - Turbidity is the cloudiness of the water. Indicate not only the cloudiness of the water but also the color of the water.
- Record statistics about the organisms in the microcosm.
  - Groups of students will be assigned to make and observe wet mounts from different areas of the microcosm.

See page 163 for Notes on Materials.

Microcosms do not always cooperate. You may want to have the class set up several (or set up one or two yourself) so that you will be able to replace one if it happens to go bad. This will add extra time, as you will need to follow the succession from the start on multiple microcosms; but it adds additional data for comparison, even if they all survive.

The lids or glass plates covering the microcosms help prevent evaporation. Any condensation on the lid should be returned to the jar. If your classroom is exceptionally dry and evaporation is a problem, mark the water level on the outside of the jar at the beginning of the experiment and add distilled water now and then to return the fluid content to that point. (Allow time for the fluid to settle before the next observation.)

If you are doing this exercise as a class project, consider having certain groups of students do certain observations. For example, if one group of students always tests the pH, measures the temperature, and records the turbidity, the group can become experienced at these skills and do them quickly. The groups observing the organisms at different levels can also become proficient. This method also reduces the number of variables in the experiment.

Introduction

This exercise, though rewarding, is time consuming. It is best conducted over a period of several weeks, taking the observations every second to third day.

It is important to begin the exercise early enough. Plan ahead so that the class will be making the final observations during their study of the chapter on ecology, or else the results will not be of much value to them.

Required / Extra / Omit

You may wish to do only the succession or only the pollution section. If you do only one part as a class, the succession part is recommended. The other section can be used as a group project for extra credit.

Your plan for doing this exercise (as a group project, extra credit, or as a required class project) will determine which parts are required. For example, you may want to consider the pollution section (pp. L163–L164) as extra credit for a class but required for a group.

Unless you have an extremely dedicated student who has plenty of time, it is best not to permit this exercise to be done by an individual.

If you are doing this exercise as a class project, make the bulletin board into an observation chart.

- ❖ One group will obtain the material for its wet mount from the surface of the microcosm, another from the middle, and another from the bottom. Disturb the microcosm as little as possible.
- ❖ Although each group may make and observe several slides, only one entry for each microcosmic area should be made on the chart.

○ Identify as many of the organisms as you can.

- ❖ Use a pictorial key to identify pond organisms or protozoans, if necessary.
- ❖ If you cannot locate the name of an organism you have found, make a reference sketch of it and assign it a number.
- ❖ Record the name or number of the organism on the chart and indicate whether the organism was very abundant, abundant, rare, or very rare in the material on your slide.

○ Do a specimen count.

- ❖ With a microscope focused on the populated area of your slide, count for fifteen seconds the organisms you see in your microscope field. Include any that move into the field while you are counting as well as those that were there when you started.
- ❖ Moving the slide slightly each time, repeat the procedure three more times.
- ❖ Average your results and record your fifteen-second specimen count on the classroom chart.

II. Every other day for two or three weeks, repeat the observations and record your results on the chart. You should be able to complete this during the first few minutes of class.

III. Answer the following questions concerning your class's observations.

- Regarding the number and types of organisms
  - ○ As the microcosm progresses toward its climax stage, how does its population change?
    ☐ increases ☐ decreases
  - ○ As the microcosm progresses towards its climax, are there more or fewer types of organisms?
    ☐ more ☐ fewer
  - ○ What progression of the number and type of organisms would you expect in an ecosystem passing through succession? In typical succession the pioneer stages have few species, with large populations of each. Those stages closer to climax will have many species, with smaller populations of each.

  Did your microcosm follow this progression? ☒ yes ☐ no usually yes
- Regarding the type of organism
  - ○ What types of organisms are most abundant in the pioneer stages? Answers will vary.
  - ○ What types of organisms are most abundant as the microcosm approaches climax?
    Answers will vary.
  - ○ Is this progression of organism types what you would expect in an ecosystem passing through succession? ☒ yes ☐ no

    Why or why not? In typical succession you would expect a large number of producers in the early stages with a few smaller consumers. In later stages you would expect more of a balance. However, that may not happen in certain cases.

Succession and Pollution as a Group Project

This whole laboratory exercise may work best as a group project or as a set of group projects. The microcosm(s) should be begun several weeks before the time you plan to cover succession and pollution. As the subject is discussed in class, the groups can give the results of their experimentation and observations for the class to analyze. If you decide to follow this suggestion, consider the following:

- Inform the students of your intention and, if the exercise is to be done for extra credit, have those interested read the material.
- Indicate that each member of the group will receive a specified amount of credit (or extra credit) if he is faithful in completing the project. If the exercise is extra credit, it will need to be done outside of class time.
- Ask for volunteers to make the observations. If enough students volunteer, only a few members of the group will need to make the observations on specific dates. Since different students will be making the observations, they must make adequate records of what they have seen. It is mandatory that they make diagrams of the organisms upon their initial observations.
- The entire group may need to meet once a week (under your supervision) to set up a schedule of observations and to carry on the project effectively.

- Conclusions
  - What can you conclude about the progression of the relative sizes of the individual organisms during succession? In typical succession the organisms are smaller in the pioneer stages and larger as succession continues.
  - What is the effect of the turbidity and pH of the microcosm on its number of organisms and its succession? In typical succession of a microcosm, the turbidity and pH will increase as succession continues. These two factors are the major causes of changes in populations. Often the death of the organisms in a microcosm is due to the rise of the pH.

Microcosm Observations

Date	Temperature	pH	Turbidity	Organisms	Specimen Count
2/14 Day 3	32° C	8	Little turbidity, white material in water.	Top: 1. (small circular algae)—abundant 2. Paramecium—rare 3. Small flagellate—abundant Middle: 4. Paramecium—rare Bottom: 5. Amoeba—rare 6. Small flagellate—abundant	Top 5 Middle 2 Bottom 8
2/16 Day 5	33°C	8.3	Little turbidity	Top: 1. (small circular algae)—abun…	Top 8

Observing Pollution and Succession

In an ecosystem passing through succession, a pollutant may be defined as any substance or factor that alters normal succession. In the following exercise you are asked to add a single pollutant to various microcosms and note how it affects the succession of each microcosm.

I. Prepare an aquatic microcosm as described in the box on page L161.

II. When the microcosm is two or three days old, divide it.
- Thoroughly mix the microcosm to distribute the organisms equally.
- While the culture is mixed, divide it into four or five equal portions. Each portion will make up one small microcosm.
- Place each portion in a jar large enough to be only half filled.

III. Select and introduce pollutants.
- Organisms are a form of pollutant. Introduce to one of the small microcosms a few of a specific type of organism from an individual laboratory culture of algae, protozoans, or small aquatic organisms (*Daphnia*, for example).

When obtaining vegetation from a pond, obtain emergent plants, plants floating or rooted in the water, and plants that are lying on the bottom. Also, try to include some pond scum (algae) with the vegetation. Mix the plant materials thoroughly and leave them in a shallow pan outdoors in the shade to air-dry. Do not overheat the materials. When they are dry, store them in a cool, dry place until you are ready to use them.

Broad-spectrum pH test papers, like those used to test aquarium water, are recommended for this exercise. These test papers and various types of freshwater pH test kits are available at some pet shops.

If you use live cultures of protozoans or algae for the second portion of the lab, select one of the types used in Lab 11.

Consider expanding this experiment with better equipment. Water quality test kits are available from suppliers of scientific materials. These kits can be used to supply precise data on the various factors (chemicals, minerals, and others) and the concentrations found in your microcosm. To use this data to determine the succession of your microcosm, first do research to find out exactly what organisms you have in your microcosm. Then determine how each organism helps to increase or decrease factor concentration, thus affecting your microcosm. Finally, compile your knowledge of the factors, the organisms, and the progressive effects of these different organisms on the factors. You can then estimate when a particular organism, because of its intolerance for a newly developed amount of some factor, will die out.

Allow the students to choose the pollution factors. If some specific factor has been in the news recently, they may want to try it. Some factors work well (acid rain, heat, phosphates), but some do not (nuclear wastes).

Consider placing different amounts of the same pollutant into various small microcosms. For example, three drops of vinegar in one microcosm and three tablespoons of vinegar in another should elicit different reactions.

- Another way to pollute the microcosms is to introduce a factor that will alter the physical environment. Consider adding a small quantity of one of these: vinegar (an acid), soluble plant food (nutrients), baking soda (a base), powdered lime, or hydrochloric acid. (You may need to add a little more of the substance every few days.)
- Another pollutant is the abundance of a physical environmental factor. Consider placing one of the small microcosms in direct sunlight, another in a dark cabinet, one near a heater or in a cold closet. Also consider adding sterile water to dilute the microcosm by doubling its volume.
- Be sure to keep at least one of the small microcosms as a control and treat it the same way you treated the large microcosm in the previous experiment.

IV. Observe and keep records for each of the small microcosms.

V. Write a summary of the results.

- Write a summary for each microcosm, telling of its contents and progression.
- Compare the microcosms, pointing out their differences.
- Offer probable explanations for the differences observed in the various microcosms.

Name______________________

Date______________ Hour________

20a
Readings on the Human Body Systems

Materials
- magazines
- 3 × 5 cards (ten to thirty)

Goals
- To research topics of human anatomy or physiology
- To learn material beyond what is covered in class
- To enrich class discussions

For this exercise you will read magazine articles on many aspects of each of the human systems. You will then write a brief report on each of these articles. This activity will help you learn more about the human body systems that interest you most.

I. Read articles about the human body systems (or parts of the systems).
- Find articles in magazines and on the Internet.
  - Look in the *Reader's Guide to Periodical Literature*, available in most libraries. Look under such topics as human anatomy or under a particular disease, such as bone cancer or arthritis. (Topics such as skeleton or skeletal system are general, and you may not find articles listed under them.)
  - Do not report on encyclopedia articles.
  - Do not read Internet articles that are on nonacademic sites. (If you are not sure about the site, ask your teacher for help.)
  - Choose an article of three or four pages (not including pictures). If an article is more than eight pages, it can count as two articles.
  - Recommend good articles to other students. (They must read the article for themselves, of course.)
  - Stop reading an article that is too simple or too difficult and find another.
- Read one article for each of the ten human body systems.
- Read extra articles if you wish.
  - Each article above the required number adds one point to the lab grade.
    - Ten articles (the required number) earn a grade of C.
    - Twenty articles earn a grade of B.
    - Thirty articles earn a grade of A. No extra points are given for more than thirty articles.
  - Read no more than five articles on any one body system.

II. Write a review of each article.
- Use a separate 3 × 5 card for each article.
- Use only one card for each report. Do not use extra cards to make long reports.
- Follow the format illustrated in Diagram 20a.1.
- Provide the following information in this order:
  1. *Title of article* (top line, left side). Indent on the second line if the title is long.
  2. *Human system* (top line, right side). Underline it and then write your name underneath the line.
  3. *Name of author(s)* (second line, left side).
  4. *Name of magazine* (third line, left side).
  5. *Date of article's publication*, not the date you read it (third line, right side).
  6. *Page numbers* of article (fourth line, left side). List the page numbers, not how many pages there were.
  7. *Illustrations* (fourth line, right side). List the number and types.
  8. *Material discussed* in the article. Use the remainder of the front side with the first line indented. The back of the card can be used if necessary.
  9. *Evaluation* of the article using the following scale: 1–2 very poor (you learned very little from the article); 3–4 good; 5 excellent. Write your evaluation in the lower right-hand corner and circle it.

Some teachers keep a file of good articles that they make available to students. If you do this, develop a sign-out system or require that the articles be used only in the classroom. Otherwise your articles may disappear.

Consider limiting the number of articles a student can have from one source.

INTRODUCTION

Most students have an interest in some particular field of human anatomy and physiology, whether it be new developments in the treatment of disease processes or the long-term effects of certain sports on the body (e.g., the effect of long-distance running on the feet or of repeatedly heading soccer balls). When discussing this assignment, approach it with a positive attitude. Tell the students, "Here is your chance to learn things about the human body you have always wanted to know and to get credit for learning them." Encourage them to do their readings on topics that are current and interesting.

Required / Extra / Omit

You can adjust the length of this assignment by requiring more or fewer articles for different grades.

Be strict on the card format the first time or two that you check them. You will not have to check as carefully in the future if you establish the standard in the beginning.

Allow the students to exchange the titles of articles that they enjoyed. They should *not* exchange cards.

Have a student draw a red line around the page numbers on his card if he has read an article more than eight pages long. This will call the number of pages to your attention as you check his cards, reminding you to give him credit for two articles.

Tell students to leave their reading cards upside down on their desks while they are taking the test. Go around and check the cards to make sure that the students are following the proper form and that they have all the required cards.

Have a space on the test paper where the student can indicate whether he has read the required articles for that day's test. Subtract points (as if a question or two were missed) from the test score of a student who does not have his cards.

Digestive — 2
1 — "The Vitamins You Need" Joe Student
3 — by Dr. Tom Hartman and Dr. Mary Klutz
4 — Junior Science Journal March 1978 — 5
6 — pages 43-45, 47 1 Drawing, 2 Photos — 7
8 — The article discussed the two major types of vitamins. We know very little about minimum daily requirements of vitamins. Some physicians believe there are many essential vitamins we don't even know about.
(4) — 9

20a.1
Sample article card

III. Turn in your review.
- Bring the card for each system on the test date for that system. The article is required reading for that test. The card will be checked and returned.
- Turn in the entire collection of article cards when you turn in your laboratory notebook.

It is recommended that a record of the articles read be kept so that you will know at a glance which ones are yet to be completed. The following table can be used.

System	Required	Extra
Skeletal	☐	☐ ☐ ☐ ☐
Integumentary	☐	☐ ☐ ☐ ☐
Muscular	☐	☐ ☐ ☐ ☐
Digestive	☐	☐ ☐ ☐ ☐
Respiratory	☐	☐ ☐ ☐ ☐
Circulatory	☐	☐ ☐ ☐ ☐
Excretory	☐	☐ ☐ ☐ ☐
Nervous	☐	☐ ☐ ☐ ☐
Endocrine	☐	☐ ☐ ☐ ☐
Reproductive	☐	☐ ☐ ☐ ☐

Name______________________

Date______________ Hour__________

20b The Human Body and the Skeletal System

Materials

- microscope
- preserved slides of dry ground bone, c.s.
- a model of a human skeleton
- skeleton diagrams
- colored pencils

Goals

- To learn the basic terms associated with anatomy
- To observe the typical microstructures and macrostructures of the skeletal system
- To learn the names of various bones and joints of the human body

The human body is an outstanding example of God's intricate design in creation. The more we study it, the more we understand that even the minutest details have significance. In this laboratory exercise you will learn the names of some of the obvious parts of the body and look at some details regarding the skeletal system.

Quality plastic life-sized skeletons are as effective in high school classrooms as the real ones. Plastic skeletons usually cost less than natural ones, and they are considerably more durable, making them practical for student use.

Wall charts of the bones of the human body may be used instead of a skeleton. You may be able to obtain these from your physician (charts such as these are often given away by sales representatives of various drug companies or surgical equipment distributors).

R E O

Terms of Human Anatomy

Label all of the following terms on one (or both) of the diagrams (20b.1).

I. Direction (indicate by using arrows on the diagrams): anterior, posterior, superior, inferior, medial, lateral, transverse, deep, superficial, proximal, and distal

II. Cavities: cranial, buccal, nasal, thoracic, abdominal, pelvic

III. Areas: pectoral, cervical, brachial, lumbar, trunk, thigh, calf, upper extremity, lower extremity, pelvis, and buttocks

The terms *upper extremity* and *lower extremity* are not used in the text. Tell the students to research these terms, or define the terms in a lecture.

Students sometimes have difficulty indicating the following labels on diagram 20b.1: medial, deep, superficial, proximal, distal, and cavity. Omit these labels or offer a few words of instruction. For example, cavities may be indicated by shading the appropriate areas on the diagram.

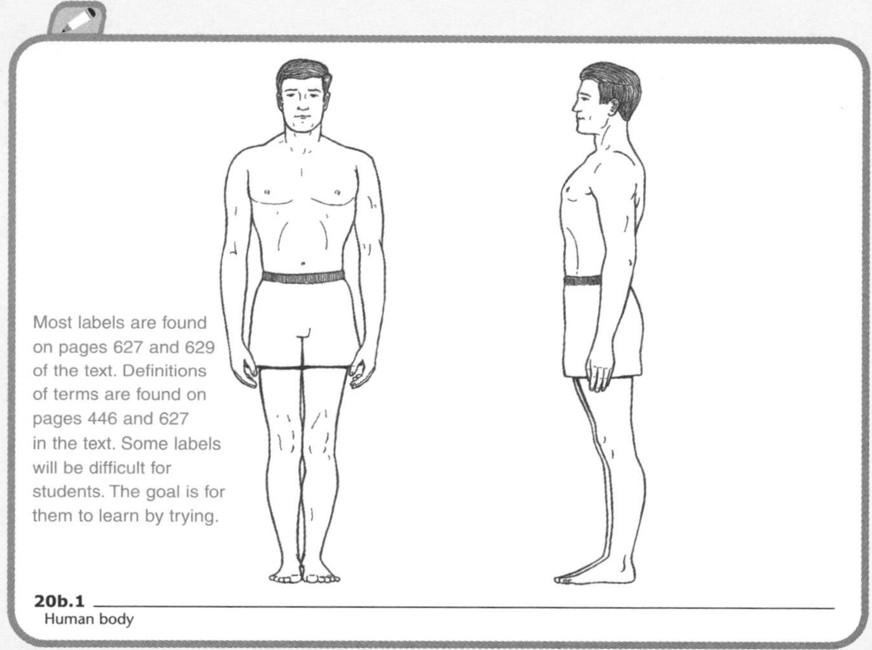

20b.1 Human body

Introduction

The main reason for this laboratory exercise is to give the students experience in using anatomical terms properly. These terms are often used by students but are not always understood. Through the activities of labeling diagrams, completing charts, and researching interesting structures, students should learn some of the material that is presented in this unit without having to memorize it.

Required / Extra / Omit

It is suggested that most of the exercise be required. Very little of it involves laboratory equipment.

If desired, the sesamoid bone section can be done for extra credit.

If the students learned a number of the major bones of the body in a junior-high life science course, you might have them learn all the bones and bone markings on pages 638–39. If, however, your students do not know a number of these structures already, you may need to trim the list considerably.

You may wish to combine Exercises 20b and 20c. See the box on the next page.

Dry ground bone is bone that was dried before it was mounted for microscopic viewing. Thus, although the Haversian canal is present, the Haversian blood vessel is not. The lacunae are there, but not the osteocytes. Tell the students that they are looking at bone that was dead and dried before it was made into a slide. This information should give them a clue as to what structures they will and will not see in a dry ground bone slide.

Students will not be able to copy from the text all the information needed to fill out the Joints of the Human Body chart in this laboratory exercise. Tell them that they will need to think carefully in order to come up with some of the answers.

The Skeletal System

The primary system of support is the skeleton. The skeleton includes the bones, ligaments, joints, and cartilage of the body. We shall begin with a microscopic study of bone and then proceed to a study of the major structures of the skeleton.

Microstructures

I. Observe the preserved slide of dry ground bone, c.s, and draw a diagram in Area A.

II. Label a complete Haversian system. Include the Haversian canal, lamellae, lacunae, canaliculi, and any other structures observed in the preserved specimen.

Macrostructures

I. Learn the bone names and markings indicated on pages 638–39 of the text. (Omit those indicated by the instructor.)
- Locate these bones on the skeleton in the laboratory.
- Label them if they are shown on Diagram 20b.2. Below the diagrams, list the bones not shown.

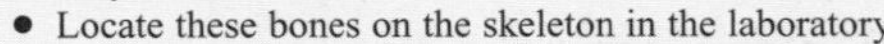

II. Learn the types of joints. Fill in the missing information on the Joints of the Human Body chart.

Joints of the Human Body

Kind	Type	Movement	Examples
Movable	Ball-and-socket	Free movement inside a cone (circumduction)	1. Shoulder 2. Hip
Movable	Hinge	Flexion and extension on one plane	1. Elbow (humerus, ulna) 2. Phalanges or knee
Movable	Pivot	Rotation	1. Humerus and radius 2. Atlas and axis
Movable	Gliding	Slight movements—often weak movements	1. Thumb 2. Wrist
Slightly movable	Cartilaginous	Bending, twisting, and slight compression	1. Between vertebrae 2. Pubic symphysis
Immovable	Suture or fibrous	No movement—two bones have grown together	1. Skull sutures 2. Union of epiphysis and shaft

Scheduling Laboratory Exercises

Laboratory Exercises 20b and 20c can be combined into a single lab period by omitting the sesamoid bone section (p. L170), the drawings of cardiac and visceral muscles (p. L171), and the skin research and reports section (p. L174). Much of these laboratory exercises will need to be done outside of class. Be sure to point out to students which items will need to be done in class and which can be done at home.

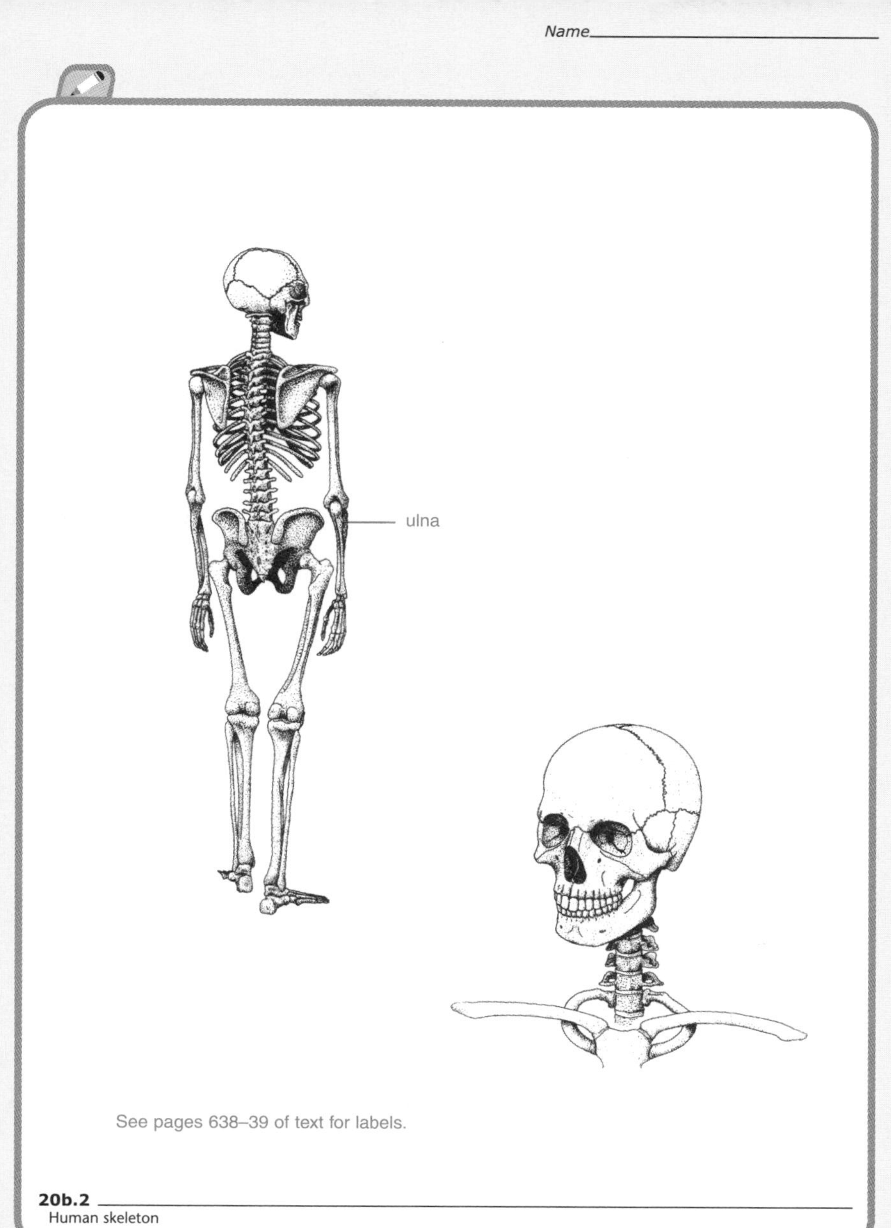

The Human Body and the Skeletal System L169

R E O

III. Do additional research on sesamoid bones. (NOTE: Although they are not always the same thing, sesamoid bones are sometimes called supernumerary bones.)

- What are sesamoid bones? Sesamoid bones are bones that are not present at birth but develop later in the tendons near the joints.
- How do they develop? Usually friction and pressure on a joint cause them to develop.
- List some examples of sesamoid bones. The kneecap and extra bones in joints of fingers and toes are examples of sesamoid bones.

Name________________________________

Date__________________ Hour__________

20c The Human Muscular and Integumentary Systems

Materials

- microscope
- preserved slides of human skin, c.s., skeletal (striated) muscle, cardiac muscle, and visceral (smooth) muscle
- human muscle diagrams
- colored pencils

Goals

- To observe the typical microstructures of the muscular and integumentary systems
- To learn the names, origins, insertions, and functions of some of the major human muscles

The human muscular system is a marvel of design. It permits not only movement but also various degrees of strength and extensive flexibility. Human skin is equally marvelous. It is tough enough to block out most substances that would invade our bodies, yet soft enough to permit sensation of minute changes in temperature, touch, and pressure—all this while remaining supple enough to bend virtually constantly without breaking. We are truly "wonderfully made" (Ps. 139:14).

The Muscular System

The primary system of movement is the muscular system. We will begin by studying the structures of muscular tissue and then study some of the major muscles of the human body.

Microstructures

R E O

I. Observe a preserved slide of a section of skeletal muscle. In Area A draw a diagram of what you see. Label all the structures you observe.

A

B

R E O

II. Observe the preserved slides of visceral and cardiac muscle. In Area B draw a diagram of what you see. Label all the structures you observe.

The skin slides must be of human skin; however, the various muscle slides can come from any mammal.

Good charts of the human muscles, both front and back, are recommended. Although life-sized charts are expensive, they are exceptionally good in the classroom and are ideal for use with this laboratory exercise.

When the students are observing muscle, they should see nuclei and possibly striations. Actin and myosin as individual proteins cannot be seen using a light microscope.

Introduction

The main reason for this laboratory exercise is to give the students experience in working with the muscles and skin so that they can learn the names and structures without having to memorize them.

Required / Extra / Omit

It is suggested that most of the exercise be required. Very little of it requires laboratory equipment.

Sections that can be done for extra credit include the cardiac and visceral muscle drawings (p. L171), the skin microscope observations (p. L173), and the reports on skin research (p. L174).

The reports on various structures, diseases, or disorders of the human skin can be very profitable if they are assigned in advance. Some teachers may find it best to assign different topics to groups of students and then have each group present an oral report. (You may wish to consult Exercise 16c and corresponding teacher notes for some ideas regarding having groups of students present oral reports.) Other teachers may find it best to prepare a list of topics for all students to select from and prepare written reports on. Another use of the section would be to have those students who want extra credit prepare a written report on an approved topic related to skin. You can select the best ones to be presented as oral reports, awarding additional extra credit for those who give good oral reports to the class.

You may wish to combine Laboratory Exercises 20b and 20c. See the box on page 168.

III. Fill in the missing spaces in The Three Types of Muscles chart.

The Three Types of Muscles			
Type	**Other names**	**Control**	**Location (L.) and function (F.)**
Skeletal	1. Striated 2. Voluntary	☒ Conscious ☐ Subconscious	L. Attached to bones and bony parts F. Moves body
Visceral	1. Smooth 2. Involuntary	☐ Conscious ☒ Subconscious	L. Lines internal ogans and ducts F. Moves substances internally
Cardiac	Heart	☐ Conscious ☒ Subconscious	L. The heart F. Pumps blood

Macrostructures

I. Study carefully the information on pages 650–52 of the text regarding the attachments and naming of muscles.

II. Answer the following questions:

- What is the linea alba? It is a ligament.
- Where is it located? It runs from the sternum to the pubic bones.
- Where is the Achilles tendon? It extends from the distal gastrocnemius to the heel bone.

Students may need to do research to determine that the linea alba is a ligament.

III. Learn the name, origin, insertion, and function for each of the human muscles listed on page 651. Include the diaphragm, which is discussed on pages 559 and 658. Omit those muscles indicated by the instructor.

- The following suggestions are helpful when learning the required muscles:
  - Locate each of the muscles on your body by putting your hand over it and then performing its function. You should be able to feel the muscle working.
  - Locate the origin and insertion while you perform the muscle's function. The function should seem logical when you know the origin and insertion.
  - Consult a human muscle chart to make sure you have located the origin and insertion correctly. Note carefully the location of the muscle.
- On the human body outlines (Diagram 20c.1), use colored pencils to sketch and label each of the muscles you are assigned to know. (NOTE: One diagram is a dorsal view, and the other is ventral, but both are in anatomical position.)

The diaphragm originates on the sternum, ribs, and lower vertebrae and inserts on the central tendon of the diaphragm. Its function is to increase the space of the thoracic cavity during respiration.

Name______________________________

See page 652 of text for labels and muscle drawings.

Ventral

Dorsal

20c.1 ______________________________
Human muscles

The Integumentary System

The primary function of the integumentary system is protection. Several varied types of skin are found on the body. The thick, tough skin of the palms of the hands and the soles of the feet is considerably different from the thin skin of the face, the arms, and the abdomen.

R E O **Observe Human Skin**

Observe a preserved slide of human skin. In Area C draw and label the structures you are able to identify.

Students often find the drawing of muscles in the body outlines a little confusing. Consider drawing the biceps brachii in a human body outline on the overhead projector. Discuss what the students need to know to make the drawing and what they should learn as they are doing the drawing. Try to help them understand that this is not to be a busywork assignment but an assignment that will help them learn the muscles you have selected for them to know.

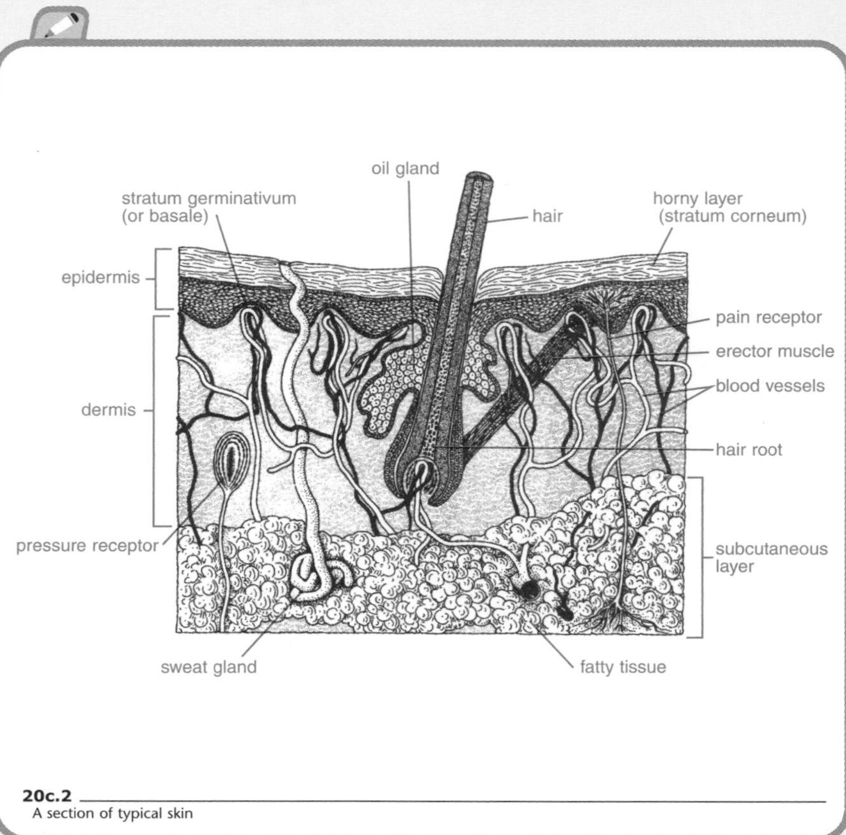

20c.2
A section of typical skin

Label Structures of Human Skin

Identify and label as many structures as possible in Diagram 20c.2.

Prepare a Report About Human Skin

I. Read about some skin-related topic or problem.
- Burns, tans, skin cancer, baldness, warts, moles, birthmarks, oily skin, dry skin, skin transplants, skin wrinkles, aging of the skin, and face-lifts are possible topics.
- Consult at least three sources and read at least five pages regarding your topic.

II. Prepare a brief report based on your research.
- Written reports must be at least one hundred words long and should be submitted with this lab.
- Oral reports should be three to five minutes long and will be assigned in place of written reports for some students.

Name____________________________

Date__________________ Hour__________

21a The Human Respiratory System

Materials

- lung volume bag
- rubber band
- mouthpiece
- paper towels
- stethoscope
- isopropyl (rubbing) alcohol

Goals

- To measure average lung capacity
- To learn structures of the respiratory system

The first section of this laboratory exercise will be done as a class demonstration. Various lung volume tests will supply the data to use in answering the questions. Following the lung volume demonstration there are several exercises that deal with the structures of the respiratory system.

> A water-displacement spirometer is a good piece of equipment to have, but it is very expensive. If you have access to one, you can modify the lung volume experiments to use it.
>
> Lung volume bags and kits are available from suppliers of scientific materials.

Air Volume Measurement

R E O

A **spirometer** is a device used to measure the volume of air a person exhales. A long plastic bag calibrated in liters may be used instead of the relatively expensive spirometer. The lung volume bag is not as accurate, but for the purposes of this exercise it will serve well.

Preparing a Lung Volume Bag

I. Select three students of average size and select an assistant for each.

II. Prepare the lung volume bags.
- Insert the mouthpiece partway into the open end of the lung volume bag and secure it with a rubber band. (See Diagram 21a.1.)
- Have the assistant sit down.
- Slide the bag slowly across the assistant's knee while he presses the bag with a paper towel. This will remove all air from the lung volume bag. (See Diagram 21a.1.)

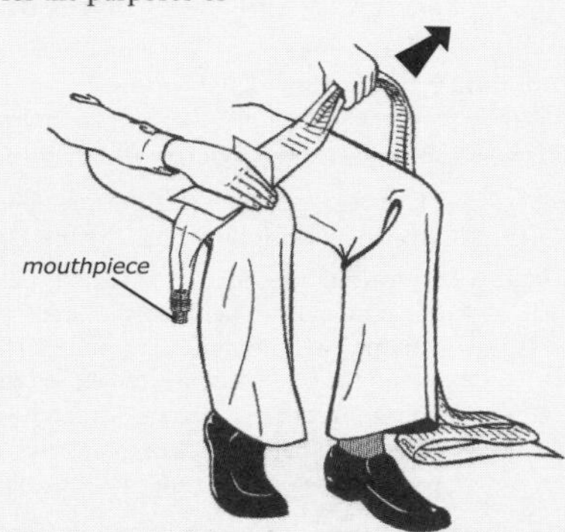

21a.1
How to empty a lung volume bag

Lung volume bags are usually not designed for all the lung capacity measurements taken in this exercise. Thus some of the experimental results will not be quite as accurate as they would be if a spirometer and different techniques were used.

Measuring Lung Volume

I. Measure tidal volume.
- Instruct the person being tested to breathe in a normal breath, pinch his nose, put the lung volume bag mouthpiece in his mouth, and breathe out a normal breath.
- Ask the assistant to take the bag and hold it closed while sliding it across his knee and pressing it with a paper towel in order to force all the air to the closed end.
- Record the data on the chalkboard. Students should fill in their Lung Volume charts from the data on the chalkboard.
- Empty the lung volume bag, using the procedure described earlier.
- Have each person tested perform this experiment two more times. Record each volume in the proper space of the Lung Volume chart.

II. Measure expiratory reserve volume.
- Have the person being tested breathe in a normal breath, breathe out a normal breath, pinch his nose, put the lung volume bag mouthpiece in his mouth, and breathe out as much as possible.
- Using the procedure described in the instructions for measuring tidal volume, measure the air and record the reading for each person.

Demonstrate how to use the lung volume bag before you ask for volunteer "breathers" and "assistants."

Because the students know that they are being tested, they often exaggerate their breathing. Emphasize that this is not a contest and that the data should be as accurate as possible. Do not be surprised, however, if your students have "normal" breath volumes that are several times larger than average.

A student should record the information on a chart (see p. L176), on the chalkboard, or on the overhead projector as the assistants call it out. This chart can also serve as your record when you grade the exercises.

Introduction

This exercise includes an enjoyable demonstration that takes about fifteen to twenty minutes of class time and an interesting activity involving the use of a stethoscope for listening to breath sounds and the voice. The rest of the exercise can be done outside of class. The experience of labeling the diagram helps the students learn the structures and functions of the respiratory system.

Scheduling Laboratory Exercises

The laboratory exercises dealing with respiration and digestion (21a and 21b) can easily be combined into a demonstration and laboratory activity period. By having abundant labeling and computing for students to do, one can have fewer stethoscopes and merely encourage students to pass them around.

Required / Extra / Omit

It is suggested that the entire laboratory exercise be required.

You may want to combine Exercises 21a and 21b into an hour-long lab.

Lung Volume

Tidal Volume

Person A	Person B	Person C	Average
1. ______	1. ______	1. ______	______ mL
2. ______	2. ______	2. ______	or
3. ______	3. ______	3. ______	______ L

Expiratory Reserve Volume

Person A	Person B	Person C	Average
1. ______	1. ______	1. ______	______ mL
2. ______	2. ______	2. ______	or
3. ______	3. ______	3. ______	______ L

Vital Capacity

Person A	Person B	Person C	Average
1. ______	1. ______	1. ______	______ mL
2. ______	2. ______	2. ______	or
3. ______	3. ______	3. ______	______ L

- Have each person tested perform this experiment two more times. Record each volume in the proper space of the Lung Volume chart.

III. Measure vital capacity.
- Have the person being tested breathe in as much as he possibly can, pinch his nose, put the lung volume bag mouthpiece in his mouth, and breathe out as much as possible.
- Using the procedure described in the instructions for measuring tidal volume, force the air to the bottom of the bag and record the reading for each person.
- Have each person tested repeat this experiment two more times. Record each volume in the proper space of the Lung Volume chart.

Computing Average Lung Capacities

I. Take all your data and determine averages for the following volumes. (Be careful to use the correct units.)
- Tidal volume: approximately 500 mL
- Expiratory reserve volume: approximately 1000 mL
- Vital capacity: approximately 4500 mL

II. Using these averages, compute the inspiratory reserve volume: approximately 3000 mL.

III. Assuming a residual volume of 1000 mL, what would be the average total lung capacity of the people tested? approximately 5500 mL

IV. According to the information on page 659 of the text, are these lung volume results considered average? ☐ yes ☐ no If not, what factors might account for the difference? Size of students, athletic ability, and diseases and disorders such as asthma can affect lung volume. Also, the testing procedure is not completely accurate.

Students should be able to compute the inspiratory reserve volume. The text states that vital capacity equals tidal volume plus inspiratory reserve volume plus expiratory reserve volume. By using algebra, students can calculate that vital capacity minus tidal volume minus expiratory reserve volume equals inspiratory reserve volume.

Name______________________________

Structures of the Respiratory System

R E O

I. Label Diagram 21a.2 as completely as possible.

II. Under each label, indicate what happens to air in that structure. Enclose this information in parentheses.

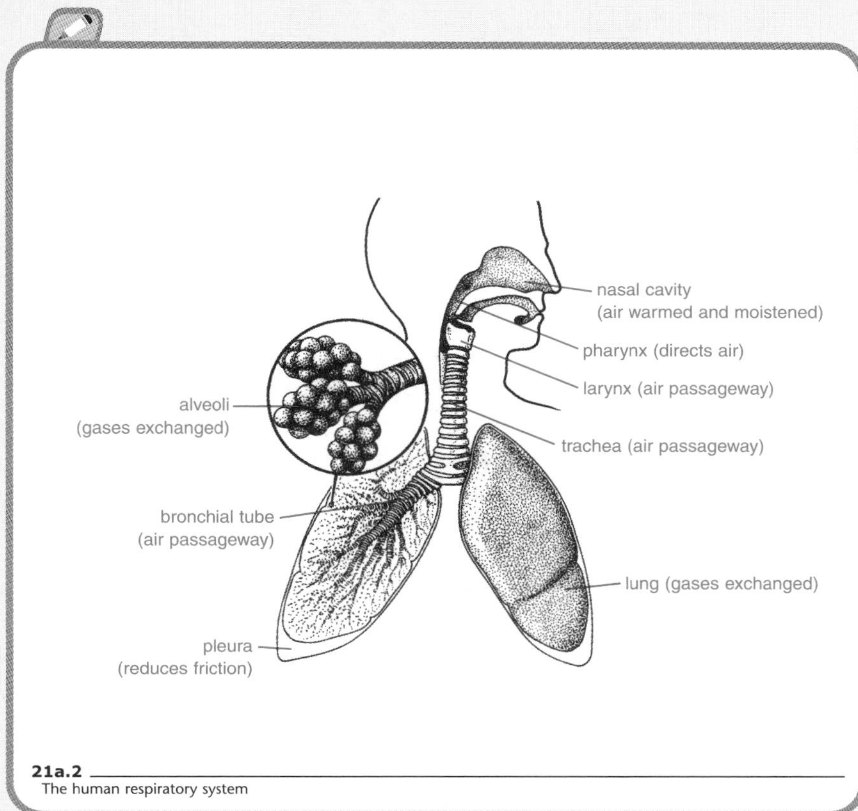

21a.2
The human respiratory system

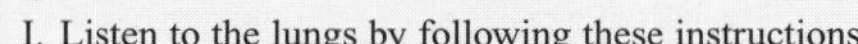

Listening to Your Lungs

Air rushing into and out of healthy respiratory structures makes various sounds. Many respiratory problems cause various abnormal sounds that a physician can hear using a stethoscope. It is hoped that you will not hear abnormal respiratory sounds when listening to your lab partner's breathing. It can be interesting, however, to listen to normal sounds of the respiratory system.

R E O

I. Listen to the lungs by following these instructions:
- Using a tissue and alcohol, clean the earpieces of a stethoscope.
- Place the stethoscope in your ears, allowing the tubes to hang freely and being careful not to hit the diaphragm on hard objects. (The noise can be very loud.)

- Place the diaphragm of the stethoscope on your lab partner's back and press lightly as he breathes normally.
- Listen to a normal breath or two in areas A–F as labeled on Diagram 21a.3. Describe the sounds you hear.

Answers will vary.

21a.3
Areas to place stethoscope

- Are the sounds you hear different in different areas? Answers will vary.
- Listen to a deep breath in the same areas. Do you hear a difference? ☐ yes ☐ no If so, describe the difference and tell what may account for it. There should be little difference in a normal, healthy person.
- Listen to areas A and E while the person coughs. Describe what you hear.
Answers will vary.
- Listen to areas A and E while the person talks. Describe what you hear.
Answers will vary. One should hear the person's voice but with a different timbre.

R E O

II. Using a stethoscope, listen to your partner's throat.
- Listen to your lab partner's breathing by placing the stethoscope in area G.
- Listen to your lab partner's voice in the same area.
- Describe what you heard. Answers will vary. One should hear little while the person is breathing and should hear the person's voice but with a different timbre when he is speaking.

Name____________________

Date____________ Hour________

21b
The Human Digestive System

Materials
none

The first part of this laboratory exercise involves identifying and labeling structures of the human digestive system and completing a chart dealing with human digestion. The last part of the exercise deals with calories, weight gain, and weight loss.

Goals

- To learn about the structures of the digestive system and the process of digestion in the human body
- To learn about calories and weight gain or loss

Structures of the Digestive System

I. Label Diagram 21b.1.
- Label as many structures as you can. You should have at least eleven structures labeled.
- Under each label indicate what activity of physical digestion happens in that structure. If the structure is not involved in physical digestion, give a brief statement of its function. Enclose this information in parentheses.

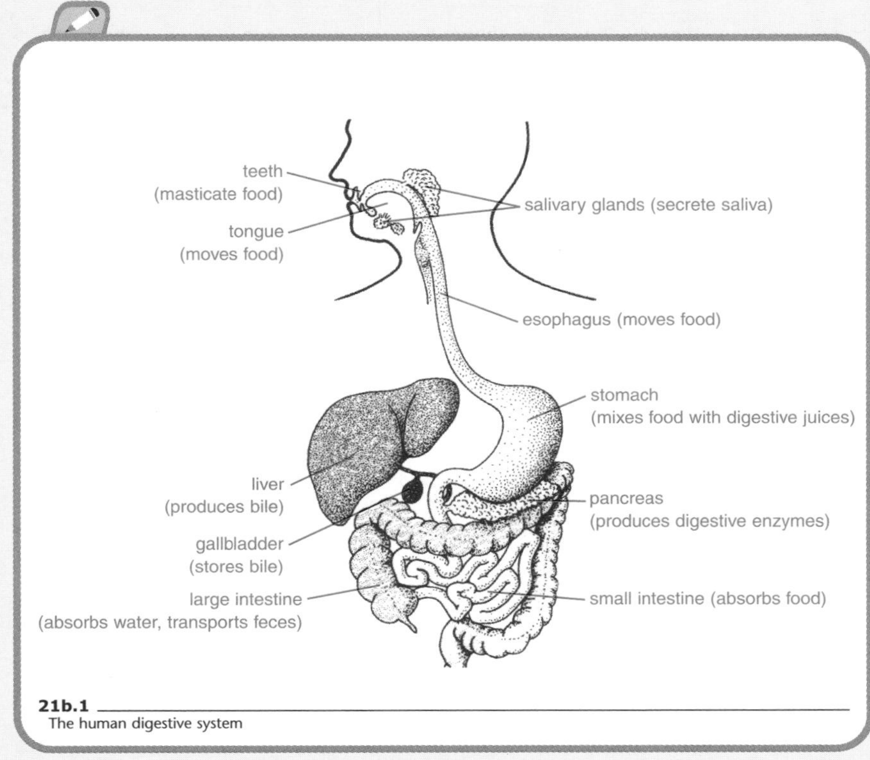

21b.1 ____________________
The human digestive system

INTRODUCTION

This exercise can all be done as homework since it requires only a pencil and the textbook (and possibly a calculator). The experience of labeling the diagram helps students learn the structures and functions of the digestive system. The problems involving calories and pounds are mathematical word problems designed to teach students the significance of the caloric value of their food and the caloric consumption of their activities.

Required / Extra / Omit

It is suggested that the entire laboratory exercise be required.

You may wish to combine these activities with Laboratory 21a. See the box on page 175.

It may be profitable to work the problems in the Calories and Pounds section (pp. L180–L182) orally in class rather than to assign them as homework.

Call the students' attention to the notes under the Chemical Digestion chart. They will need to be aware of this information before they can complete the chart accurately. You may also need to help them get started on this chart.

If you decide to work the problems in the Calories and Pounds section orally, you may want to work a sample problem and then divide the students into groups and have each group work on a different problem.

To complete these problems, use this conversion factor: 1 lb fat contains 3500 Cal. This is discussed in the text on page 676.

R E O

II. Fill in the Chemical Digestion chart. If certain foods undergo no chemical digestion in a particular area, draw a line through that space.

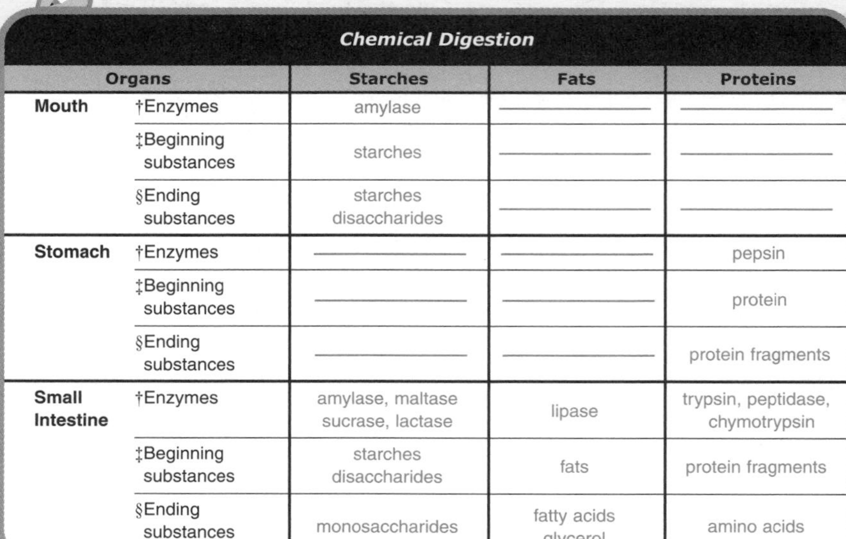

Chemical Digestion

Organs		Starches	Fats	Proteins
Mouth	†Enzymes	amylase	—	—
	‡Beginning substances	starches	—	—
	§Ending substances	starches disaccharides	—	—
Stomach	†Enzymes	—	—	pepsin
	‡Beginning substances	—	—	protein
	§Ending substances	—	—	protein fragments
Small Intestine	†Enzymes	amylase, maltase sucrase, lactase	lipase	trypsin, peptidase, chymotrypsin
	‡Beginning substances	starches disaccharides	fats	protein fragments
	§Ending substances	monosaccharides	fatty acids glycerol	amino acids

†List all the enzymes involved in chemical digestion in the proper spaces, regardless of the sequence in which they work.
‡List all the substances acted on by any of the enzymes listed.
§List the substances that result after all the enzymes act on the beginning substances you listed.

Calories and Pounds

Some people think that calories and pounds are different names for the same thing. This is not true. Calories are units of heat energy; pounds are units of weight. In the human body, however, calories and pounds are converted from one to the other. It is good to understand the relative proportions of calories contained in food to pounds of body weight.

There are many factors that could alter the numbers given in the following charts. For example, a person who is in poor physical condition or who is overweight will use more calories doing a particular physical activity. Some apples contain more sugar than others and thus would have more calories.

R E O

I. Use the figures in the chart Selected Foods and Calorie Values (p. L181) to answer the following questions.

- How many apples would one have to eat to gain a pound of body weight? 50 apples
- How many pats of butter (a pat is 1 T [tablespoon]) would one have to eat to gain a pound of body weight? 35 pats
- How many cups of ice cream would one have to eat to gain a pound of body weight? 11.9 cups
- How many cups of peanuts would one have to eat to gain a pound of body weight? 4.2 cups

Name________________________________

Selected Foods and Calorie Values

Food	Calories	Food	Calories
Fruits		**Meats, cont.**	
Apple (1 large)	70	Chicken, fried (half breast, 3.3 oz)	154
Banana (1 large)	85	Egg (1)	80
Cantaloupe ($\frac{1}{2}$)	40	Frankfurter (1)	155
Orange (1 large)	70	Hamburger, on bun (0.25 lb)	416
Raisins (1 cup)	460	Ocean perch, fried (3 oz)	195
Strawberries (1 cup)	55	**Seeds and Nuts**	
Watermelon (2 lb slice)	120	Almonds, shelled (1 cup)	850
Vegetables		Peanut butter (1 T)	90
Broccoli (1 cup)	60	Peanuts, shelled (1 cup)	840
Carrots, cooked (1 cup)	45	**Breads and Cakes**	
Celery stalk (8 in.)	5	Bread, white (1 slice)	62
Sweet corn (5 in. ear)	65	Cake, angel food (2 in. slice)	110
Cucumber (1 in. slice)	5	Cheesecake (4 oz)	215
Onions (1 in. slice)	80	Doughnut, sugar (1.8 oz)	233
Green peas (1 cup)	110	Pancake (4 in. diameter)	60
Pepper, green (1 raw)	15	Pie, Boston cream (3.3 oz)	329
Potato, baked (5 oz)	90	Pie, pumpkin (4 in. section)	265
Potatoes, French-fried (2 oz)	200	**Miscellaneous**	
Dairy Products		Cola (6 oz)	73
Butter or margarine (1 T)	100	Fudge (1 oz)	115
Cottage cheese (1 oz)	30	Honey (1 T)	60
Ice cream (1 cup)	295	Ketchup (1 T)	15
Milk, whole (1 cup)	165	Mayonnaise (1 T)	110
Yogurt (1 cup)	120	Pickle, dill (1 large)	15
Meats		Salad dressing, French (1 T)	90
Beef, roast (3 oz)	265	Soup, chicken (1 cup)	75
Beef stew (1 cup)	250	Sugar (1 T)	50

Calories Used for Selected Activities

Activity	Calories per hour	Activity	Calories per hour
Watching TV, reading	25	Walking (2.5 mph)	210
Driving car	50	Golfing, lawn mowing	250
Eating	50	Bowling	270
Sewing	50	Swimming (0.25 mph)	300
Typing	50	Volleyball, roller-skating	350
Washing dishes	75	Table tennis	360
Playing piano	75	Hiking	400
Brushing teeth or hair	100	Tennis	420
Dusting furniture	150	Shoveling	500
Mopping floors	200	Skiing	600
Bicycling (5.5 mph)	210	Running (10 mph)	900

II. Use the figures in the chart Calories Used for Selected Activities (p. L181) to answer the following questions.

- How many hours would one have to watch TV to lose a pound of body weight? (Hint: Look in your textbook to find out how many calories are equivalent to a pound of weight gain.) 140 hours
- How many hours would one have to wash dishes to lose a pound of body weight? 46.7 hours
- How many hours would one have to walk at 2.5 mph to lose a pound of body weight? 16.7 hours
- How many hours would one have to play volleyball to lose a pound of body weight? 10 hours
- How many hours would one have to run at 10 mph to lose a pound of body weight? 3.9 hours

III. Although many factors are involved in weight gain and loss, working the following problems will help you to see the relationship between the two. (Indicate whether there is a gain or a loss of weight and how many pounds are involved.)

- One day at breakfast, Tom read that the quantity of cereal he was consuming gave him a breakfast of 300 calories. He decided that two boiled eggs, two slices of toast with a quarter tablespoon of butter on each, and an orange would be a better breakfast. If Tom kept his other meals the same and did not change his amount of activity, what would be his weight change in one year? He would gain about 10.5 pounds.
- At the end of the school year, Maria discovered that her dresses were getting tight. She decided that for the thirteen weeks of summer vacation, she would invest the two hours a day she normally spent doing her school assignments in physical exercise. Maria decided that for six days a week she would spend one hour walking, a half hour in the pool swimming, and a half hour bicycling to and from the pool. If she does not change her food intake, how much weight change can she expect? She would lose 10 pounds.
- Jason enjoyed his summer job at the bank, but he noticed that for the two summers he had held that job he had gained about twenty pounds in thirteen weeks. He knew that he would do better in soccer if he could keep that weight off. Normally he had two sugar doughnuts at his morning break and another two at the afternoon break. He decided to substitute a cup of yogurt for each of these snacks. If all other factors remain the same, would the amount of weight Jason usually gains change? ☒ yes ☐ no Explain. He would still gain weight. The doughnuts accounted for about 17 pounds of weight gain per summer. The yogurt would account for about 4 pounds of weight gain. He should gain only about 7 pounds if he eats the yogurt instead.

Name____________________

Date______________ Hour__________

22a
Human Blood

Materials

- fresh blood (or simulated blood)
- glass slides
- Tallquist hemoglobin scale test booklet
- anti-A and anti-B human blood sera
- capillary tubes
- toothpicks
- microscope
- preserved slides of human blood
- sterile cotton gauze
- stopwatch or timer
- lancet

Goals

- To observe some of the clinically important characteristics of human blood
- To observe human blood cells

The circulatory system is one of the first to react to diseases and disorders in the body. The composition of the blood, the action of the heart, and the pressure of the blood in the blood vessels can give the physician a good idea of the physical well-being of his patient. Although not as sophisticated as modern medical laboratories, the following procedures form the basis for many of the diagnostic tests used to detect specific illnesses and conditions.

Your instructor will inform you if fresh or simulated blood will be used. If using fresh blood, the teacher will supply the blood for certain sections of this laboratory exercise and will perform a number of the procedures as demonstrations. If using simulated blood, you will be given additional instructions as needed.

Blood Types

Before a transfusion can be given, the blood must be accurately typed. If the wrong type is transfused, the recipient's blood may agglutinate, causing death. Blood is usually typed by testing it with sera. Blood typing serum is made from blood plasma; therefore, it contains only antibodies. Anti-A serum, then, contains anti-A antibodies and will cause blood containing A antigens to agglutinate. (See pp. 683–84 of your text.)

I. Answer the following questions regarding blood typing sera, antigens, and antibodies.

- What antigens would be found in anti-B serum? none
- What antibodies would be found in anti-B serum? B
- If the red blood cells agglutinate when anti-A serum is placed on the blood, what are the possible blood types for that person? A, AB
- If the red blood cells agglutinate when anti-A serum is placed on the blood and also when anti-B serum is placed on the blood, what blood types are possible for that person? AB
- If the red blood cells do not agglutinate when anti-A or anti-B serum is placed on the blood, what blood types are possible for that person? O

II. Your teacher will type a blood sample by following these procedures.

- Place two separate drops of blood from one person on either end of a clean, dry glass slide and lay the slide on a piece of paper that has the letter *A* marked near one end of the slide and the letter *B* marked near the other end.
- Without touching the pipet to the blood, place a drop of anti-A serum on the drop of blood closest to the letter *A*. Stir the drop of blood with a toothpick. Does the blood agglutinate? ☐ yes ☐ no

Always wear gloves (such as latex or vinyl) when working with blood or blood products. If using latex gloves, be aware that some students may have a latex allergy.

Do not touch a bleeding finger to anything except sterile gauze saturated with isopropyl alcohol.

When determining blood types, some people seek to help the blood agglutinate by adding more serum. One drop of serum per one drop of blood is all that is necessary. The absence of agglutination is just as significant as is agglutination.

Follow the manufacturer's instructions for storing the blood-typing sera; they may require refrigeration until the lab day and then may need to be kept in an ice water bath during the exercise.

Introduction

Although much can be learned in a high school classroom by the observation of blood, finger pricking for the observation of fresh blood has recently fallen from favor as an educational tool. The risk of infection is present any time the skin is broken, but since hepatitis and HIV infection are now more common (although not very likely in a high school laboratory), some educational authorities have recommended that fresh blood not be dealt with in high schools.

However, fresh blood can be dealt with safely in the high-school laboratory and has been for many years. (See pages A27–A28 for information about obtaining and handling blood in the classroom.) The decision to do sections of this laboratory activity and how or where to obtain the blood rests with you and your administration.

If you decide not to use fresh blood, you may still have the students observe and draw the preserved slide of human blood (see p. L185) and perform the typing exercise using simulated human blood; however, you cannot perform the hemoglobin or the clotting time exercises with simulated blood. Kits for blood typing that use simulated blood can be purchased from a supplier of scientific materials. If you decide to use one of these kits, you can easily modify the equipment list and the exercise using the instructions from the kit.

Required / Extra / Omit

If you are using fresh blood, it is recommended that all of the exercise except the observation of a preserved blood slide be done as demonstrations.

If time is a factor, you may wish to omit the blood clotting experiment (p. L186).

- On the blood closest to letter *B*, repeat the above operation using anti-B serum and a fresh toothpick. Does the blood agglutinate? ☐ yes ☐ no
- What type of blood was tested? Answers will vary depending on the person's blood type.
- What types of blood could safely receive the blood you tested? See chart on page 685.
- What types of blood could safely be given to the person you tested? See chart on page 685.

Hemoglobin Count

The amount of hemoglobin found in the blood determines its oxygen-carrying capacity. Because hemoglobin is a pigment, the amount of it in a quantity of blood can be measured by the color of the specimen. Although the Tallquist method has been replaced by more accurate methods of measuring hemoglobin, we will use it as a simple test.

I. Test a blood sample using the Tallquist hemoglobin count method. Follow these instructions.
- Place one drop of blood on half a section of a test paper from a Tallquist test booklet.
- Fold back the unused portion so that it absorbs the excess blood from the underside of the test paper.
- When the gloss of moisture has disappeared, match the color of the dry blood by moving it up and down behind the scale found in the test booklet. This comparison should be done in direct sunlight if possible.

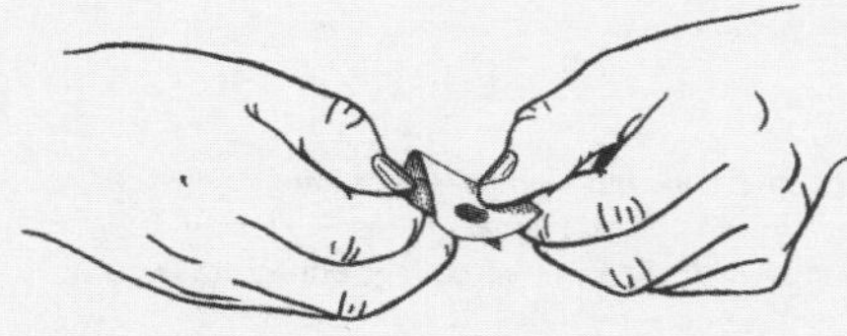

22a.1 Method of preparing a Tallquist test paper

II. Answer the following questions regarding the blood you tested.
- What percent category does the blood match most closely? Answers will vary.
- According to the information in the test booklet, what is the significance of this category? See the information in the test booklet.

- What would this test quickly tell a physician concerning a patient? Answers may vary, but the test can determine whether the person is anemic and to what degree he suffers from anemia.

Scheduling Laboratory Exercises

Laboratory Exercises 22a and 22b can be combined into a single-period laboratory exercise. If done so, it is suggested that you do the following sections in the following ways:
- Require the drawing of the blood slide (22a, p. L185).
- Choose one demonstration dealing with fresh or simulated blood from Laboratory Exercise 22a. It is recommended that you not do the blood typing section (p. L183).
- Require the students to measure their pulse and their heart rate (22b, p. L188).
- Do the heart and breathing rate exercise as a demonstration involving a single subject (22b, pp. L188–L190). Have the students do the graph and answer the questions at home.
- Have as many students as possible take their blood pressure (22b, pp. L190–L192) following a class demonstration of the procedure.

Name___________________________

Blood Cells

R E O

I. Observe a preserved slide of blood.
- Be sure to observe a section of the slide where the blood is one cell layer thick. Such an area usually appears to have nothing on it when you look at it with the naked eye.
- Observe red blood cells.
- Do you see any atypical shapes? ☐ yes ☐ no
- What might account for them? The way the slide is prepared can affect shapes of blood cells.
- Scan the slide until you find at least three white blood cells. How can you distinguish them from the red blood cells? White blood cells are larger, and they have nuclei. They do not have the biconcave disc shape, nor are they the same color as RBCs.

II. Draw blood cells in Area A.
- Draw three or four red blood cells and at least two white blood cells.
- Label all the features of white blood cells you can identify.

A

R E O

Blood-Clotting Time

The time it takes for blood to clot is significant in surgery and other clinical procedures. If a patient's blood clots too slowly or too quickly, the physician may have to give the patient medications to adjust the clotting time. The following simple test can be used to determine clotting time. You will need a large drop of very fresh, uncontaminated blood.

I. Fill a capillary tube with blood.
- Use a drop of blood about the size of a small pea that has formed on the person's finger in fewer than ten seconds.
- Holding the capillary tube almost parallel to the floor, touch one end of the tube to the blood.
- The blood will flow into the capillary tube. It should flow almost completely to the opposite end, without air bubbles in the tube. If it does not, either you had an obstruction in your capillary tube or the blood was not fresh. Wipe the finger with sterile cotton and try again.

II. Time the clotting.
- As soon as the tube is filled, begin timing the clotting, using either a stopwatch or the second hand on a clock.
- Wait one minute.
- Break off a short section of the capillary tube, being careful not to get broken glass in your finger.
- As you pull the broken piece away from the larger piece, look for solidified blood within the tube. The solidified blood is the blood clot.
- If no clot is visible, wait thirty seconds and break off another piece, looking for the blood clot.
- Break off a piece every thirty seconds until you see the blood clot. Record the time when a clot is seen. ______________ minutes
- Normal clotting time is from two to six minutes.

III. Answer the following questions.
- How long did it take the blood to begin clotting? Answers will vary.
- Why would some blood have a shorter clotting time than others? Answers may vary but could include the idea that there is too much thrombin in the blood, that there are abnormal platelets, or that certain medications are present.

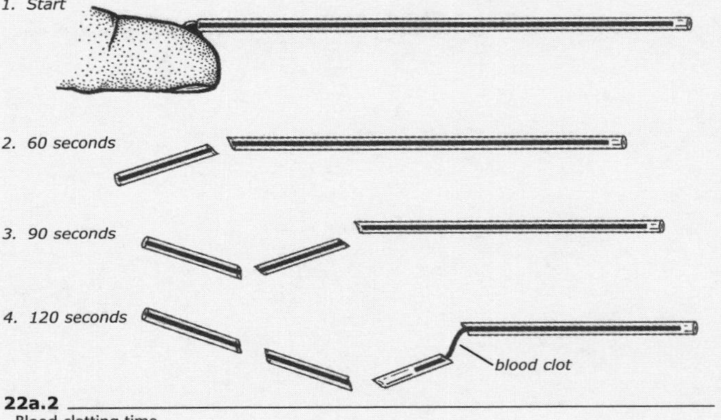

22a.2
Blood-clotting time

Name________________________

Date_______________ Hour_________

22b
Human Blood Circulation

Materials
- sphygmomanometer
- stethoscope
- stopwatch (or clock with second hand)

Goals
- To learn to take a pulse
- To listen to the heart
- To learn how blood pressure is measured
- To compare changes in the pulse rate and the breathing rate

During almost every physical exam your pulse rate and your blood pressure will be measured. Many different diseases or disorders can affect one's pulse rate and blood pressure. By knowing these statistics, a physician can begin to form his diagnosis of his patient's condition.

In this laboratory exercise you will also listen to the sounds of a person's heart. Many conditions of the heart can be determined by listening to the sounds made by the closing of its valves.

Counting Your Pulse and Listening to Your Heart

An irregular heartbeat is an indication of disease, disorder, or emotional trauma. One of the first things a health care provider wants to know about a patient is his pulse rate. Another part of almost every physical examination is listening to sounds of the heart. In this exercise you will count your partner's pulse rate, and he will count his own heart rate while he engages in various activities. Afterwards you will compare the different rates.

Where to Find Your Pulse

Use one of the two methods described below to find your pulse. Your radial pulse can be monitored by someone else. The carotid pulse is the usual method a person uses to find his own pulse rate. (It is recommended that you learn to take a pulse using both methods.)

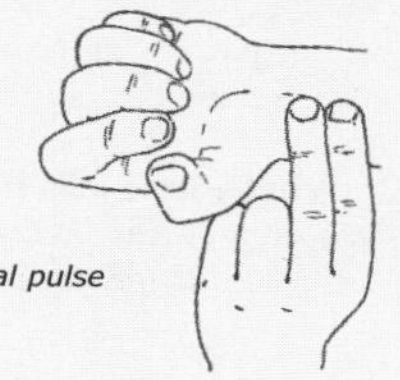

radial pulse

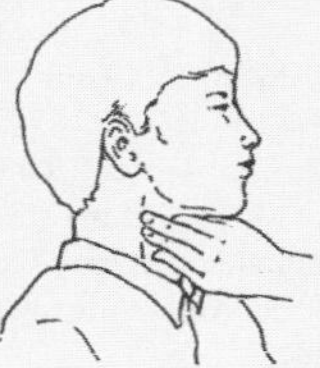

carotid pulse

22b.1
Locating radial and carotid pulse

The Radial Pulse
- Have your partner sit quietly for about four minutes. (Work on other sections of the lab.)
- While he is seated, find his radial pulse by placing your fingertips (not your thumb) over the area where the radial artery passes over the radius of the wrist.

The Carotid Pulse
- Sit quietly for about four minutes. (Work on other sections of the lab.)
- Hold your head so that your jaw is horizontal or slightly elevated.
- Place the anterior (palm) side of your index and middle fingers on the side of your neck below the jaw, under the ear, in the area of the carotid artery. Press lightly.

A mercury sphygmomanometer is not essential; in fact, mercury is considered a hazardous material, and should it be spilled, special materials are required to clean up the spill. Most healthcare providers use sphygmomanometers that use a dial pressure gauge.

Automatic digital-readout sphygmomanometers are available. Although some of these battery-operated devices require the pumping up of the cuff, many are fully automatic and need no additional equipment. If you are going to demonstrate the use of a sphygmomanometer, use one of the manual models. If an automated sphygmomanometer is available, you may want to have students use it to measure their blood pressure.

Introduction

This exercise is designed to teach students about some of the common medical practices involving the circulatory system: taking the pulse, listening to the heart, and measuring blood pressure. The exercise is relatively simple and can be completed in less than a single period.

Required / Extra / Omit

It is suggested that students be required to measure their own pulse rate and to take the radial pulse of another person.

It is suggested that students be required to listen to their own heart and compare the heart and pulse rates.

The comparison of heart and breathing rates can be omitted, or it can be done as a demonstration, using a single subject for the entire class. The graph and the questions can then be answered individually at home, or the graph can be put on the overhead projector and the questions answered in a class discussion. Rather than asking a student to run, you may have the student engage in another type of aerobic activity such as running in place or performing jumping jacks (side-straddle-hops) for four to five minutes. If you do substitute a different form of aerobic activity, it should not affect the answers to the questions in this section.

It is suggested that each student try to take a person's blood pressure. If equipment or time is limited, you may wish to do this section as a demonstration.

You may wish to combine the two laboratory exercises of this chapter into a single-period laboratory exercise. (See the box on p. 184.)

The Pulse and Heart Rate

I. Take a pulse.
- Determine your pulse by using a stopwatch or a clock with a second hand.
  - Count the number of pulses that occur in fifteen seconds.
  - Multiply by four to get the rate per minute. Record the number.
  - Repeat the procedure two more times and average the results.
- What is your pulse rate while you are seated? ________________ beats per minute

II. Listen to your heart.
- While seated, listen to your own heart, following these instructions.
  - Using a tissue and alcohol, clean the earpieces of a stethoscope.
  - Place the stethoscope in your ears, allowing the tubes to hang freely.
  - Place the diaphragm of the stethoscope just below your third rib, slightly to the left of the sternum.
  - Using a stopwatch or a clock with a second hand, count the number of beats that take place in fifteen seconds. The "lubb-dubb" sound counts as one beat, not two.
  - Multiply by four to get the rate per minute. Record this number.
  - Repeat the procedure two more times and average the results.
- What is your seated heart rate? ________________ beats per minute

III. Compare your pulse rate and your heart rate.
- Should your pulse rate and your heart rate be the same? ☒ yes ☐ no
- Explain your answer. The pulse and heart rate should be the same because the beating of a person's heart causes his pulse.

Pulse and Breathing Rates During Activity

I. One member of a laboratory group should perform the following physical activities. The data of this one person should be used by everyone to make graphs individually (Section II) and to answer the questions (Section III).
- Seated
  - You should already have your subject's seated pulse rate; transfer that information to the box that follows this section.
  - After your subject has sat quietly for four minutes (working on his lab), count his breathing rate for thirty seconds, and multiply this number by two. Record this information in the box.
- Standing
  - Have your subject stand quietly (while working on his lab) for three minutes.
  - Count his breathing for thirty seconds. Multiply the number by two and record the information.
  - Simultaneously, have him take his pulse for fifteen seconds. Multiply the number by four and record the information.
- Walking
  - Have your subject walk the distance prescribed by your instructor. As soon as he returns, do the following.
  - Count his breathing for thirty seconds, multiply the number by two, and record the information.
  - Simultaneously, have him take his pulse for fifteen seconds. Multiply the number by four and record the information.
- Running
  - Have your subject run the distance prescribed by the instructor. As soon as he returns, do the following.
  - Count his breathing for thirty seconds. Multiply the number by two and record the information.
  - Simultaneously, have him take his pulse for fifteen seconds. Multiply the number by four and record the information.

Name______________________________

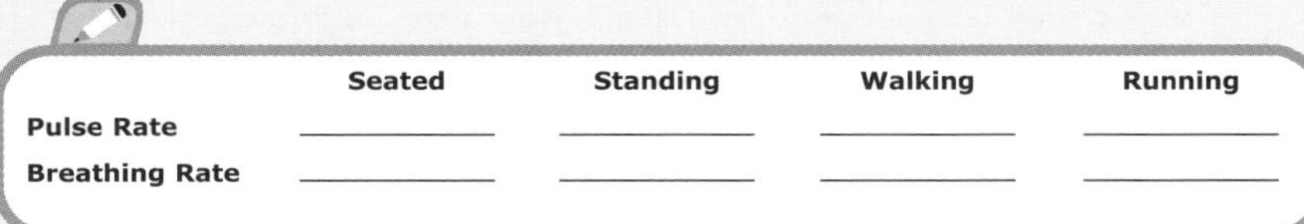

	Seated	Standing	Walking	Running
Pulse Rate	____________	____________	____________	____________
Breathing Rate	____________	____________	____________	____________

II. Plot the preceding information on the graph provided, using one color for the pulse rate and another for the breathing rate.

Pulse and Breathing Rates

	Seated	Standing	Walking	Running
200				
195				
190				
185				
180				
175				
170				
165				
160				
155				
150				
145				
140				
135				
130				
125				
120				
115				
110				
105				
100				
95				
90				
85				
80				
75				
70				
65				
60				
55				
50				
45				
40				
35				
30				
25				
20				
15				
10				

A thorough class presentation of blood pressure and its significance, along with a demonstration of the use of a sphygmomanometer, is recommended. It should be followed by a period of time when students can take their blood pressure using an automatic device. (See notes about the sphygmomanometer.)

Stress that each student must clean the earpieces before using the stethoscope.

III. Answer the following questions.

- Between which two adjacent activities is there the largest increase in the pulse rate?
  Answers will vary. What explanation can you offer? Answers will vary.
  Normally there will be the largest increase between walking and running. Walking is an activity for which most people are in condition, while running is generally a strain on the body.
- Between which two adjacent activities is there the largest increase in breathing rate?
  Answers will vary. What explanation can you offer? The answer should be the same as the largest increase in pulse rate and for the same reason.
- Would you expect the largest increases in both pulse rate and breathing rate to be between the same two activities? ☒ yes ☐ no Why or why not? The reason for increasing the pulse is to get more oxygenated blood to the cells. The reason for increasing the breathing rate is to get more blood oxygenated. These two activities are part of the same process of delivering oxygen to the cells to be used in cellular respiration.
- Based on your data, is the largest increase in pulse rate and breathing rate between the same two activities? ☒ yes ☐ no If this is not in keeping with your hypothesis (in the previous question), account for the difference. Answers will vary depending upon the subject and conditions.

Measuring Your Systolic Blood Pressure

Blood pressure is the pressure the blood exerts against the walls of the arteries. Carefully read the section on blood pressure in your text (p. 695). Although professionals take blood pressure readings quickly and easily, the process is not as easy as it looks. Health care providers often spend long hours learning the proper techniques. For this laboratory exercise you will record only the systolic pressure, which is easy to determine. (Instructions for finding the diastolic blood pressure are also given for those who would like to try.)

Taking a Person's Systolic Blood Pressure

I. Set up the sphygmomanometer.

- Place the cuff around your lab partner's arm in the area of the belly of the biceps brachii. It should be snug, but not tight.
- Turn the thumbscrew near the squeeze bulb until the valve is closed.
- Have your lab partner bend his arm and place it palm up on the table.
- Place the stethoscope earpieces in your ears. Be careful not to hit the diaphragm against any object.
- Find your partner's radial pulse with your fingers.

II. Take the systolic blood pressure of your partner.

- While feeling your partner's radial pulse, squeeze the bulb repeatedly until you can no longer feel a pulse in the radial artery.

Name________________________

> ***Warning!*** *The remainder of the exercise must be done within thirty seconds. If you are unable to complete it in thirty seconds, you must release the pressure on the arm and permit the blood to flow freely into the arm for a minute before you try again.* ***Do not cut off the circulation in the arm for more than thirty seconds.*** *Also,* ***do not*** *flex the arm muscles while the cuff is tight. Such movements can destroy a mercury sphygmomanometer.*

  - Keep your eye on the pressure gauge (mercury level or dial gauge). The pulse should stop near 140 mm Hg.
  - As soon as the pulse ceases, increase the pressure about twenty points on the scale; then stop squeezing the bulb.
- Place the diaphragm of the stethoscope in the cubital fossa (pit in the bend of the arm).
- Partially release the thumbscrew. You will hear the air hiss out and see the pressure gauge drop.
  - Listen for the sound of the first spurt of blood as it passes through the partially closed artery.
  - When you first hear the sound, note the number indicated on the pressure gauge. (If it is a mercury gauge, the mercury should take a quick little jump as the sound starts; the needle on a dial gauge will slightly move also.)
- Immediately release the thumbscrew completely. NOTE: If you must repeat the procedure more than three times in order to do it right, switch the cuff to the other arm.

III. Answer the following questions.

- What was the person's systolic blood pressure? Answers will vary.
- Normal systolic blood pressure for adults is about 120 mm Hg; for young people it is slightly lower. What could cause a higher than normal pressure? (List three possible explanations.)

  Reasons could include being overweight; eating too much salt; or having thickening or hardening of the artery walls, which makes the arteries smaller in diameter.

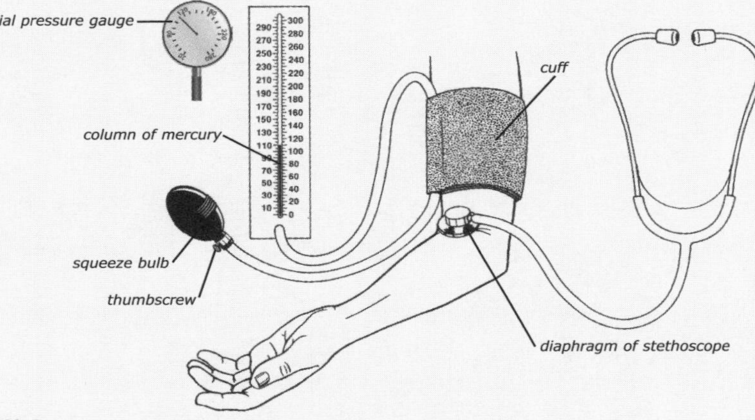

22b.2
A sphygmomanometer and stethoscope set up to take a person's blood pressure

Although it should not be necessary, it is safe to let the pressure rise to over 190 mm Hg when taking blood pressure. At about 200 mm Hg the person will begin feeling discomfort that may continue even after the cuff is removed. Although this may cause alarm, if the cuff pressure was not held that high for more than a few seconds, there will not be significant problems for normal people.

A student should not feel pain as his blood pressure is taken. It is, however, normal to feel the pressure of the cuff and a "coolness" or tingling in the hand while the cuff is inflated. If a student does feel pain, something may be seriously wrong with the technique or the equipment. Stop the process immediately.

Taking a Person's Diastolic Blood Pressure

R E O

I. Procedure
- After taking the systolic blood pressure, instead of releasing the thumbscrew rapidly, continue to allow the air to escape slowly.
- Continue listening to the sounds.
  - At one point the sounds will become softer and muffled.
  - At this point the pressure gauge indicates the diastolic blood pressure.

II. Answer the following questions.
- What is your partner's diastolic blood pressure? Answers will vary.
- How would that blood pressure (BP) normally be written? The systolic number is written above the diastolic number, as in 120/60.
- Is your partner's blood pressure normal for his age? ☐ yes ☐ no usually yes

  If not, what may account for the irregularity? Excessive weight, disease or disorder, or being an exceptionally well-conditioned athlete may account for abnormal blood pressure.

Name______________________________

Date__________________ Hour__________

23a
Human Reflexes

Materials
- reflex mallet
- penlight

Goals
- To perform some simple tests on various structures of the nervous system
- To note the clinical value of such tests to a physician

A reflex is considered the lowest level of human behavior because it involves responses that do not involve conscious decision making. In other words, your body performs reflexes without your having to think about them. As you study the reflex arc and various human reflexes, you should come to understand why they are important and how they operate.

The Reflex Arc

Reflexes originate at receptors found in the skin, tendons, muscles, and other body structures. When stimulated, these receptors send impulses over sensory neurons (*afferent neurons*) to the central nervous system. In the CNS, connections are often made through interneurons (*association neurons*) to motor neurons (*efferent neurons*). As impulses travel over these motor neurons, they cause effectors (muscles) to contract, producing the reflex action. These innate (inborn) behaviors are unlearned, nearly instantaneous reactions to a single, simple stimulus.

R E O

Demonstrating the Patellar (Knee-Jerk) Reflex

I. Sit comfortably in a chair and cross your legs above the knees, or sit on a high surface so that your feet do not touch the floor. Keep the thigh of your leg relaxed.

II. Have your lab partner tap your patellar tendon just below the patella with the reflex mallet. Do not watch as the tendon is struck. What is the reaction? The thigh muscles tighten, causing the knee to jerk the leg in a kicking motion.

III. Try variations of the patellar reflex. Try to stiffen your bent leg so that the reflex will not work. Is it possible to tense the leg so much that the reflex will not work? ☒ yes ☐ no

- Try the patellar reflex with the leg at different degrees of straightness (with the knee at different angles).
  - Does this affect the strength of the reflex? ☒ yes ☐ no
  - Does the reflex get weaker or stronger as the knee is straightened? ☒ weaker ☐ stronger

R E O

Studying a Reflex Arc

I. Label the following terms on Diagram 23a.1: *receptor, sensory neuron, axon of sensory neuron, dendrites of sensory neuron, central nervous system, interneurons, motor neuron, axon of motor neuron, dendrite of motor neuron, effector.*

II. A doctor tests reflexes for several reasons. List at least two. He can determine whether there is damage to the nerve or other structures. He can also determine at what level there is damage to the central nervous system.

Any firm but blunt item will do in place of a reflex mallet. Consider wrapping cloth around a piece of wood. The end that taps the tendon should be less than an inch wide. Tapping with the bound edge of a narrow paperbound book will work.

You may wish to demonstrate each of the reflexes to save time.

Be sure to caution students regarding how hard to tap the tendons in order to get the proper response.

Introduction

This laboratory exercise involves a brief demonstration of three reflex arcs. It can easily be accomplished in a few minutes.

Required / Extra / Omit

It is suggested that the entire exercise be required.

If time is lacking, you may wish to make the Achilles reflex and the pupillary reflex extra credit.

Turning off most of the lights in the room should make it dim enough for the pupillary reflex experiment. In some rooms, just turning the lights back on will be enough to effect the desired response. If demonstrating this response, consider having a student sit with his eyes closed and a thick blindfold on for a few minutes. When he removes the blindfold and looks at the classroom light, the pupillary reflex should be visible.

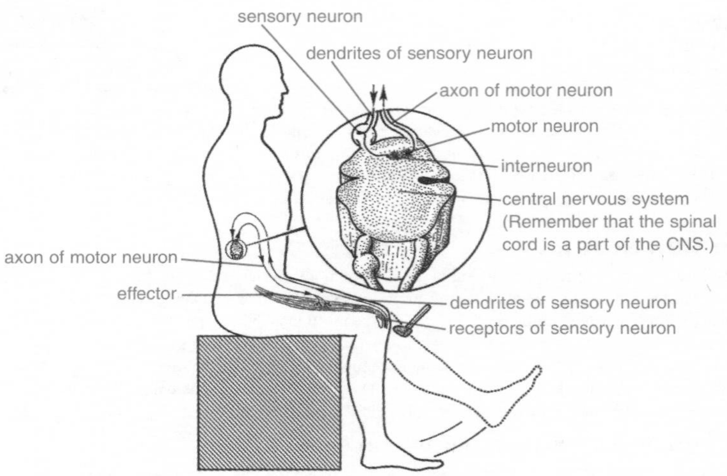

23a.1 ______

The patellar reflex arc

Demonstrating Other Human Reflexes

R E O

I. The Achilles (ankle-jerk) reflex
- Have your partner kneel on a chair with his feet hanging over the edge.
- Tap his Achilles tendon with the blunt end of the reflex mallet.
- Describe the reflex action. The tendon tightens, causing the foot to extend.

R E O

II. The pupillary reflex
- In a dimly lit area, shine the beam of a penlight into your partner's right eye, being careful not to shine the beam into the left eye.
- What happens to the pupil of the right eye? It becomes smaller.
- What happens to the pupil of the left eye? It also becomes smaller.
- Try the experiment again, shining the beam into the left eye this time. Are the results the same?

☒ yes ☐ no If not, why not? ______

Scheduling Laboratory Exercises

Laboratory Exercises 23a, 23b, and 23c can be combined into a single-period laboratory exercise. Consider the following:
- Do the patellar reflex (23a) as a demonstration and require the labeling of the reflex arc (pp. L193–L194).
- The Achilles and pupillary reflexes (23a, p. L194) can be done for extra credit outside class.
- The Senses of Taste and Smell (23b, pp. L195–L196) should be required.
- The Sensation of Heat and Cold on the Skin, first part (23b, p. L196), should be done as a demonstration. The second part should be extra credit or omitted.
- The Sense of Balance (23b, pp. L197–L198) should be omitted or done for extra credit.
- All of the eye materials should be required (23c, pp. L199–L203). Those sections that do not require laboratory equipment should be done at home.
- Do the Hearing section as a demonstration or omit it (23c, pp. L203–L205).

Name__________

Date__________ Hour__________

23b
Minor Senses in Humans

Materials

- metal or glass rods
- hot water
- ice water
- beakers
- washable-ink pen
- sugar cubes
- vanilla extract
- cotton swabs
- ruler
- paper towels
- swivel chair
- stopwatch (or clock with a second hand)

Goal

- To perform some simple tests on various minor senses of the human body

Although called the minor senses, taste, smell, balance, and touch (including pressure, pain, and temperature sensations) are all important to one's well-being. Because these senses are often thought of as being less important than sight and hearing, they are often taken for granted. But if one of these senses is not working properly, a person is handicapped. In this exercise you will test some of these not-so-minor senses.

The Senses of Taste and Smell

Two closely allied senses are the senses of taste and smell. Having a cold shows you that many of the tastes you enjoy are actually smells. Try these experiments to determine some of the relationships between taste and smell.

R E O

The Taste and Smell of Sugar

I. Smell a sugar cube.

- Describe the smell. There is no smell.
- Based on the smell, what would you expect sugar to taste like? Based on smell it should have no taste.

II. The taste of sugar

- Rinse your mouth with clean water.
- Stick your tongue out of your mouth and dry it with a paper towel.
- Place a sugar cube on the center of your dry tongue. Do not pull your tongue back into your mouth.
- Record the time it takes for you to taste the sugar. __________ seconds
- Remove the sugar cube as soon as you taste it.
- Rinse your mouth with clean water.
- Stick your tongue out of your mouth and wet it with clean water. Do not pull it back into your mouth.
- Place the opposite side of the same sugar cube on the same area of your tongue.
- Record the time it takes to taste the sugar. __________ seconds
- Explain the differences in time it took to taste the sugar. The sugar must dissolve before it can enter the taste buds to be tasted. Dissolving should take less time on the wet tongue.

The metal or glass rods used for the hot and cold sensing demonstration should be about half the width of a normal pencil. The procedure goes more rapidly if each group has several rods for the hot and several rods for the cold. Have one person prepare the rods for another person to touch to the hand of a third person. Sixteen-penny nails work well for the rods. They have a uniform size and composition and are readily available in sufficient quantities from hardware or home improvement stores. Dull the point of the nail to reduce the risk of injury.

Until the tests on tasting have been completed, discourage the students from eating sugar cubes. Only one member of each lab group needs to do the sugar cube test. If more than one member does it, students are wasting time (and sugar cubes).

Introduction

This laboratory exercise is an interesting collection of tests that the students will enjoy performing on themselves. Because this exercise can be fun, students have a tendency to get carried away and may need a few words of warning at the beginning of class. Tell them that they should go no further than the laboratory instructions tell them to go and emphasize the importance of following instructions exactly.

Required / Extra / Omit

Since the experiments on the senses of taste and smell (pp. L195–L196) are easily accomplished at home, you could assign them as an extra-credit section and spend more time in class on the experiments requiring laboratory equipment.

The first part of the testing of heat and cold sensations can be accomplished easily and quickly. It is recommended that you require your students to do this experiment or that you do it as a demonstration.

The second part of testing of heat and cold sensation on the skin requires much time. It may be wise to omit this section or to permit it to be done for extra credit.

It may be best to omit the section on balance (pp. L197–L198) if your students are prone to be silly. The activity makes a good demonstration. Since it is an experiment that requires only a swivel chair and two people, many students could do it at home for extra credit.

See the scheduling box on page 194 for suggestions for combining Exercises 23a, 23b, and 23c.

The Taste and Smell of Vanilla

R E O

I. Smell the vanilla extract and then describe the smell. It has a rich, deep, "vanilla" smell.

II. Dip a cotton swab into some vanilla extract and touch the swab to your tongue. (You may need to touch it to several areas of the tongue.) Describe the taste. It has a bitter taste.

- Does vanilla extract taste the way it smells? ☐ yes ☒ no
- Which sense do you think accounts for the taste we normally call vanilla (such as in vanilla ice cream and vanilla pudding)? smell

Sensation of Heat and Cold on the Skin

Your skin receives numerous sensations. Your sense of touch involves only one set of nerves. Pain, temperature, and pressure (and possibly other sensations) are perceived by other nerve endings in the skin. In this exercise you are asked to determine whether heat and cold are different sensations of the same nerve or are the sensations of two different nerves.

Sensing Hot and Cold

R E O

I. Obtain a beaker of hot water and place a blunt metal or glass rod in it. Make sure that the water is not hot enough to burn the skin. Also obtain a beaker of ice water and place a similar rod in it.

II. Test your partner's sense of hot or cold.

- With washable ink, place six small dots on the back of your partner's hand separated by at least 1.0 cm. On paper, diagram the hand, draw in the dots, and assign each dot a letter.
- Blindfold your partner.
- Randomly place either the hot or cold rod on each of the six dots until every dot has been tested twice for hot and twice for cold.
  - Quickly dry the rod before placing it on the dot.
  - Touch the rods with the same pressure to the skin.
  - Leave the rods in contact with the skin for three seconds, after which your partner must identify whether the rod was hot or cold.
  - Return the rods to the proper beaker between tests to keep them at the proper temperature.
  - Record the number of correct and incorrect responses for both hot and cold for each dot.

III. Answer the following questions.

- Which was your partner more often correct in sensing? ☐ hot ☐ cold Answers will vary.
- Was each of the dots equally sensitive to hot and cold, or were some dots more prone to be correct about one temperature or the other? Answers will vary.
  - If different areas were sensitive to different temperatures, what would this result suggest? The nerve endings for hot and cold are not distributed evenly in the skin.
  - If all areas were equally sensitive to different temperatures, what would this result suggest? The nerve endings for hot and cold are evenly distributed in the skin.

Name_______________

Plotting the Sensation of Heat and Cold

I. With washable ink, mark an area one-inch square on the back of your partner's hand and then draw a grid in the square, dividing each side into sixths. (See the boxes below.)

Cold   Heat

II. Using hot and cold rods as described above
- Test all of the areas within the square with the cold probe. Locate and mark on the diagram all the areas that were sensitive to the cold probe.
- Test all of the areas within the square with the hot probe. Locate and mark on the diagram all the areas that were sensitive to the hot probe.

III. According to your experiment, are heat and cold receptors in identical locations on the hand?
☐ yes ☒ no From this fact, what can you conclude about temperature receptors?
Heat and cold receptors must be different since they are located in different areas of the skin.

The Sense of Balance

Your inner ear contains the delicate structures responsible for the sense of balance. These structures are dependent upon the properties of fluids. Moving fluids are used to send the information necessary for your brain to know your position and movements. Your sense of balance is usually quite accurate; however, under certain circumstances the inner ear fluids can send impulses to your brain that do not reflect reality.

I. Test normal visual and motor coordination.
- Have your partner sit cross-legged in a swivel chair.
- Place your extended index finger about twenty inches in front of his chest and test his ability to touch your finger.
  - Have him raise his arm above his head.
  - Have him extend his index finger and quickly drop his arm until his finger comes into contact with yours. Did his finger make contact on the first try? ☐ yes ☐ no
  - Repeat this experiment eight times. Record the number correct. _______________
- Have your partner repeat the experiment with his eyes closed.
  - Did his finger make contact? ☐ yes ☐ no

    If not, by how much did he miss? _______________
  - Repeat this experiment eight times. Record the number correct. _______________

One must be spun rapidly enough to cause dizziness, but not so fast as to be unsafe.

II. Test visual and motor coordination after movement.
- While your partner has his eyes open, twirl him rapidly in the chair for fifteen seconds.
  - Stop him abruptly and tell him to try the finger-touching experiment.
  - How many tries did it take for him to make contact as well as he did before twirling? ______
- When he is no longer dizzy, have him close his eyes and repeat the twirling-chair test.
  - He should then open his eyes, note where your finger is, close his eyes, raise his hand above his head, and try to make contact.
  - How many tries did it take for him to make contact as well as he did before twirling? ______
- When he is no longer dizzy, repeat the twirling-chair test with his eyes closed.
  - This time have him keep his eyes open as he tries to touch your finger.
  - How many tries did it take him to make contact? ______

III. Answer the following questions. (Some may require careful reasoning.)
- When did he perform better? ☐ before being twirled ☐ after being twirled

  Explain your answer, telling what structures are responsible. The spinning fluid in the semicircular canals results in multiple, overlapping, and thus confused impulses to the brain. This confusion accounts for his not being able to make finger contact as well after being twirled.
- Compared to performing the experiment without twirling and with eyes open, how difficult would it be to perform the following actions?
  - Without twirling and with eyes closed while he tries to make contact

    It should be slightly more difficult.
  - With eyes open while he twirls and with eyes open while he tries to make contact

    It should be more difficult.
  - With eyes closed while he twirls and with eyes closed while he tries to make contact

    It should be considerably more difficult.
  - With eyes closed while he twirls and with eyes open while he tries to make contact

    It should be slightly more difficult.
- What would account for these differences in difficulty? Answers may vary. Vision does help, but in a normal person, impulses from semicircular canals affect the movement of the eyes, making focusing on a stationary object difficult after twirling.

Name____________________

Date____________ Hour_______

23c
The Human Eye and Ear

Materials

- Snellen eye chart
- penlight
- red and green cellophane
- tape measure
- white paper
- Holmgren color vision test
- tuning forks of assorted frequencies (including 128 and 256 cps)

Goals

- To perform some simple vision and hearing tests
- To note the clinical value of such tests to a physician

A minor shortcoming of one's vision or hearing may go unnoticed for years. For example, astigmatism in one eye may be compensated for by the other eye so that a person may not be aware that he has blurred vision. Some people who have red-green color blindness (one of the most common forms of color blindness) do not realize it until they are adults. In this exercise you will perform some simple tests on your eyes and ears.

The Eye and Sight

Vision is one of the senses on which humans rely most. It is also more prone to minor disorders than are other senses. In the following exercises, you will perform some simple tests on your vision (or your lab partner's vision).

Structures of the Eye

I. Examine your partner's eye (or use a mirror to examine your own eye) and identify the following structures. Give definitions where required.

- Lids: flaps of tissue that cover the eyes
- Conjunctiva: the lining of the eyelid and transparent covering of the anterior eyeball, except the cornea
- Openings of nasolacrimal ducts: openings of the tubes (ducts) that carry tears from the eyes into the nose
- Cornea: clear front portion of the eye
- Sclera: white of the eye
- Pupil: dark opening in the center of the iris
- Iris: colored part of the eye

II. Label as many structures of the eye as possible on Diagram 23c.1.

Snellen Test for Visual Acuity

A person's visual acuity (visual sharpness) can be tested with a Snellen eye chart, which consists of rows of black letters of different sizes printed on a white card. The distance from which those letters can be read by the normal eye is printed beside each line of letters.

I. Check your visual acuity by doing the following:

- Remove glasses if you wear them. (If possible, remove contact lenses.)
- Stand twenty feet from the chart and cover your left eye with your hand. (Keep the covered eye open.)
- Have your lab partner point out the line of letters that is marked "20 ft." Read the lines as your partner checks to see if you are correct. If you can read most of the letters on this line correctly, you have 20/20 vision for that eye.
    - If you are able to read the line marked "20 ft," try the next smaller line. Continue until you can no longer read most of the letters accurately.

The Materials Lists on pages A6–A20 indicate several sources and substitutions for most of the items needed for this exercise.

Students will be able to see the openings of their nasolacrimal ducts by looking into a mirror. Gently evert the lower lid. The opening of the nasolacrimal duct is about the diameter of a pin and can be seen at the medial-most aspect of the lash-bearing portion of the lower lid. They will not be able to label these structures on the diagram on page L200.

Make a mark on the floor with chalk or masking tape showing the proper distance for using the Snellen eye test. The eye test chart should be at eye level on a flat, light-colored wall.

Introduction

This laboratory exercise is an interesting collection of clinical tests that the students enjoy performing on themselves. Because they perform these tests without the thorough knowledge and experience that a professional would have, these tests cannot truly be considered "clinical" in a classroom situation.

Because this exercise can be fun, students have a tendency to get carried away and may need a few words of warning at the beginning of the class. First, tell them that they should go no further than the laboratory instructions tell them to go. Second, emphasize the importance of following the instructions exactly. Third, admonish them to keep the noise down.

Required / Extra / Omit

It is suggested that you require all of the Eye and Sight section (pp. L199–L203). Several of these experiments can be done at home. The astigmatism, blind spot, and visual accommodation sections (pp. L200–L202) can be done without laboratory equipment.

The hearing section should be required. If experiments must be omitted for the sake of time, note that the tests for unilateral sound-conduction and acoustic nerve deafness (p. L205) take the most time and are the most difficult. See the scheduling box on page 194 for suggestions about combining Exercises 23a, 23b, and 23c.

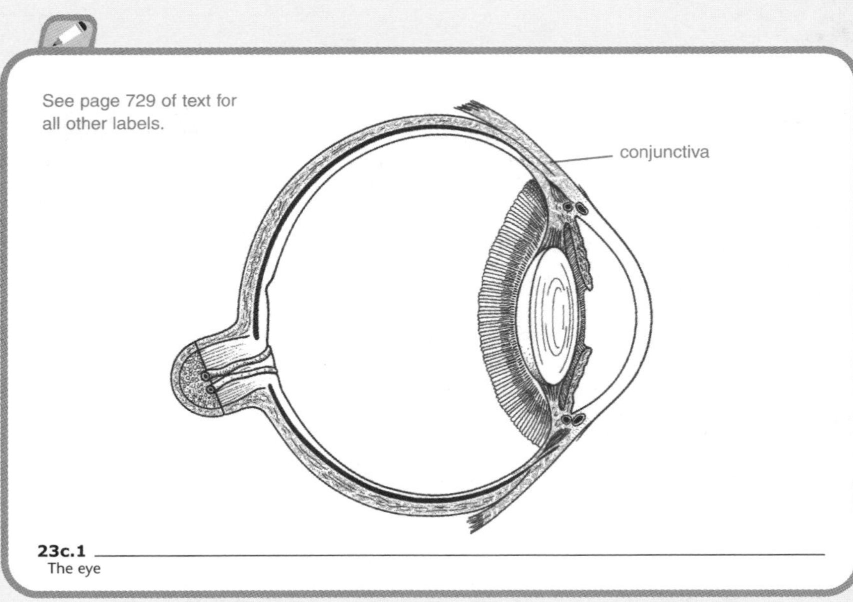

23c.1 The eye

- If you cannot read the line marked "20 ft," have your partner point to the line with the next larger size of type, and so on, until you can read accurately most of the letters on the line that he indicates. (Your partner should point out the letters in the line at random so that you do not memorize the order of the letters.)

II. Check the reading recorded for your right eye's vision: ☐ 20/15 ☐ 20/20 ☐ 20/25 ☐ 20/30 ☐ 20/40 ☐ 20/50 ☐ 20/70 ☐ 20/100 ☐ 20/200.

III. Repeat this test, covering your right eye to test your left eye's vision. Check the reading recorded for your left eye's vision: ☐ 20/15 ☐ 20/20 ☐ 20/25 ☐ 20/30 ☐ 20/40 ☐ 20/50 ☐ 20/70 ☐ 20/100 ☐ 20/200.

R E O

Testing for Astigmatism

I. Define *astigmatism*. Astigmatism is an uneven area of the cornea or lens. An area of blurred vision results.

II. Check yourself for astigmatism.

- Cover your left eye and hold the diagram for testing astigmatism (Diagram 23c.2) about six inches in front of your right eye.
- Look directly into the center of the empty circle of the diagram. Be sure your pupil is directly over the central white area.
- If any of the lines appear blurred, you probably have astigmatism in the corresponding area of your right eye.
- Do you have astigmatism in your right eye? ☐ yes ☐ no If so, in which areas (indicated by numbers at ends of lines)? ______

Name________________________________

- Repeat the procedure, covering the right eye and observing with the left eye.
- Do you have astigmatism in your left eye? ☐ yes ☐ no If so, in which areas?

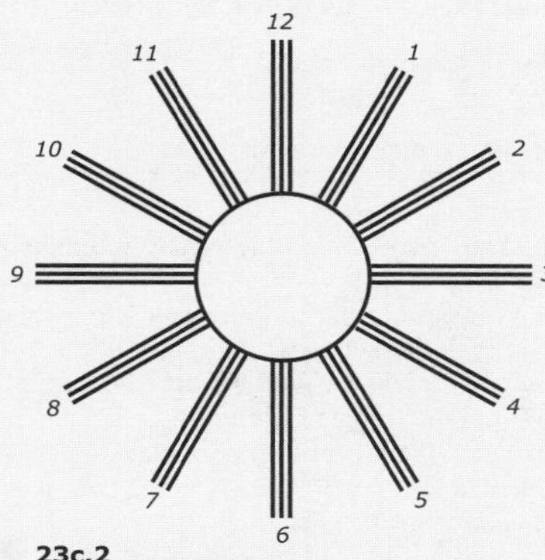

23c.2
Test for astigmatism

R E O

Demonstration of the Blind Spot

I. Read about the blind spot on page 729 of your text.

II. Find your blind spot by using Diagram 23c.3.

- Position the diagram so that the dot is to the right of the plus sign.
- Hold the diagram about eighteen inches from your eye, with the plus sign directly in front of your right eye. Cover your left eye.
- Move the diagram slowly toward you as you stare at the plus sign. At a certain point the dot will disappear. The dot is then in your blind spot.
- Have your partner measure the distance from your eye to the paper. What is the distance? usually 8–12 in.
- Repeat for your left eye. With the dot to the left, place the plus sign directly in front of your left eye and cover your right eye. At what distance does the dot disappear? usually 8–12 in.

III. What effect would the blind spot have on a person who has only one eye? Should such a person be allowed to drive? ☐ yes ☐ no Why or why not? Answers will vary. Most one-eyed (monocular) people are not aware of the blind spot because their brains fill in the image.

23c.3
Blind spot test

If the darkened area in your classroom is not dark enough, the afterimage experiment may not work. It may be best to use a stockroom or a large closet. The experiments do not, however, require total darkness.

R E O

Visual Accommodation

I. Read about visual accommodation on page 729 in your text.

II. Demonstrate visual accommodation.

- Have your partner look at an object across the room while you hold a pencil about eighteen inches in front of his nose. Then ask him to look at the pencil.
- What was the change in the size of the pupils? They became smaller.
- Did his eyes move in any other way? ☒ yes ☐ no

  If so, how? The eyes direct the pupils toward his nose.

III. Demonstrate near-point accommodation.

- Another important part of accommodation is near-point accommodation. The near point is the closest distance at which sharp focus is attained.
- Determine the near point of your eyes by covering your left eye and focusing with your right eye on the *D* at the beginning of this sentence.
  - Move this page toward your right eye until the letter no longer appears sharp and clear.
  - Move the page away until the letter is clear again.
  - Have your partner measure the distance from the page to your eye.
- Repeat the process for the left eye.
- Record your near-point accommodation distance.

  Left eye ____________ Right eye ____________
- The near-point accommodation distance increases with age because the lens of the eye loses its elasticity.
  - Is your near-point accommodation distance normal for your age? ☐ yes ☐ no
  - When a person can no longer focus on the print of a book at a "comfortable" distance (about 20 in.), he needs reading glasses. Based on your present near-point accommodation distance, at what age should you expect to need reading glasses?

    ____________ years old

Average Near-Point Accommodation by Age

Age	Distance in inches
15	3.5
25	4.5
35	6.8
45	20.5
55	33.0

R E O

Afterimages

I. An afterimage is the image that a person sees after he stops looking at an object. Such images are most common after looking at an object that is in sharp contrast to its background.

- A positive afterimage is one that is the same color as the object observed.
- A negative afterimage is the complementary color. Negative afterimages are caused by bleaching (fatigue of visual pigments).

II. Observe afterimages.

- Sit in a darkened area.
- Flash a penlight into one eye for not more than one second. Then close your eyes. Is the afterimage positive or negative? ☒ positive ☐ negative
- Holding a piece of red cellophane between the light and the eye, flash a penlight into one eye for not more than one second. Then close your eyes. Is the afterimage positive or negative? ☒ positive ☐ negative
- Repeat this test, using a piece of green cellophane. Is the afterimage positive or negative? ☒ positive ☐ negative
- Shine a penlight steadily into one eye for about twenty seconds and then quickly look at a piece of white paper. (Blinking your eyes will help the appearance of the afterimage.) Is the afterimage positive or negative? ☒ positive ☐ negative

- Holding a piece of red cellophane between the light and your eye, repeat this test. Is the afterimage positive or negative? ☐ positive ☒ negative
- Repeat this test using a piece of green cellophane. Is the afterimage positive or negative? ☐ positive ☒ negative

Testing for Colorblindness

The Holmgren color vision test consists of a set of colored wool strands that matches a set of mounted wool strands. NOTE: More specific and more accurate tests must be taken to determine colorblindness accurately. The Holmgren test merely indicates that other tests may be necessary. Even a very poor performance on the Holmgren test may not mean that a person is colorblind.

I. Ask your partner to match the loose strands with the mounted ones as rapidly as possible.

II. Note any of the following reactions in your partner:
- Hesitation before placing a colored strand by the one it matches
- Comparisons (laying a strand beside various mounted threads to determine which one it matches)
- Mistakes (whether or not they are corrected)

III. If your partner shows any of these reactions, note which colors caused the problems. Did your partner show colorblindness tendency? ☐ yes ☐ no If so, in what color range? ______________

The Holmgren test is just one of several types of tests used to diagnose colorblindness. Check with your local ophthalmologist for suggestions or to see if the materials for the vision test can be borrowed for this exercise.

Hearing

You depend greatly on your sense of hearing. The ear plays a vital role in sound perception. Your ears tell you more than just the kind and volume of sound, as some of these experiments will demonstrate.

How to Use a Tuning Fork

The tuning fork is an instrument used to produce a specific pitch. This instrument can be used to test for possible hearing problems. You will use it in the next few experiments. A tuning fork consists of a base and a forked pair of prongs. The base supports the prongs, allowing them to vibrate and produce sound when they are struck.

There are two things to remember when using a tuning fork:

- Hold it at its base only. Touching the fork along the prongs stops their vibrating and thus stops the sound. (This may be done after you complete an experiment.)
- Strike the fork against only the palm of your hand or your thigh. Do not strike it on any hard surface since resulting dents may alter its frequency.

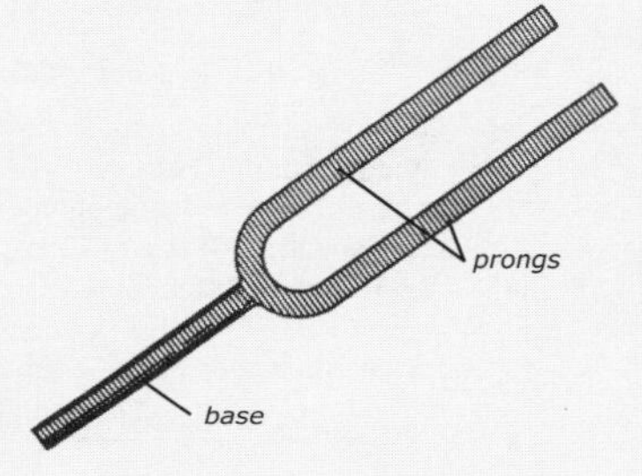

23c.4 ______________
Tuning Fork

Testing Your Hearing

I. Localizing sound

- Sit in a quiet room with your eyes closed.
- Your partner will strike the fork on his hand and hold it eight to ten inches away from the sides, top, and then back of your head.
- As he moves the fork to different positions around your head, point to the direction from which the sound is coming.
- Your partner may need to strike the tuning fork each time he moves it.
- Were you able to locate sound near the sides of your head? ☐ yes ☐ no Back of your head? ☐ yes ☐ no Top of your head? ☐ yes ☐ no
- Place your index finger over the opening of one of your ears and repeat the experiment.
- Was there any change in the results? ☒ yes ☐ no
- Why or why not? Answers may vary. Both ears are needed to establish sound direction.

II. Bone conduction

- Conduction of sound through the skull
  - Sit quietly and plug both ears with your fingers.
  - Your partner will strike the tuning fork and rest the base of the fork on the top of your head.
  - Signal by a slight movement of your head when you hear the fork.
  - Your partner will remove the fork. Can you still hear the sound? ☐ yes ☐ no
  - Your partner will immediately replace the tuning fork on your head. Can you hear the sound? ☐ yes ☐ no
- Conduction of sound through the teeth
  - Sit quietly and plug both ears with your fingers.
  - Your partner will rinse and dry both the tuning fork and his hands. He will strike the fork and place its base (not the vibrating prongs) between your teeth. Only the teeth should come into contact with the tuning fork. (Your lips should not touch it.) Can you hear the sound? ☐ yes ☐ no
  - Remove the fork and wipe it dry.
  - Is there any difference between the sounds heard in these bone conduction experiments? ☒ yes ☐ no If so, how did the sounds differ? Volume is the main difference. Pitch may also vary.
- Conduction of sound through the temple
  - Sit quietly and plug both ears with your fingers.
  - Your partner will strike the tuning fork and place its base against your right temple. Do you hear the sound? ☐ yes ☐ no
  - Now repeat the test on the left temple. Do you hear the sound? ☐ yes ☐ no
  - Was there any major difference between what you heard when the right temple was tested and what you heard when the left was tested? ☐ yes ☐ no Give the probable reason for your answer. One side's sounding softer would indicate a type of nerve deafness on that side.

Testing for Deafness

Deafness can result when structures malfunction in any of three different areas: within the parts of the ear that conduct the sound waves (eardrum, ossicles, and other structures), within the nerves and sensory cells of the inner ear, or within the central nervous system. Often sound-conduction deafness affects only one ear. This unilateral (one-sided) sound-conduction deafness is caused by a blockage of sound waves. A person is said to have acoustic nerve deafness if he cannot hear because of problems in his inner ear.

During this exercise, the classroom may become too noisy for students to test their hearing accurately. You may want to place a chair or two in the hall and tell the students that they can sit there for the hearing tests. Emphasize that they should only whisper in the hall. Demonstrate how to strike a tuning fork.

Name________________

I. Test for unilateral sound-conduction deafness.

- While you sit quietly, your partner will strike a 128 or 256 cps tuning fork and carefully place the base of the fork on the center of your forehead.
- Where does the sound seem loudest? ☐ right ☐ center ☐ left
- If you hear the sound better in the left ear or the right ear, you may have sound-conduction deafness. This type of deafness eliminates the background noise that a normal ear hears. Because there is less surrounding noise to distract a sound-conduction deaf ear, the sound heard from the tuning fork on the skull registers more volume in that ear.
  - Is there a tendency toward sound-conduction deafness in your right ear? ☐ yes ☐ no
  - Is there a tendency toward sound-conduction deafness in your left ear? ☐ yes ☐ no
- What can correct unilateral sound-conduction deafness? Hearing aids may help. Surgery can loosen stiff joints or replace ossicles that are fused together.

R E O

II. Test for acoustic nerve deafness

- While you sit quietly, your partner will strike a 128 or 256 cps tuning fork and carefully place the base of the fork on the center of your forehead.
- Plug your right ear. In which ear is the sound louder? ☐ right ☐ left ☐ no difference
- Repeat the experiment, this time plugging the left ear. In which ear is the sound louder? ☐ right ☐ left ☐ no difference
- If the right ear is plugged and the sound is heard better in the left ear, there may be nerve deafness on the right side. Sound conducted through the skull is naturally transmitted better (more loudly) to a plugged ear than to an open ear. If the sound is louder in the unplugged ear, some difficulty other than conduction must be causing the problem.
  - Is there any tendency toward acoustic nerve deafness in your right ear? ☐ yes ☐ no
  - Is there any tendency toward acoustic nerve deafness in your left ear? ☐ yes ☐ no
- What can be done for acoustic nerve deafness? Hearing aids can increase the volume of the sound. Surgery does not help because the problem is in the nerves.

Name________________________________

Date____________________ Hour__________

24
Drugs in Our Culture

Materials
- library

Goals
- To learn about the physical effects of various psychoactive drugs
- To learn about the effects of psychoactive drugs in our culture

According to many people, the abuse of psychoactive drugs is one of the major problems faced by our culture. These drugs begin with mental effects, but soon they physically affect the one who takes them. In many cases these drugs leave mental, emotional, and physical scars that may trouble the drug user for the rest of his life even though he quits using them. The drug abuse also affects his family and his friends in different, often serious and always harmful, ways.

The economic effect on our society involves not only the money exchanged on the black market but also the millions spent on law enforcement and public and private rehabilitation. It is estimated that the yearly cost of the productivity lost to drugs in the workplace is in the hundreds of millions of dollars.

In this exercise you (or a group of students, if your class does this exercise as a group project) will select or be assigned a drug to research. Only when you know about the psychoactive drugs and their effects can you make intelligent decisions about drug-related concerns in our society. It may be easy for you to decide not to be involved with drugs. But since drugs pervade our society, you will need to make decisions regarding everything from the spending of public money to counseling friends regarding their position on drugs and drug-related issues. This project is designed to help you become ready to face these problems.

I. Select a drug (or a group of drugs) and research the effects of the drug.
- Use a library's catalog to locate books that contain information about the drug.
- Read those parts that contain pertinent information.
- Consult the *Reader's Guide to Periodical Literature* for the past several years to find articles containing information about the drug. Read those that contain pertinent information.
- Perform an Internet search for the drug. Use reliable sources such as law enforcement agencies, federal, state, or local government sites, and educational sites. Avoid chat rooms or other unregulated sites.
- Information regarding drugs and their use is frequently available from physicians, hospitals, pharmacists, law enforcement authorities, drug rehabilitation centers, and government agencies responsible for drug education. Consult these or other similar sources regarding material about the drug.
- Try to find the following information about the drug. Be more specific than the information found in the text.
  - Briefly describe the history of the drug. Who first used it? Where? When was it introduced into the modern drug culture?
  - List the physical symptoms caused by the drug. Distinguish between long-term and short-term effects and between those experienced by "casual users" and "heavy users."
  - List the drug's mental/emotional effects that cause people to want to take it. Describe these effects on both "casual users" and "heavy users."
  - How is the drug taken? What problems does a person who uses this drug encounter because of the way it is taken?
  - What is the source of the drug (synthetic, a foreign country, etc.)? How difficult is it to produce/refine?
  - Are there international difficulties (problems between governments) because of the illegal trade of this drug? How extensive are they?

You may wish to take several of the points from the list (such as the ones dealing with drug education, cost of drugs, cost of rehabilitation, or the number of people who take the drug) and give these to a special group who are to contact the proper authorities (by phone or appointment) to glean information regarding illegal drugs in general. Often statistics regarding the amount of money spent on law enforcement, for example, are not broken down by specific drugs.

INTRODUCTION

The illegal traffic in psychoactive drugs (and a few other drugs, such as anabolic steroids) is a major topic not only in the streets and in the media but also in the legislatures, courts, hospitals, police stations, prisons, public schools, sports locker rooms, counseling centers, and even churches of our land. Unfortunately, there are not very many Christian-oriented drug education programs. Sometimes secular antidrug programs are overly simplistic or, in their attempts to reach certain groups, are offensive to many Christians.

This exercise is designed to compel students to look a little deeper than the popular media to find out about drugs. Once a person finds out the truth about drugs, he is less likely to be lured into starting to use them and will be better able to make wise decisions regarding how to deal with the drug problems of others. When trying to convince a person of a truth, it is frequently more efficient for the teacher to have the person find the information for himself rather than merely to have another lecture on the subject. But too often the person who may need the most convincing will be the one least likely to find the information. For these reasons doing this activity as group work is recommended.

Required / Extra / Omit

It is recommended that you assign this exercise as group projects with oral reports trimmed to fit your classroom situation.

If you elect to assign this exercise as individual rather than group projects, consider omitting the hard-to-find sections from the list of required information.

- ❍ How much is spent by government agencies (federal, state, local) to control the supply of this drug? How effective is the control? Is there a short supply of the drug because of these control efforts?
- ❍ What kinds (groups) of people use this drug (level of education, age, economic group, etc.)? How often do people use this drug and how much of this drug do the different groups use?
- ❍ What kinds of drug education programs are aimed at people not using this drug? What kind of drug education programs are aimed at people using this drug? Are the drug education programs considered effective?
- ❍ Approximately how many people use (or are addicted to) the drug in the United States? in your state? in a nearby major city?
- ❍ How much does the drug cost ("street price") for a single dose? to support a "casual" or mild habit? to support a major addiction?
- ❍ What kind of drug rehabilitation is offered for abusers of this drug? How much does this rehabilitation of one person cost? How effective is it? Who pays for this rehabilitation?
- ❍ Does this drug have legitimate medical uses? What are they? What measures do physicians take to make sure their patients do not abuse this drug?

II. Prepare a report about the information you find.

- Prepare a written report.
  - ❍ Write a three- to five-page report on the drug you researched.
    - ❖ The introduction and conclusion of your report should be in paragraph form.
    - ❖ The main part of your report can be in paragraph form, or it can be in the form of a list of statements dealing with the answers to the questions asked above.
  - ❍ Include a complete bibliography of the sources from which you obtained information.
- Prepare an oral report.
  - ❍ Prepare a four- to seven-minute oral report on the drug you researched.
  - ❍ Cover as many of the questions presented above as possible.
  - ❍ Be sure to include references to any source other than printed sources from which you obtained information. (In other words, you do not need to tell about library research sources, but if you talked to someone about this material, you should mention him as part of your report.)
  - ❍ Present material you think would be interesting and valuable to the class.

Name____________________

Date____________ Hour________

25 Chicken Embryology

Materials

- fertilized chicken eggs
- incubator
- scissors
- dropping pipet
- shallow dishes (finger bowls or large culture dishes)
- forceps
- physiological saline
- scalpel

Goals

- To observe chicken embryos at different stages of development
- To compare the embryonic growth rate of different structures
- To learn about various embryonic structures

Embryology is the study of the process through which a single cell grows, divides, and gives rise to thousands of individual cells of many different types. In a relatively short time, these individual cells are able to work together to sustain life. Embryology is a fascinating study, and researchers are working hard to understand the process by which cells with identical genetic makeup can differentiate to form tissues such as bone, muscle, liver, thyroid gland, and cartilage. There is also intense research about how cells develop in the right places so that they all fit together in a workable, complete organism. The embryo is too tiny for general observation, and any experimentation greatly affects it. The intricate chemical messengers that turn genes on and off to cause cell differentiation are an area of great importance in embryology as well as biotechnology. This laboratory exercise will look at several stages of the embryological growth of a chicken egg in an attempt to observe some of these marvels.

Incubating Chicken Eggs

Fresh fertilized eggs can be kept at a cool room temperature without incubation for several days. This lowered temperature temporarily stops the embryo's development. Then, when the eggs are placed in an incubator set at 38 °C (100 °F), embryonic growth starts again. If incubated for twenty-one days, normal fertilized chicken eggs will hatch.

Before the laboratory period begins, eggs should be placed in an incubator at intervals so that on the appointed day the egg will have been incubated the proper amount of time. For this exercise, about four different embryonic stages are recommended. Eggs incubated four, nine, twelve, and fourteen days would be ideal. For large classes, however, eggs incubated three, six, nine, twelve, fifteen, and eighteen days could be used.

Several eggs should be incubated for each time period desired so that if one is infertile or if an accident should happen, there are still other eggs to observe. With a pencil, mark on each egg the date and time that its incubation began. Twice a day during the incubation period the eggs should be turned over so that the chick embryos do not become attached to their shell. A shallow pan of water should be kept in the incubator so that the eggs do not dehydrate.

The class should be divided into groups, with each group responsible for opening an egg of a different age. As each egg is opened, each student should observe the egg and record his observation in the proper spaces on page L212.

Opening a Chicken Egg

Eggs Incubated Three to Nine Days

I. Without rolling the egg, take it from the incubator. The embryo should be on top of the yolk. If you cut and remove the top part of the shell, you should be able to find the embryo without having to rotate the yolk.

The best source for buying fertilized eggs is usually a local farm supplier. Consult the Yellow Pages under *Poultry* or *Feed Dealers* to locate the possible sources. Occasionally the biology department of a nearby college can tell you of a good local source.

You can make normal saline (physiological saline) by mixing 7 grams of NaCl (table salt) in 1 liter of distilled water.

Introduction

This is a difficult laboratory exercise because it requires the student to use some very precise techniques. For this reason, you may wish to modify the requirements or choose to omit the entire exercise. It is possible for you to perform the various egg openings the night before and to leave them covered in physiological saline. Thus the students would need to do only the observations. You may want to have students open only the three-, six-, and possibly nine-day-old eggs (which are easiest to open) and omit the later eggs or have them already opened. It is also possible to purchase preserved and mounted specimens and then modify the exercise accordingly. Or you might open the eggs beforehand and go from egg to egg, pointing out the structures as a class demonstration.

Some students have difficulty observing a living chicken embryo with its heart beating. For others, removing a chick from the egg, realizing that it is going to die, may be repulsive. Some may consider this exercise cruel. It is wise to introduce the exercise a day or two in advance, indicating what the students might see and be inclined to feel. Inform them that such reactions are normal for some people, but that they should try not to give in to these reactions. This will help them to cope with their emotions.

Emphasize that experimentation with animals is fundamentally different from experimentation with humans. This might be a good time to review the Dominion Mandate in Chapter 7, pages 180–81, and Facet: Animal Rights and Wrongs, pages 608–11. Also, explain that there is a vast difference between taking an egg from a robin's nest and taking an egg that is being cultured for food. Tell the students that the embryos in the eggs will be killed soon after the observations are done. (Place them in a strong alcohol solution after the students have left.) If you feel that your students will be extremely squeamish, you may wish to perform the egg openings in advance and to

Before the laboratory period begins, eggs should be placed in an incubator at intervals so that on the appointed day the egg will have been incubated the proper amount of time. For example, you will need to begin incubating the eighteen-day eggs about two and a half weeks before the day they are to be observed. To ensure freshness, do not purchase all the eggs at once, but obtain each set of eggs just before you incubate them.

Be sure to incubate several eggs for each time period.

To prevent students from having a psychological attachment to the eggs and the embryos, it is suggested that you do all the incubation and bring out the eggs on lab day without fanfare. Having live chicks or pictures of newly hatched chicks in the classroom at this time would be unwise.

II. With the egg lying on its side, draw an oval on the egg as illustrated in Diagram 25.1.

III. Carefully insert the point of a pair of scissors a short distance through the shell and cut cautiously around the oval.

IV. Using forceps, remove the loose piece of shell and locate the embryo.
- If the embryo is not visible, use forceps to grasp the chalaza (see the diagram on p. 553 of your text) and rotate the yolk.
- Remove some albumen with a dropping pipet to see the embryo more easily.
- With eggs incubated four to nine days, you will need to cut the amnion to see the embryo clearly. Be sure the other students see these membranes before you cut them.

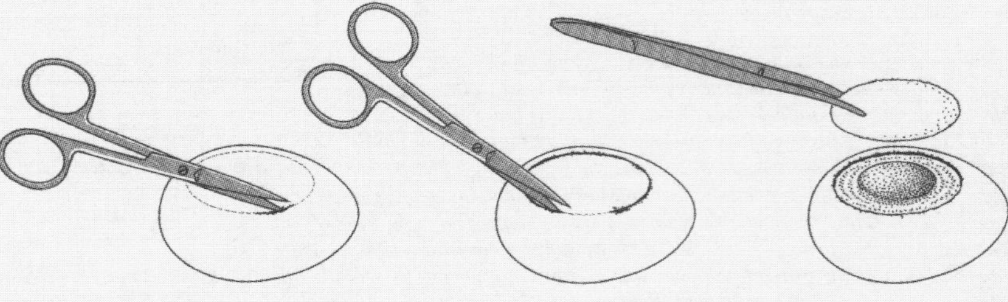

25.1
Opening an egg incubated fewer than ten days

Eggs Incubated Ten Days or More

I. Obtain the eggs from the incubator.

II. Tap the large end of the egg with the handle of a pair of scissors or a scalpel to crack the shell. (See Diagram 25.2.)

III. Using forceps, pick away the shell, being careful not to break the shell membrane.
- After a portion of the shell has been removed, place the egg in a shallow dish of physiological saline.
- Continue picking off the shell until it is completely removed.

IV. After observations have been made with the shell membrane intact, break the shell membrane and observe the structures inside.

V. Various membranes will need to be cut before the embryo is clearly visible. Be sure the other students in the class see the membranes before you cut them.

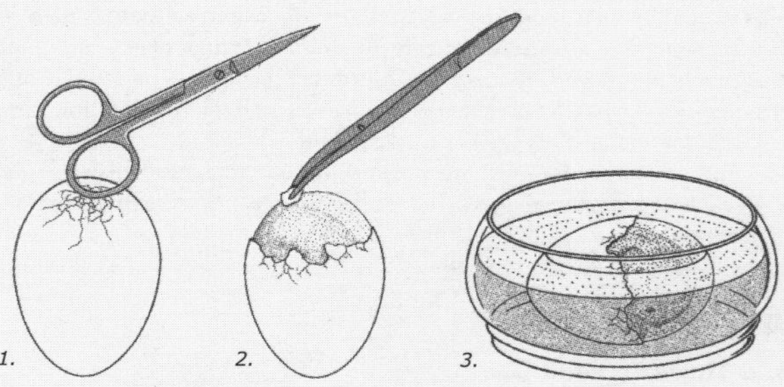

25.2
Opening an egg incubated ten days or more

make sure that the embryos are dead (by adding alcohol) before the students arrive. If you do not feel that your students will be squeamish, do not invite problems by dwelling on the topic.

See page A29 for a chart on chick embryo development.

Required / Extra / Omit

Unless you modify the experiment by opening the eggs for the students or by having preserved specimens, it is suggested that you require all of this exercise.

You may wish to modify or consider as extra credit one or more of the reports asked for on page L212.

Observing a Chicken Embryo

I. Look for these structures as you observe.

- **Yolk and yolk sac.** The yolk is the stored food for the embryo. Blood vessels formed by the embryo grow to encircle the yolk sac. As the yolk is used, the yolk sac decreases in size.
- **Shell membrane.** The shell membrane is just inside the eggshell and surrounds the albumen (egg white).
- **Amnion and amniotic fluid.** See page 531 of the text.
- **Allantois.** See page 531 of the text.
- **Somites.** Somites are lumps of tissue along the back of the young embryo. These structures develop into the vertebrae, ribs, and muscles of the chicken's body. The column of somites extends beyond the area of the arm and leg buds. But as the body grows, the arm and leg buds appear to move to their proper positions.
- **Blood, heart, and blood vessels.** Blood is one of the first obvious tissues formed by the embryo. The heart is one of the first organs formed. It begins as a pumping tube, which then twists back on itself and becomes a four-chambered pumping organ. At first it is outside the body, but later it is enclosed inside the body cavity. Visible blood vessels go to various egg structures to accomplish different functions.
- **Brain and spinal cord.** The heads of embryos are generally large in comparison to their bodies. The spinal cord is one of the first organs to be recognizable.
- **Limbs.** Starting as bumps on the sides of the body, the limbs slowly take form. Feathers, claws, and scales form before the chick hatches.
- **Eyes and ears.** The eyes form early in embryonic development. They are complex organs that must be fully functional when the chick is hatched. Eyelids form after the eyes do and then grow closed over the eyes. The ear openings can be found along the neck.
- **Mouth and beak.** The mouth begins as an opening to a hollow tube. The tube becomes the alimentary canal. In time, the opening of the tube becomes a mouth and then develops a beak and an egg tooth. The egg tooth is a structure that the chick uses to break the shell when it hatches.

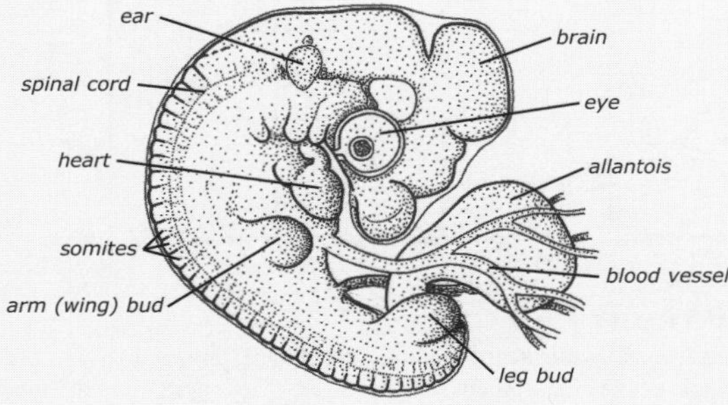

25.3 ____
A chick embryo incubated four days

II. Record your observations on the Chicken Embryo Development chart.

- Read the summary (p. L212) to find out what types of observations you need to make.
- Be sure that you observe all the eggs when they are first opened and record any observations you may have at that time.
  - Observe the embryos when they have been removed from their protective membranes.
  - In the spaces provided on the Chicken Embryo Development chart, describe extensively the development of each of the structures listed. Use additional paper if necessary.

It is good to have a number of illustrations available in the laboratory for reference. Even when a student sees the embryos, he is not always able to recognize the structures, especially in the earlier stages.

Although the students may have done careful observations and thoroughly completed the Embryo Development chart, they may experience difficulties trying to prepare the reports. A few words of explanation stressing what you expect will help.

Chicken Embryo Development

Structures	___ Days	___ Days	___ Days	___ Days	___ Days	___ Days
Yolk and yolk sac						
Amnion and amniotic fluid						
Allantois						
Somites						
Blood, heart, and blood vessels						
Brain and spinal cord						
Limbs						
Eyes						
Ears						
Mouth and beak						

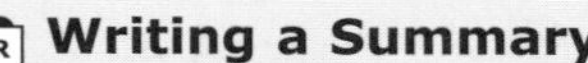

Writing a Summary

I. Prepare a report (one to two pages) discussing the changes in the yolk, yolk sac, amnion, amniotic fluid, and allantois of the chicken eggs you observed. Keeping in mind the functions of these structures, give probable reasons for the changes you observed.

II. Prepare a report (one to two pages) discussing the development of the heart, blood, blood vessels, brain, spinal cord, and somites of the chicken embryos you observed. Describe their changes as the embryo becomes larger. Keeping in mind the function of each of these structures in the adult chicken, give probable reasons for the different rates of growth you observed.

III. Prepare a report (one to two pages) discussing the relative developments of the front and back limbs, eyes, ears, mouth, and beak of the chicken embryos you observed. Keeping in mind what a chick has to do as soon as it is hatched, explain why the sequence of development in each of these structures is logical.

Name________________________________

Date____________________ Hour__________

Laboratory Final Examination: The Frog

Materials

- preserved frog
- dissection pan
- dissection kit
- pins
- reference materials
- mounted frog skeleton
- plastic bag

Goals

- To demonstrate, as a final exam project, the level of your laboratory skills
- To review the subphylum Vertebrata, class Amphibia, as well as human anatomy and physiology
- To learn about the frog

The Frog Lab (as this laboratory final examination will be called) will serve as a final test of your laboratory skills. The value of this lab will be one hundred twenty points. These points will be earned through written quizzes and the demonstration of laboratory skills. This laboratory exercise has no blanks to fill in, no drawings to make, and no illustrations to label. Instead, you are asked to know the answers to the questions and to know the material presented. Whether or not you have learned this material will be indicated by how well you do on the quizzes.

You will have your own specimen for dissection and will be graded individually on all parts of the Frog Lab. Your ability to follow directions and your skills in performing laboratory procedures can then be judged by the quality of your work. You must do your own work. You may consult your classmates or your instructor about information, sources, or directions, but you must do the dissection yourself. You are encouraged to study with other students, quizzing one another over the material, to prepare for the quizzes.

Contents

Preparing for the Frog Lab

I. Read before you begin.

- Read the *entire* Frog Lab before you come to class.
- Read completely Chapter 17 in your text.
- Plan to read and consult other texts as you work on the Frog Lab. You will not find in your text all the information you need to know to complete the dissections and the quizzes successfully. The books listed on page L214 are recommended; your instructor may suggest others. You may also find some information on the Internet. A search for "frog dissection" or "frog anatomy" may yield good results.

INTRODUCTION

The Frog Lab is designed to test the students' laboratory skills, to help students review the human body systems, and to teach them about the frog. If you have completed the *BIOLOGY for Christian Schools* textbook, your students should be ready for the Frog Lab. Since the Frog Lab is basically a review, it would be good to schedule it for the last few days before the written final exam. The Frog Lab serves to keep the students busy in profitable activities by providing them with physical goals to accomplish, an activity that is challenging, and the chance to improve (or at least maintain) their grades.

The Frog Lab should take four or five class days. Students should be able to complete the laboratory work and the quizzes during that time. If at all possible, the laboratory should be open for extra times after school, through the lunch periods, during an evening, and/or on a Saturday. Emphasize that these extra times are for the students to work ahead (or to catch up if they are behind). The homework for the Frog Lab should be to prepare for the dissection and to study for the quizzes.

To encourage students to work ahead and finish the Frog Lab on time, consider announcing, with administrative approval, that after they finish the Frog Master Quiz, they will not be required to come to biology class (except to report for attendance) until the end of the time allotted for the Frog Lab. This policy is especially helpful if you have several biology classes and have an after-school lab time as the last time students can finish the exercise. If you do not give this kind of encouragement to finish early, you may have more students than your classroom can hold during the last laboratory session of the Frog Lab.

Before the Frog Lab Starts

A few days before the Frog Lab, take a few minutes to present its goals. State the policies and procedures that will be in effect,

Suggested References for the Frog Lab

Bohensky, Fred. *Photo Manual and Dissection Guide of the Frog.* N.p.: Square One Education Guides, 2002.

Boolootian, Richard A., and Donald Heyneman. *An Illustrated Laboratory Text in Zoology.* 5th ed. Philadelphia: Saunders College Publishing, 1991.

Boolootian, Richard A., and Karl A. Stiles. *College Zoology.* 9th ed. New York: Macmillan Publishing Company, Inc., 1976.

Gilbert, Stephen G. *Pictorial Anatomy of the Frog.* Seattle: University of Washington Press, 1965.

Hickman, Cleveland P., et al. *Integrated Principles of Zoology.* 12th ed. St. Louis: C. V. Mosby Company, 2003.

Hofrichter, Robert, ed. *Amphibians: The World of Frogs, Toads, Salamanders and Newts.* Buffalo, NY: Firefly Books, 2000.

Storer, Tracy I., et al. *General Zoology.* 6th ed. New York: McGraw-Hill Company, 1979.

Underhill, Raymond A. *Laboratory Anatomy of the Frog and Toad.* 6th ed. Dubuque, IA: Wm. C. Brown Publishers, 1995.

Wells, T. A.G. *The Frog: A Practical Guide.* New York: Dover Publications, 1986.

Wingerd, Bruce D. *Frog Dissection Manual.* Baltimore: The Johns Hopkins University Press, 1988.

II. Understand the requirements and grading.

- This lab must be done in the order presented in the table of contents.
- The Muscle, Bone, and Skin Quiz; the Systems-Functions Quiz; and the Frog Master Quiz are your primary opportunities to earn points.
- While you are taking the Muscle, Bone, and Skin Quiz and the Systems-Functions Quiz, the quality of your dissection skill will be judged, and points will be awarded for your dissection work.
- You may take the quizzes at any time during the time allotted for the Frog Lab.
  - You may study your dissected frog for as long as you wish before coming to take a quiz.
  - You must take the quiz before you go on to the next section of the lab.
  - Allow yourself enough time to complete the quiz. Once you begin a quiz, it counts, whether you finish it by the end of the class period or not.
- Plan ahead for the lab times.
  - You will work on the Frog Lab in class from ____________ to ____________.
  - Your instructor may announce additional times that the laboratory will be open for work on the Frog Lab. The times are ____.
  - The entire Frog Lab must be finished and the Score Sheet handed in by ______________.
- After reading the Frog Lab, make a schedule to help you budget your time. On the Score Sheet are listed the values of the various sections of the Frog Lab. You should not spend days skinning the frog. Removing the skin in one piece is valued at only five points. To spend so much time skinning the frog, therefore, is unwise.

III. Take care of your frog.

- Frogs need moist habitats. As you work on your frog, keep it moist. As it is exposed to the air, it dries out and becomes brittle, breaking easily and costing valuable points.
- When storing your frog overnight, place its internal structures in its body cavity and then wrap the entire organism in a very wet paper towel. Place this in a plastic bag. Remove as much air as possible, close the bag tightly, and tie or zip it shut. Write your name on the bag with a pen or marker.
- You may keep your dissected frog after the dissection if you wish. Place it in a small jar of alcohol, and it will keep for years. Otherwise, when you are finished with a portion of it and your work has been graded, you may wrap it in a paper towel and throw it away.

especially those that the students may find confusing. Major points to cover include the following:

- Stress the importance of this examination to the students' grade. You should make the value of the Frog Lab equal to about one and a half or two regular test grades. If the points suggested on the Score Sheet (p. L227) need to be altered, do so at this time. Some teachers prefer to count the laboratory examination as one half and the written final examination as the other half of the students' final examination grade.
- Go over the form of the quizzes, giving a few sample questions. Stress that dissected specimens will be included on some of the quizzes. Each student will need to know the functions of a frog's structures and be able to recognize the frog's structures from a diagram and from a real specimen.
- Point out that each student will have his own specimen, will be responsible for his own work, and will be graded on the quality of his dissection. Tell your students how you expect them to present their dissected frog sections to you and explain that you will evaluate how well they have followed the directions.
- Emphasize the importance of budgeting time. Tell the students the dates they are to work on the Frog Lab in class and any extra laboratory times available to them. Have them record this information on page L214.
- Announce the date and time that the Frog Lab must be completed. Have the students record this information on page L214 and on the Score Sheet (p. L227). Emphasize that unless they make arrangements with you *in advance*, this date and time are inflexible. Exceptions should be made only for extreme emergencies or unexpected circumstances.
- Tell the students that there are no blanks to fill in on the Frog Lab and no diagrams for them to label. However, there are

Name________________________

Observing the External Structures of the Frog

I. Learn the external structures of a frog well enough to do the following:

- Identify on your specimen each of the structures listed below.
  1. Nostrils
  2. Nictitating membrane
  3. Tympanic membrane
  4. Forelimb
  5. Hind limb
  6. Anus
  7. Mouth (buccal cavity)
     a. Maxillary teeth
     b. Vomerine teeth
     c. Internal nares (nostril openings)
     d. Tongue
     e. Opening of eustachian tube
     f. Opening to vocal sac
     g. Glottis
     h. Opening to esophagus
  8. Skin
- Know how each structure operates and what its functions are.
- Know the system to which each structure belongs.

II. Be able to answer the following questions about the frog's external structures:

- Do the nostrils connect with the buccal cavity? If so, of what importance is this connection?
- What is the function of the eustachian tube?
- How do frogs make noise (croak)?
- How do frogs breathe (take in and force out air)?
- How do a frog's teeth differ from those of a human?
- How does a frog catch flies?
- How many toes does a frog have on its forelimbs? on its hind limbs? What are the toes like? What is the ratio of their extended length to the length of the leg? Compare toes on the hind limb and forelimb.
- What causes the skin of the frog to have color? to change color?
- How is the coloration of the frog different from the ventral to the dorsal side? What is this called and what is its significance?
- Frogs have thin, moist skin. Explain what keeps the skin moist and why it is thin.
- What is important about the thumbs of a frog?

NOTE:

- You should make several quick diagrams of these external structures.
- As you do your research, jot down notes about pertinent facts you discover and list any questions you have.
- Use these diagrams and notes as a study guide when preparing for the quizzes.

questions that they will need to study and diagrams that contain information that they will need to know in order to do well on the quizzes.

- Students sometimes become panicky when they see the diagrams of frog bones and muscles (pp. L217–L218) and the chart on the frog muscles (p. L219). Remind them that one of the purposes of the Frog Lab is to help them review for the written final and then calm their fears by pointing out that these are basically the same muscles and bones that they learned for the human body. Not all the human bones and muscles have significant counterparts in the frog, however; so not all the structures that the students learned for the human are included in this exercise. Also, some major frog bones and muscles that do not have significant human counterparts have been added (urostyle and mylohyoid, for example). If the students learned the bones and muscles when they studied Chapter 20, they should have no problems with the Frog Lab. If you did not cover certain bones and muscles while the students were studying Chapter 20, you may wish to skip the same ones in this exercise. You may also want to omit some of the muscles and bones in the Frog Lab even though you covered all the ones suggested in Chapter 20. The time to mention this is while you are giving the students the preliminary instructions.
- If you are going to modify any instructions or if you are going to add any activities, announce these changes now.
- Inform the students of the resources available to them. Keep in your classroom copies of as many of the books listed on page L214 as possible. Some of these books (especially the ones by Gilbert, Underhill, and Wells) are inexpensive, and you may want to have several in your classroom. A few of the older titles are out of print but may still be available through online used book sources. You may want to suggest other references and to put several books on reserve in the school library. The Internet is another source of information that can

Skinning the Frog

I. Remove the skin of the frog following these instructions.
- Make a cut on the ventral side of your frog from the lower abdomen to the lip (Diagram FL.1, from point A to point D).
- From this cut (line AD) make extensions toward the ends of the extremities of the limbs (lines BF and CE, both right and left sides).
- Starting at the previous cut to the lip (point D), cut the skin around the lips (Diagram FL.2).
- Remove the frog's skin.
  - Be careful around the eyes, tympanic membranes, and anus, where additional cuts may be necessary.
  - Mesenteries (connective tissues) and blood vessels hold the skin of the frog to its body. Most of these will pull apart easily. A few will need to be cut.
  - The skin of the front and hind feet will come off like gloves. Do not leave skin on the toes.
  - The skin of the frog should come off in one piece.

II. Save the skin of the frog for grading.
- Wrap all of the frog skin in a wet paper towel and save it until you are ready to take the Muscle, Bone, and Skin Quiz.
- As you take the Muscle, Bone, and Skin Quiz, your instructor will grade your frog skin. He will be looking for the following:
  - Directions followed accurately
  - Neatness
  - The skin taken off in one piece without being torn

FL.1
Removing frog skin

FL.2
Cutting around the lips

Observing the Bones and Muscles of the Frog

I. Learn the bones of the frog.
- Study carefully Diagram FL.3.
- Study carefully the mounted frog skeleton in the classroom, if available.

II. Note these facts about the frog skeleton.
- Know the structures in Diagram FL.3. The structures you are asked to learn are basically the same structures you learned for humans.
- There are several differences between human skeletons and frog skeletons, all of which you should recognize. Note the differences in the areas listed below:
  1. Ribs
  2. Number of vertebrae
  3. Ilium

be helpful, if used judiciously. There are some sites with detailed instructions, photos, and even virtual dissections.

- Inform the students that since this is an examination on which their dissection skills are being graded, they may not take their partially dissected frogs home.
- Stress to the students that they will do their own work and that you will be offering little assistance. Remind them that you have been giving assistance all year; by now they should be able to proceed with the Frog Lab by themselves. After all, this examination tests their laboratory skills, and teachers do not normally give help on tests.

During the Frog Lab

After a class period or so, most of your time in the laboratory will be spent grading dissected frogs and administering and grading quizzes. This will actually encourage the students to work on their own. If the teacher is wandering about the classroom with nothing to do, students are prone to ask about anything that may be causing them the slightest problem. If, however, asking the teacher a question means that they must go to the front of the classroom and wait for a turn, many students will think through their problem and arrive at their own decision. That is an important goal of this examination—to judge how well students think things through for themselves, follow directions, and learn material presented only by the printed page.

Sometimes students become concerned if their frog is unusual. For example, occasionally a frog stiffens into a contorted position. It may be a little more difficult to skin the frog, but the rest of the operations should not be hampered. If the frog is in some way maimed (for example, missing a front foot), note this on the student's Score Sheet so that you will take that into account as you grade the skin. Sometimes a frog has somehow everted one of its lungs into its mouth, making the removal of the respiratory system in one piece impossible. Again, such a problem should be noted on the student's Score Sheet. Occasionally when a body cav-

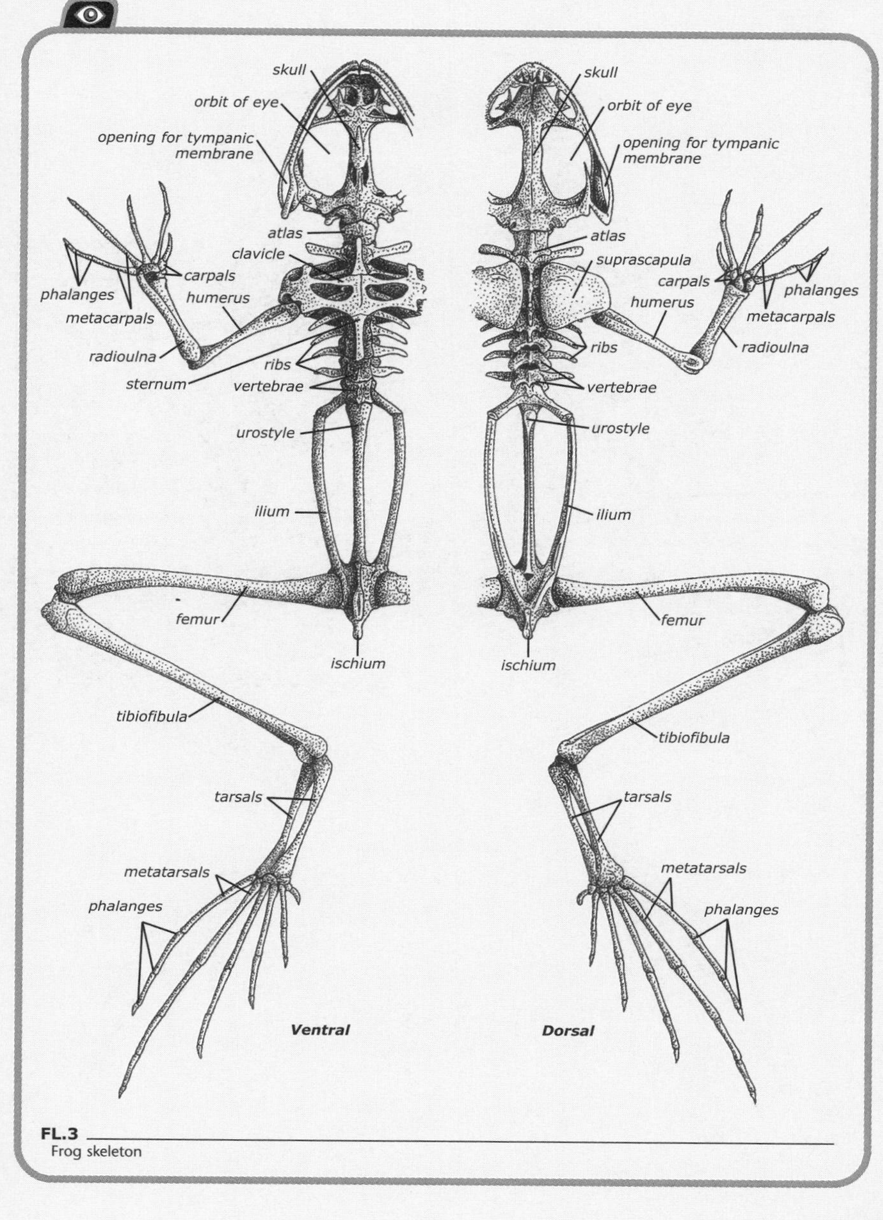

FL.3
Frog skeleton

ity is opened, the entrails are an unidentifiable mass. (One wonders how the frog could have lived long enough to reach adult size with whatever problems caused the internal disfigurement.) In this case, have the student get another frog. Tell him to quickly remove the skin from the new frog so that he can get to the point of opening the body cavity.

A student will occasionally ask a question that comes directly from the laboratory exercise. Immediately reply, "Where have you looked for the answer?" If he indicates that he has not done any research, tell him that he should start. If he did research but still did not find the answer, ask what books he used. Help him find the answer by pointing him to a source that he did not use or by telling him that he overlooked the answer when consulting a particular source. Of course, you must be familiar with the sources that are in your classroom. If some of the questions asked in the exercise are not discussed in the references your students have available, you should try to supply the answer for them ahead of time. Some of the questions in the Frog Lab can easily be figured out with a little thought on the student's part. Other questions (such as "How do frogs make noise [croak]?") are not answered in the text but are found in most other sources. A few questions (such as "What is important about the thumbs of a frog?") are not found in all the sources and may be confusing to some students, even if they have read an explanation. (The thumbs of the males of some species become enlarged prior to amplexus. Some sources indicate that this helps the male frog to clasp the female.) Unless the sources available to your students have the information clearly stated, some questions may require an explanation from you during the announcements. If you decide to omit such a question, tell your students during your preliminary announcements.

Some students become tense during the Frog Lab. Help your students relax a bit by having a collection of "froggie funnies." Look for cartoons or comic strips about

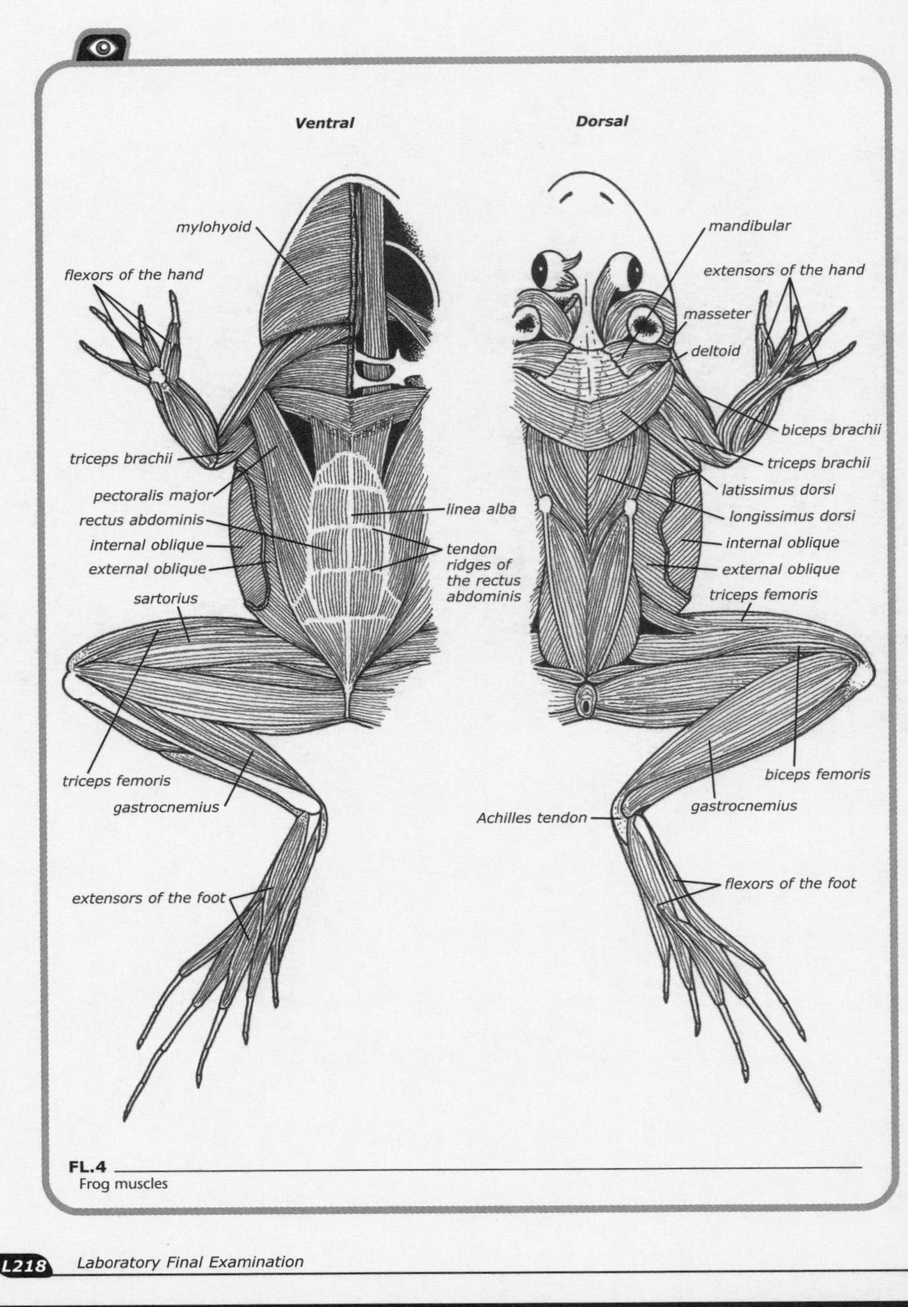

FL.4
Frog muscles

frogs and put them on the bulletin board during the Frog Lab. Also look for good posters of frogs. Consider changing bulletin boards in your classroom daily. There are many frog jokes and poems that make excellent "start-your-lab-day-off-right" material. After prayer and announcements, read the poem "What a Wonderful Bird the Frog Are" or an excerpt from Mark Twain's "The Celebrated Jumping Frog of Calaveras County" that extols the glory of frogs. A good giggle or an "awwww" while the students are getting their materials helps to keep the atmosphere relaxed.

Frog Lab Quizzes

The Muscle, Bone, and Skin Quiz and the Systems-Functions Quiz should include dissected specimens that have been labeled with colors or letters. Normally three or four dissected specimens per quiz are adequate. This number allows you to have several body positions and different systems in a quiz.

Dissected specimens for the quizzes should be placed in an area of the classroom where students usually do not go during the normal class hour. Perhaps some portable office divider panels could enclose a corner. If you have an adjoining stockroom or an empty classroom nearby, those would be ideal locations. Scatter the specimens in the area where students are taking the quiz to reduce the possibility of cheating. Also consider having several forms of the quizzes, often with many of the same questions asked in a different order, as another method of preventing cheating. Have students bring something to write with and a blank sheet of paper to serve as a cover sheet when they come to pick up a quiz. Encourage students who are not taking a quiz to keep noise down while other students are taking a quiz. Emphasize that they are not to discuss answers while quizzes are being taken.

These quizzes should be prepared in advance and copied so that they can be taken without the aid of a teacher (unless your class is so small that you can administer quizzes individually to every student). Questions such as "Name the muscle that is marked

Name________________________

Muscles of the Frog

Name	Origin	Insertion	Function
Biceps brachii (*flexor antibrachii*)	Proximal humerus	Proximal radioulna	Flexes forearm
Biceps femoris (*iliofibularis*)	Ilium	Tibiofibula	Extends thigh and flexes leg
Deltoid	Scapula, clavicle	Humerus	Abducts arm
External oblique	Scapula, vertebrae	Sternum, linea alba	Compresses abdomen
Gastrocnemius	Distal femur	Achilles tendon to metatarsals	Flexes leg and extends foot
Internal oblique (*transversus*)	Ilium, vertebrae	Sternum, linea alba	Compresses abdomen
Latissimus dorsi	Dorsal skin, vertebrae	Humerus	Extends arm posteriorly; rotates arm
Longissimus dorsi	Urostyle	Skull, vertebrae	Elevates head; extends back
Mandibular	Skull (near tympanic membrane)	Mandible	Lowers mandible
Masseter	Zygomatic process	Mandible	Raises mandible
Mylohyoid	Margin of mandible	Central tendon of mylohyoid	Raises floor of the mouth (breathing)
Pectoralis major	Sternum, rectus abdominis	Upper humerus	Adducts shoulder forward
Rectus abdominis	Pubic symphysis (of pelvic bone)	Sternum	Compresses abdomen; flexes trunk
Sartorius	Pubis	Tibiofibula	Flexes thigh at hip; flexes leg
Triceps brachii (*anconeus*)	Scapula	Radioulna	Extends forearm
Triceps femoris (includes the rectus femoris)	Ilium	Tibiofibula	Extends leg; flexes thigh
Extensors of the hand	Radioulna (dorsal)	Carpals and metacarpals (dorsal)	Extend hand
Extensors of the foot	Tibiofibula (ventral)	Tarsals and metatarsals (ventral)	Extend foot
Flexors of the hand	Radioulna (ventral)	Carpals and metacarpals (ventral)	Flex hand
Flexors of the foot	Tibiofibula (dorsal)	Tarsals and metatarsals (dorsal)	Flex foot

Muscle names in italics are used in some books and are included here for reference.

with a blue tag in specimen number 1" or "What is the function of the muscle marked with a green tag in specimen number 3?" are recommended. For the Muscle, Bone, and Skin Quiz and the Systems-Functions Quiz, it is better to have the students write out the answer in a blank than to choose the proper answer from a list. However, the Frog Master Quiz should be predominantly multiple-choice, matching, and true-false questions, with some direct recall and a few subjective questions.

One method of preparing quiz specimens is to dissect several specimens, position them in dissection pans, and place pins with various colors of tags attached to them (or with various colors of pinheads) through different structures. A specimen prepared in this way should either have wet cloths placed over it or be placed in a pan with a small amount of water in the bottom and covered with a glass plate. You will occasionally need to check the specimens to make sure that the pins have not moved (or been moved) and that the organism is not deteriorating. A more permanent method is to tie dissected specimens to glass plates (glass cut to fit a jar) with monofilament fish line. Then, using a needle, tie black thread around specific structures or insert the thread through them. Attach the other ends of the threads to colored tapes stuck to the glass or to lettered labels attached to the glass with tape. Place the glass plates in jars filled with a preservative solution. Formaldehyde, long the standard for specimen preservation, is a known carcinogen. Formalin, a dilute 10% solution of formaldehyde, is still readily available but should be handled according to MSDS precautions. Other safer but less effective chemicals are also available. (You may need to experiment with tapes and inks to find those that will not smear or lose their color in the preservative.) Once you prepare these materials, they will last many years. If you decide to make permanent quiz specimens, it is suggested that you include a few more labels than you expect to use. In this way you can alter the quizzes in future years and will not need to adjust the specimens in the bottles.

4. Radius and ulna; tibia and fibula
5. Carpals and tarsals
6. Sternum
7. Clavicle and scapula (suprascapula)

III. Learn the muscles of the frog.
- Be able to identify the muscles listed in the chart on page L219 and illustrated in Diagram FL.4 when they are pointed out.
- Know the meaning and application of the terms *origin* and *insertion.*
- Be able to list the origin and insertion of each muscle.
- Be able to demonstrate the function of each muscle.

IV. Observe these notes about frog muscles.
- The muscles and structures you are asked to know are basically the same as the ones you learned for humans.
- Muscle functions in the frog are often different from those in the human because of the difference between the body positions. The origins and insertions, however, are generally the same.
- You will need to make no further cuts on your frog to be able to see all of the muscles indicated, with the exception of the internal oblique.
- The masseter may have been torn as you opened the mouth of the frog to see the structures inside.
- You may use your probe to locate and slightly separate the muscles.

V. Review with your classmates by pointing out the structures for each other and asking questions (about function, modification, origin, and so forth) until you have mastered the material.

Muscle, Bone, and Skin Quiz

I. About the quiz
- The Muscle, Bone, and Skin Quiz is a written fifteen-point quiz that includes specimens with numbered labels.
- You may take the quiz anytime you wish, and you may spend as much time on it as you need. Remember, though, that you must turn in any quiz at the end of the class period. (The average time is about fifteen minutes. Check the clock before you begin to make sure you have adequate time to complete the quiz.)

II. Taking the quiz
- When you come to obtain your copy of the quiz from the instructor, bring the following:
  - Your dissection pan, with the skinned frog and the frog skin
  - Your Score Sheet
- While you take the quiz, your frog skin will be graded and your score entered on the Score Sheet.
- When you have finished the quiz, hand it in and pick up your dissection pan and Score Sheet.

III. After the quiz
- **Do not discuss the content of the Muscle, Bone, and Skin Quiz with anyone.**
- Your score on the quiz will be given to you as soon as it is graded, and you will have a chance to review it at that time.
- You will have no further need of your frog skin and may discard it if you wish.

About two-thirds of the questions on both the Muscle, Bone, and Skin Quiz and the Systems-Functions Quiz should cover the names and functions of the structures seen in the dissected organisms. The other questions should come from material that is either presented or asked about in the Frog Lab. (Of course, all the questions should relate to the frog.) Some of the questions should be answered from the text (Chapter 17C and other chapters), while others should be answered only from the reference books used to research material in the Frog Lab.

The Frog Master Quiz should contain questions that require students to apply knowledge of the frog and questions that ask merely for fact. If you include essays in the Frog Master Quiz, do not ask general essay questions like those you answered in upper-level college courses. If you do, students will write vague, rambling replies that may or may not deal with the topic. It is best to prepare essay questions that provide students with a structure for their answers. A good example is the question "List and describe three differences between the respiratory systems of a tadpole and a frog." The question limits the answers to three differences, and thus it encourages students to select the most significant details.

See pages A30–A31 for sample questions for frog lab quizzes.

Name________________________________

Opening the Frog's Body Cavity

NOTE:
- Be careful not to cut the internal organs as you make the incisions described below.
- Do not cut off limbs or any other structures unless you are instructed to do so.
- There are many ways to open the body cavity (coelom) of a frog. The method described below is recommended. It usually results in fewer damaged organs.

I. Cut along the linea alba from the lower part of the rectus abdominis (Diagram FL.5, point A) to the lip (point D).

II. Cut around the sternum (point B to point C).
- You will need to cut through bone in this area.
- Be careful not to cut so deeply that you damage the heart. It may help to tilt your scissors sideways.
- When cutting in the area of the mylohyoid, be careful not to damage other structures in the mouth.

III. Carefully cut from above the sternum to just above the shoulders on both sides (point C to point E).

IV. Carefully cut laterally from just above the origin of the rectus abdominis (point F) to the dorsal surface of the sides (point G).

V. The forelimbs of the frog should be bent dorsally, breaking the sternum and opening the flaps of the body wall to reveal the internal organs.

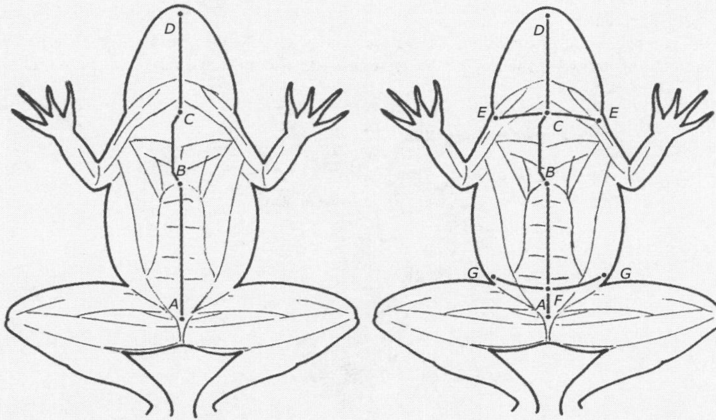

FL.5
Opening the frog's body cavity

Removing the Frog's Internal Systems

I. Do the following first.
- Identify all the internal structures that you can see.
- If you find eggs, use your probe to remove all of them, wrap them in a paper towel, and dispose of them.

- Mesenteries (thin, clear connective tissues with blood vessels running through them) hold the organs in place. Using a probe, loosen these mesenteries so that all the internal viscera are visible.
- Before you go on, locate all the following structures. Some of them are on the dorsal side of the body cavity, and you will need to use a probe to find them. **Do not cut any structures.**
  1. Right atrium of heart
  2. Left atrium of heart
  3. Ventricle of heart
  4. Venae cavae
  5. Artery leading from heart
  6. Liver
  7. Stomach
  8. Small intestine
  9. Colon (large intestine)
  10. Spleen
  11. Mesenteries
  12. Trachea
  13. Lungs
  14. Pulmocutaneous artery and pulmonary vein
  15. Gallbladder
  16. Bile duct
  17. Hepatic portal vein
  18. Kidneys
  19. Fat bodies
  20. Adrenal glands
  21. Ovaries or testes (Ovaries may have been removed with the eggs.)
  22. Urinary bladder
  23. Spinal cord
- As you begin your dissection of the various systems, remember that **each part must be entire and connected with the rest of the system** if you are to receive full credit for the dissection.

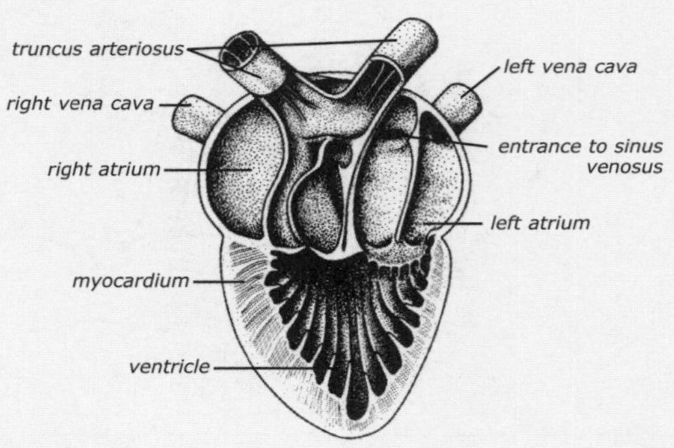

FL.6 ____________________
Frog heart, l.s.

II. Remove the circulatory system.

- It is easy to remove the heart, but identifying its structures after it has been removed from the body cavity can be difficult. While it is in its natural position, identify each of the following:
  1. Truncus arteriosus
  2. Right and left atria

3. Ventricle
4. Right and left anterior venae cavae
5. Posterior vena cava
6. Sinus venosus
7. Pulmonary vein

- Be able to trace the blood flow through the frog's heart and to tell the oxygen content of the blood at all the various stages of the cardiac cycle of the frog.
- Remove the heart with as much of each blood vessel as possible (approximately one-half inch).
- Wrap the circulatory system structures in a wet paper towel and set them aside for further study and evaluation.

III. Remove the respiratory system.

- Identify the structures of the respiratory system.
  - Locate the lungs, found dorsal to the digestive system.
  - Find the trachea. It is very short and connects the lungs. It is sometimes helpful to put a probe down the proper opening of the mouth in order to find the trachea.

NOTE: Some students find it easier to remove the digestive and respiratory systems together (see the instructions below on how to remove the digestive system) and then to separate the systems when they are both out of the body cavity. This may be advisable, especially with smaller frogs.

- Cut the trachea as near the buccal cavity as possible.
  - Do not cut the alimentary canal or damage the spine or spinal nerves.
    - ❖ The alimentary canal will be removed in another section.
    - ❖ If you cut into the back, the nerves will be damaged.
  - If the trachea is cut properly, the lungs will come out attached to each other.
  - Mesenteries holding the trachea and the alimentary canal together should be removed.
- Study carefully the method the frog uses to breathe. Be able to answer the following questions.
  - Are the lungs large enough to obtain oxygen for the frog's entire body?
  - Without a diaphragm and a rib cage, how does the frog force air into and out of its lungs?
  - What are the three respiratory surfaces used by the frog?
  - How do frogs make the croaking sound?
- Wrap the respiratory system in a wet paper towel and save it for future study and evaluation.

IV. Remove the digestive system.

- Carefully cut the lining of the mouth as close to the lips as possible. This will permit the mouth with the tongue attached to be removed as part of the alimentary canal. (See Diagram FL.7.)

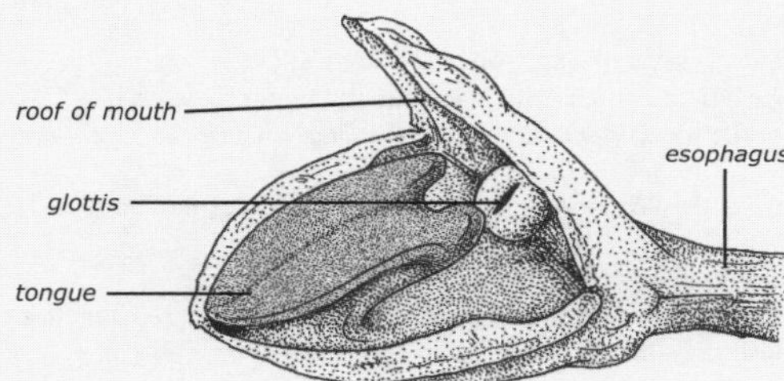

FL.7
Frog mouth as removed for Frog Lab

- Cut the large intestine just above the place where the urinary bladder joins the alimentary canal. Be careful not to cut the urinary bladder or any other structure. NOTE: Be careful not to ruin kidneys, fat bodies, and other structures of the urogenital system or nervous system by carelessly removing them with the digestive system.
- Carefully separate any mesenteries connecting digestive organs to parts of the urogenital system and the vertebrae.
- Remove the entire digestive system with the liver, gallbladder, spleen, and pancreas intact. (NOTE: Figure 17C.9 on p. 526 of your text does not show the mouth with the digestive system, but your specimen should.)
- Slowly tease the mesenteries with your probe so that the alimentary canal can be straightened.
    - Be careful not to cut the bile duct or pancreatic duct. The liver and the pancreas should be attached to the alimentary canal at the proper place (the duodenum).
    - The spleen is attached to the digestive system only by mesenteries. Leave it attached.
- Know all the structures of the digestive system in order (Figure 17C.9, p. 526 of the text) and their functions. The functions are the same as in humans.
- Be able to answer the following questions.
    - How long is the alimentary canal?
    - How long is it in relation to the length of the frog?
    - Is this proportional to the relationship between human height and the length of the human alimentary canal?
    - In regard to the frog and other vertebrates, what is the relationship between an animal's diet and the length of the intestine?

V. Remove the urogenital system.

- The excretory system and the reproductive system (along with parts of the endocrine, digestive, and other systems) will count as one system, the urogenital system.
- Carefully locate the following structures, which will be considered part of the urogenital system.
    1. Fat bodies
    2. Dorsal aorta and vena cava
    3. Renal arteries and veins
    4. Testes or ovaries (If eggs have been removed, ovaries have usually been destroyed.)
    5. Kidneys
    6. Adrenal glands (difficult to see)
    7. Ureters
    8. Vasa efferentia (difficult to see)
    9. Oviducts or seminal vesicles (Oviducts may have been destroyed when the eggs were removed.)
    10. Urinary bladder
    11. Cloaca
    12. Anal opening
- Cut the mesenteries connecting these structures to the body wall.
    - Be careful not to cut the ureters, the oviducts, the vasa efferentia, or the renal arteries and veins.
    - Carefully lift the urogenital system from the body wall.
    - Do not disturb the spinal nerves, which are directly under these organs.
- Cut the cloaca below the place where the urinary bladder attaches to it. Be careful not to cut any nerves.
- Cut the dorsal aorta and the vena cava just anterior to the top of the kidneys. Be careful not to cut any nerves.
- Remove the urogenital system as a unit.
- Know all the structures of the urogenital system listed above and their functions. They are basically the same as those of humans.
- Know the substances that empty into and pass through the cloaca.
- Wrap the urogenital system in a wet paper towel and save it for future study and evaluation.

VI. Reveal the nervous system.

- Observe the nerves as they appear in the dorsal area of the body cavity.
  - Compare them with Figure 17A.5 on page 505 and 17C.11 on page 528 of the text and Diagram FL.8. Be sure you know the labeled structures.
  - Note the color and texture of the nerves.
- Follow the spinal nerves as they branch down the limbs.
  - Cut away the muscles and the bones of the limbs. Muscles and bones may be discarded. If possible, trace the nerves to the toes.
  - Keep the structures moist.

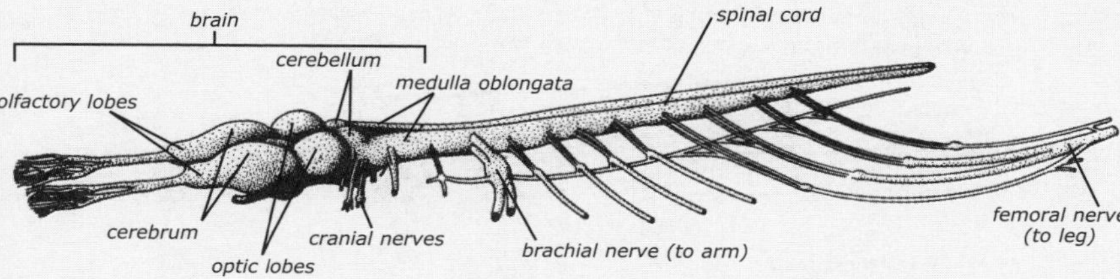

FL.8
Nervous system of the frog

- Remove enough of the skull to reveal the brain.
  - Removing the dorsal side of the skull is recommended; however, you can also reveal the ventral side of the brain.
  - A good way to get to the brain is to crack the skull with the handle end of the scalpel and then carefully remove the pieces of the skull. Be careful; the brain is easily damaged.
  - All the brain lobes should be visible.
- Cut away the tissue around the anterior end of the frog so that only the muscle-covered skull and vertebral column (with nerves coming out of it) remain.
- Cut away one or two of the vertebrae on the dorsal side to reveal the spinal cord.
- Know all the structures and functions of the nervous system in Figure 17C.11 on page 528 of your text. They are basically the same as the structures and functions in humans. Include olfactory nerves, nasal sac, and spinal nerves (not labeled in text).
- Note the eyes and tympanic membranes of the frog and know their structures and functions.
- Wrap the nervous system in a wet paper towel and save it for future study and evaluation.

Systems-Functions Quiz

I. About the quiz
- The Systems-Functions Quiz is a written fifteen-point quiz involving labeled specimens.
- Follow the instructions for taking the Muscle, Bone, and Skin Quiz (p. L220), but this time present the dissected frog systems in your dissection pan, as illustrated in Diagram FL.9.

II. After the quiz
- **Do not discuss the content of the Systems-Functions Quiz with anyone.**
- You will have no further need of your frog, and you may discard it or put it in a jar to keep. Frog parts should be put in the trash, not down the drain.

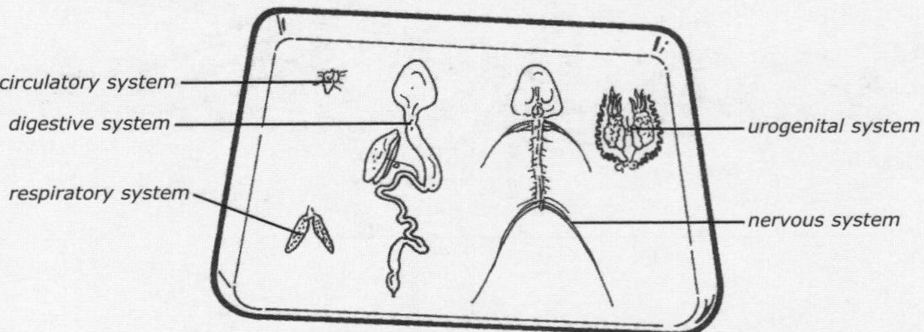

FL.9
Dissected frog (all systems dorsal side up)

Frog Master Quiz

I. The quiz
- The Frog Master Quiz is a written sixty-point quiz (half of the total value of the Frog Lab) that does not involve specimens but does have drawings, objective questions, and essay questions.
- The quiz takes about thirty minutes. Before you ask for the quiz, make sure that you have enough time to complete it.
- To prepare for the quiz, be sure to do the following:
  - Read the supplemental materials suggested in the Frog Lab, take notes on material not covered in your text, and review these notes.
  - Know the structures mentioned in the Frog Lab and their functions.
  - Know the answers to all questions asked in the Frog Lab.

II. Taking the quiz
- When you are ready, ask your instructor for the quiz. You will need a blank sheet of paper on which to write your essay answers.
- When you hand in the Frog Master Quiz, attach your Score Sheet to it. You are now finished with the Frog Lab.
- **Do not discuss the content of the Frog Master Quiz with anyone.**

Name____________________________

Laboratory Final Examination Score Sheet

I. Dissection and quizzes

- Present this Score Sheet to your instructor when you come to take your Muscle, Bone, and Skin Quiz and when you come to take your Systems-Functions Quiz.
- Leave the Score Sheet with your dissected frog so that scores for your laboratory skills can be recorded.
- After you have taken the quiz and it has been graded, take the score sheet with your quiz score on it and keep it in a safe place.

II. Frog Master Quiz

- You must turn in this Score Sheet attached to the Frog Master Quiz.
- You must turn it in by ____________ on ____________ to receive any credit for your Frog Lab.
- You need to turn in only this sheet with the Frog Master Quiz. You should not turn in the rest of the Frog Lab or any dissected frog parts.

Scores

Quizzes	Points Possible	Points Earned
• Muscle, Bone, and Skin Quiz	15	__________
• Systems-Functions Quiz	15	__________
• Frog Master Quiz	60	__________
Skills	**Points Possible**	**Points Earned**
• Skin	5	__________
• Circulatory System	4	__________
• Digestive System	5	__________
• Respiratory System	3	__________
• Urogenital System	4	__________
• Nervous System	5	__________
• General Skill	4	__________
Total	120	__________
	Grade	__________

Appendix

The Science Laboratory in a Christian Secondary School

Science, basically, is what man observes about God's creation. The primary purpose, then, of a laboratory science course in a Christian secondary school should be to observe God's creation. Before looking at what a Christian school's approach to a science laboratory should be, let us examine the history of classroom laboratories.

Several hundred years ago, almost all that was known on the subject of "natural science" (the term then used for what is now called biology) could have been observed by walking outside. At that time the life sciences were almost completely descriptive. The habitats and scientific names of various organisms were about all that was known of biology. Teaching with objects and specimens was almost unheard of. Only the highest levels of the academic ladder had natural history museums where students could look at dried specimens, skeletons, and perhaps a living organism or two. Supposedly they had already learned about these things from books. Such museums were looked on as avant-garde and considered more a toy or a curiosity than a true academic tool. During that time, academic pursuits of natural science were limited to teaching and studying what had been written.

As the scientific method of thinking spread, the classroom became populated by as many skeletons, dried specimens, and caged animals as the four walls could hold. The prevailing belief was that students could learn by observing things. Since they were later to make their own observations that would increase scientific knowledge, how scientific observations and conclusions should be made was paramount in the teaching of science. Thus, to a large extent, classroom specimens replaced books, and the classroom laboratory was firmly established.

As the years passed, scientific information began to increase. The trained research scientist was setting up observations in increasingly complex situations. These highly refined experiments were not easily duplicated by instructors or students. Thus scientific education again became book oriented. Teachers reasoned, "Since most students will not enter a scientific vocation, a firsthand knowledge of scientific apparatus and a practical knowledge of the scientific method of thinking are not so important as just knowing as many facts as we can get them to learn." This was the state of American science education in the early 1900s.

In the mid-1900s, however, the flight of *Sputnik* alerted government leaders to the fact that America was scientifically behind. Billions of government dollars were poured into science instruction. Whether you taught first grade or graduate school, obtaining scientific materials for your classroom was easy. The avalanche of government funds did the trick: the United States took the lead in space technology and regained superiority in technology development.

In the push for excellence in science education, the secondary school classroom became glutted with microscopes, plastic-mounted specimens, electrocardiograms, large and colorful models, and paraphernalia ad infinitum. All of this can be effectively used in teaching, but few teachers or students can handle it all. Today, in some science classrooms where materials abound, students are expected to learn by merely passing through the maze of things to look at, touch, cut, turn, and adjust. With the cry that students learn naturally by such exposure to scientific apparatus, we hear of educational movements such as the "hands-on approach" or "inquiry-based learning."

The task of the Christian educator in science is to achieve the proper balance between book learning and scientific-materials learning. Each of these has its place, but neither, if used exclusively, is very effective.

Goals of a Laboratory Science Class in a Christian Secondary School

If an educator reduces a secondary school science class to purely academic book study, he ignores several educationally sound and scripturally significant points.

Objects in the classroom serve as reinforcement of the facts and principles being taught. Most educators agree that showing students a picture of something while describing it is a better teaching technique than mere lecturing. Most educators also agree that bringing an object into the classroom is even better than using a picture. Of course, a student does not automatically learn all the significant material about planarians, for example, by having one placed in a dish in front of him. It may arouse his curiosity, but without a meaningful framework established by previous study and without some direction of his observation of the planarian, he will assimilate very little meaningful information. However, without the planarian in the classroom, the teacher may talk until he is blue in the face, and the textbooks may be worn out with reading and study, yet the student may still not grasp what a planarian is *really* like (even though he may correctly answer written test questions about it). However, he will not soon forget even one brief exposure to a planarian in a properly directed study. Pictures and lectures provide the main exposure to the subject, but properly directed laboratory activities serve as excellent reinforcement.

Students learn to think critically and logically by doing laboratory work. Good laboratory exercises require students to analyze observations, weigh conclusions, and evaluate their work and others' work. These are necessary skills that are taught better by putting the student into a position where he must perform them himself than by merely lecturing to him about them or by having him rely on others to think for him. Satan continually tries to cloud issues and confuse our thinking. Therefore, it is good for students to gain practical experience in critical thinking and logic that can be applied to spiritual matters too.

Students learn various practical skills from laboratory work that cannot be taught by lectures and books alone. Such skills as cooperation, the ability to read and follow directions carefully, and manual dexterity with certain tools are best taught in laboratory situations. (Although many of the scientific tools used in laboratory exercises will not be used by most of the students later, similar tools will be.) Observation skills, which are important both in science and in everyday life, can be taught and improved by laboratory work.

Students learn about the scientific method and its limitations by firsthand observations and by formulating their own conclusions. The limitations of science, a significant topic in any Christian school science course, are best illustrated by having students make their own observations and reach their own conclusions. The resulting difficulties and discrepancies can be used to reinforce the fact that science, since it is of men, is fallible.

By observing the details of the physical world, students learn of the God Who created it. God is revealed in His creation (Ps. 19:1). His power as Creator and Sustainer is revealed by close observation of the physical world. A carefully directed study of God's creation reveals considerably more than does a random glance at the world or a glimpse of it through the eyes of others, which is all that lectures and books can provide.

There is a growing movement that discredits the educational value of dissections in the biology classroom. Adherents of this position claim that a student can learn as much or more by viewing diagrams or using various software tools developed for this purpose. Consequently, a number of dissection alternatives are available. The primary motivation behind this action is to eliminate the killing of animals; this trend is promoted by the animal rights movement. For a Christian student, there should be no ethical or emotional issues surrounding the use of real animals for dissection. All have been bred for the purpose and are humanely euthanized. If the dissections are introduced in a professional manner with clear expectations, the students should have no difficulty with completing the assigned tasks.

An alternative dissection experience may be useful, though, for a student with a physical disability that prevents his participation in actual dissections.

The "No-Laboratory" Philosophy in Christian Schools

An attitude prevalent in some Christian educational circles today is that high-school science can be taught without laboratory work. No sensible person would argue with that statement. However, the relative qualities of a course with and a course without laboratory experiences must be compared.

Most states require that to receive credit for a high-school science course, students must spend a minimum of 20 percent of the instructional time in laboratory work. Although some Christian educators do not like the idea of conforming in any way to state regulations, requiring laboratory work does not contradict a scriptural command or principle. Most high-school graduates have spent time in a high-school science laboratory. Most schools and states require students to have one to three years of a laboratory science before they graduate. Laboratory work does make good educational sense and, if conducted properly, will effectively support the goals that any biblically based school should have for its science course.

The main argument against teaching a laboratory science course that meets state requirements appears to be that many Christian schools cannot afford it. Hence, the desire to teach biology and other sciences without laboratory experiences is usually based on economic rather than educational considerations, since no scriptural conviction is involved and the educational value of laboratory work cannot be denied. All too frequently a school's sports team receives hundreds of dollars for new equipment, while the science teacher's request for a microscope is denied because it is considered beyond the budget and not as necessary as other items. Such practice is shortsighted and will result in an education deficient in the quality that Christian schools are so quick to say they offer.

Of course, the science department is but one department of a good Christian school, and it is one of the more expensive ones to maintain. However, it is one of the major academic departments and deserves to be adequately supplied. No area of a school should be emphasized to the detriment of another. Priorities and balance are needed.

The Biology Laboratory in a Home School

Laboratory experiences are just as critical to home school students as to those in a traditional classroom. Sometimes this can be accomplished by regular sessions with other home school students at a school or other facility with lab space and equipment. If this is not possible, the educational rewards are worth the extra effort to provide the supplies for these labs. Many of the materials can be obtained locally. Consider reducing costs by sharing the purchase of some of the more expensive equipment with another family. If you have more than one child who will be home schooled in biology or if you have a student who is especially interested in the life sciences, buy the best microscope you can afford. A good instrument will give you years of service and will have good resale value.

The Biology Laboratory in a Christian High School

Few Christian schools can afford to spend the amount of money on their high-school laboratories that most public schools do. This book has been written with the Christian school in mind. The laboratory experiences in this book have been selected for their value as educational tools, for their ability to accomplish the goals described earlier, and for their practicality in a Christian school. Christians must be good stewards of what the Lord has given them. Thus, careful consideration has been given to the equipment needed for these laboratory exercises. This equipment is not cheap, but it is reasonably priced, and the materials purchased will be well worth the money spent if they are used properly.

New Christian schools just beginning to furnish their laboratories often have difficulty knowing what to do first. The booklet *Science Laboratories: A Practical Guide to Design and Equipment,* published by BJU Press, is recommended (call toll free 1.800.845.5731 for information). A list of materials needed to conduct the laboratory exercises in this book is found on pages A6–A20. For convenience, the materials list has been divided into several categories.

Laboratory equipment

- ***Available locally.*** These items can be purchased in grocery stores, hardware stores, or drugstores. Often they can be found in attics or at yard sales, or they can be collected with the help of students and parents.
- ***Available from a supplier of scientific materials.*** Although some of these items can be improvised or borrowed (see the Notes section of the Materials List), most of them will probably need to be purchased.

- ***Preserved microscope slides.*** Few teachers have the skill, and fewer, the equipment, to make these. Most of these slides must be purchased from suppliers of scientific materials.
- ***Preserved specimens.*** Many of these items can be collected and preserved by you, the students, or friends. Some of them will need to be purchased.

Consumables

- ***Available locally.***
  1. *Nonperishable.* These items are found in grocery stores or drugstores.
  2. *Perishable.* These items are found in grocery stores or drugstores.
- ***Available from a supplier of scientific materials.***
  1. *Nonperishable.* Some of these items can be improvised, and some may be available from local suppliers, but most must be purchased from suppliers of scientific materials.
  2. *Perishable.* Some of these items may be obtained locally, but most must be ordered from suppliers just prior to use.

Living Organisms for the Laboratory

A good high-school laboratory needs to have a few living organisms in it. Every biology teacher should maintain several live plants on a window ledge or in some other lighted area. If you do not have a green thumb, develop one or get help from a friend. The secret is in finding the proper hardy plant for your classroom, not in adapting the spot you have to grow some exotic, temperamental variety. Those plants that grow well in a home window should grow well in the classroom. You will find a potted plant an excellent visual aid when teaching such subjects as photosynthesis and leaf venation. Plants will also be necessary in certain laboratory exercises. For example, in Exercise 13b, having a plant with epidermal hairs on its leaves will save having to find a friend willing to give you a leaf of his African violet. When collecting the specimens for Exercise 13a, you will find it easy to hang a few numbers on pots of living plants and thereby add interest to the exercise.

Another must for biology classrooms is a well-stocked aquarium. An aquarium will not only add interest but will also provide the live fish needed for Exercise 17a. A simple freshwater aquarium is relatively inexpensive and easy to set up and maintain. For a real challenge that is worth the time and expense, try a saltwater aquarium. Maintaining starfish, sea anemones, coral, and other exotic saltwater organisms can greatly enhance the class's study of invertebrate zoology, especially if you live away from the coast.

Hamsters in a cage, a terrarium with an anole or toad, a caged bird (though sometimes noisy), or other classroom pets increase students' interest and serve as good illustrations. If you can induce the hamster to produce a litter (this is easy) or the parakeets to lay eggs in your classroom, you will have some very interesting visual aids. Even invertebrates such as African millipedes and hissing cockroaches are great teaching tools and have simple husbandry needs.

Remember that each of these creatures has unique food, temperature, and housing needs. You must plan accordingly and allow time for their care. A diverse collection may require several hours each week. Consider having a student aide help with this.

Stocking the Laboratory

New Christian high schools often find that they have limited funds for purchasing the necessary laboratory equipment. Actually, few Christian high schools, even though they may have been in existence for several years, can boast a well-stocked science laboratory. The following suggestions may help you in procuring some of the basics for your laboratory.

Some items can be borrowed from local professionals. Physicians, for example, often have old or spare stethoscopes or eye charts that they will either lend or donate to your school. Many have older models of organs or bones that would be wonderful teaching aids. Usually some handyman can be found who is willing to cut and sand a section of a tree trunk so that your classes can observe tree rings. A farmer can supply you with bird feathers, and his son may be willing to obtain the fur of some small animal for your laboratory collection. In somebody's basement is an old aquarium that once belonged to a youngster who has now graduated to other hobbies. Perhaps it even comes with an air pump, gravel, and a heater—all necessary to set up and maintain a thriving aquarium. You may even find a tropical fish hobbyist who has been wondering what to do with his surplus swordtails and *Cabomba* plants. States, counties, and public school districts sometimes hold public auctions to dispose of surplus supplies and older equipment. You have to be selective with the equipment, but glassware and hardware is often quite usable.

James's admonition "ye have not, because ye ask not" (James 4:2) may not have been intended for the high-school science laboratory, but it certainly applies. Let your needs be known by getting permission to make an announcement at a parent-teacher fellowship, an evening church service, a ladies meeting, the adult Sunday school class, the senior adult fellowship, or other church or school gatherings. Provide a list of the items needed for those who may be interested in donating articles to the laboratory. The items in the Available Locally Materials Lists (pp. A6 and A13–A14) can be used to make up your list of needs. Post the list, and as items are obtained, check them off. You may find it helpful to let the students know of the needs. They often can bring in supplies from their basements or garages. If your school has a service club, perhaps its members could make a project of finding all the materials on the list.

You may go a step further. Some people may be willing to help purchase items that are needed in your laboratory. A list of items that are inexpensive to moderately expensive could be posted, and some people may respond either by purchasing them or by giving the money to purchase them. Occasionally someone may be willing to donate an amount of money equal to the price of something more expensive, such as a sphygmomanometer (measures blood pressure) or even larger items.

Few families have surplus microscopes of the quality necessary for satisfactory high-school biology laboratory work. Although it is possible that you may find a donor capable of purchasing the needed equipment, you will probably have to take other measures to obtain such expensive items. Many Christian schools sell candy, magazines, or other items to raise money for everything from new soccer uniforms to tables for the lunchroom. Why not consider doing the same thing for stocking the laboratory with the more expensive equipment?

Another option is to charge a small laboratory fee. It may be wise for you to suggest that the school administration consider adding a laboratory fee to help supply consumable equipment—perhaps fifteen or twenty dollars per student per semester. After the expensive basics have been obtained, this amount (if you have enough students) can take care of consumables, equipment replacements, and minor additions.

When you have completed your purchase list, submit the list to two or more science suppliers for bids. Address it to the attention of the quotation department. On large orders, they will often give a significant discount in order to gain your future business.

Sources for Biological Supplies and Teaching Aids

It is recommended that catalogs be requested from the following companies:

Carolina Biological Supply Co.
Fisher Science Education
Frey Scientific Co.
Hubbard Scientific
JLM Visuals
Nasco
National Geographic Society
School Publishing
Sargent-Welch Scientific Co.
Schoolmasters Science
Science Kit & Boreal Laboratories

Materials Lists

Laboratory Equipment—Available Locally

Material	Quantity*	Laboratory Exercise	Priority	Notes
aquariums, gallon-sized	5/C	19, others	1	Typical all-glass fishbowls are best, but wide-mouthed gallon jars work well. These should have lids or glass plates to cover them.
blocks, metal or plastic	12/C	4	1	See teacher's notes for Exercise 4.
cellophane, green and red pieces	1/C	23c	2	Often available around Easter, material used to cover theatrical lights is suitable (need 3-inch squares).
chair, swivel	1/C	23b	3	See the school secretary.
cups, clear plastic	1/S	7	1	Use 8 oz size or larger.
hot plate	1/C	several	1	Any plate capable of boiling water can be used.
illuminators, general	2/C	3b, 4, 15c, others	2	High-intensity desk lamps are acceptable. One or two are needed at first; increase to one or two per student.
illuminators for microscopes (if not built-in)	1/microscope	1b, others	4	Desk lamps can be used, but illuminators designed for microscopes are recommended.
jars, quart	20/C	19, others	1	Mayonnaise or peanut butter jars are recommended.
jars, small	20/C	several	1	Baby-food jars are recommended.
knife	1/C	14, others	1	Sharp one is recommended.
nuts (hardware)	5/C	3a	1	Purchase size to fit cork. See teacher's notes for Exercise 3a.
pan	1/C	several	1	A two-quart (at least) non-Teflon, non-aluminum saucepan is suitable.
penlights	2/C	23a, 23c	2	Small flashlights are suitable.
photographs/posters	several of each			The teacher should collect assorted posters and calendar or magazine photographs.
animals		9	2	
insects		9, 16c	2	
plants		9	2	
razor blade, single edged	1/C	3a, 14	1	Obtain this at a drugstore or hardware store.
rubber bands	several	21a	2	
stopwatches	several	22a–b	1	These may be available through the PE department. A watch or clock with a second hand may be used.
tape measure	1/C	23c	1	

*Quantity column indicates the number needed per class (C) or number needed per student (S). Examples: 1/C means one per class; 1/2S means one for every two students; 1 box/5S means one box of the item for every five students. Teaching several classes of the same course may or may not mean that more equipment is needed. If the equipment is to be set up and left for a period of time (growing bacteria in petri dishes, for example), more equipment will be needed for each class. Most equipment, however, is reusable class after class.

Laboratory Equipment—Available from Suppliers of Scientific Equipment

Material	Quantity	Laboratory Exercise	Priority	Notes
bags, lung volume measurement	3/C	21a	2	Bags come with rubber bands and a set of mouthpieces. Additional mouthpieces will be needed for future use. (See notes for Exercise 21a.)
beakers	20/C	several	3	Small jars or glasses can be substituted.
bottles, dropping	12/C	several	4	These are convenient and safe for dispensing drops of stain and solutions, although dropping pipets and small jars may also be used.
bottles, plastic squeeze	4/C	2, 7	1	Small-necked wash bottle type is required.
burner, Bunsen (with wing top)	1/C	10a	2	A propane torch is also suitable and is recommended for small schools.
culture dishes, large	1/2S	several	2	Large, deep dishes (cereal bowl size) may be used.
culture dishes, small (watch glasses)	1/2S	15b, 15c, 16a, 17b, others	1	Shallow dishes, preferably clear, may be used.
dissection kits (which include the following items)	1/2S	3a, 3b, 15a–d, 16a, 17b, 18a, Final		Standard high-school dissection kit including the items listed is recommended (one kit per student is ideal).
dropping pipets	1/2S	2, 10a, 11, 12, 15b, 19, 25	1	
forceps	1/2S	11, 13b, 25	1	
probes	1/2S	several	1	Large pins or nutpicks can be substituted.
rulers	1/2S	1a, 2, 4, 18b, 23b, others	1	Six-inch plastic rulers with metric units on one side are recommended.
scalpels	1/2S	13b, 14, 25	1	Single-edged razor blades can be substituted.
scissors	1/2S	11b, 25	1	
dissection pans	1/2S	15d, 16a–b, 17b, Final	1	A thin slab of cork in a 9″ × 13″ baking pan (one pan per student is ideal) can be substituted.
dissection pins	1 box/C	15d, 16a, 17b, Final, others	1	Large straight pins may be used.
funnels, glass	4/C	5	2	These should be medium-sized to fit in beaker.
hand lenses	1/4S	1b, 11a, 12, 13b, 15a–d, 17b, others	1	Good magnifying glasses may be used.
Holmgren color vision test	1/C	23c	2	This or a similar color vision test can sometimes be borrowed from optometrists.
incubator	1/C	10a, 25	3	This may be borrowed from a poultry farmer; small size is sufficient; it may be purchased in conjunction with an oven (useful in physical sciences).
mallet, reflex	1/C	23a	3	You may substitute a small rubber hammer or a wooden dowel (about the size of an 18-inch broomstick).

Material	Quantity	Laboratory Exercise	Priority	Notes
meter sticks	1/2S	1a	1	
microscopes	1/2S	1b, 3a–b, 5a, 10a, 11a–b, 12, 13b, 15a–c, 18a, 19, 20b–c, 22a	1	See note A.*
osmometers (semi-permeable membrane, thistle-shaped bulb, tube, beakers)	4/C	2	1	Purchased osmometers with animal membranes are recommended. See Exercise 2, teacher's notes.
petri dishes, divided	3/C	10a–b	2	See note B.*
petri dishes, undivided	3/C	10a	2	See note B.*
rods, metal or glass	10/C	7, 23b	3	Glass stirring rods are recommended. Large metal nails with heads removed and points made smooth can be used.
slides and coverslips	50/C	3a–b, 11, 12, 13b, 15a–b, 19, 22a	1	Purchase glass slides and plastic disposable coverslips.
slides, concavity	1/2S	3b, 15b–c, others	3	
slide storage boxes	several	several	3	Preserved microscope slides are best stored flat but not stacked. Small, specially designed plastic boxes are recommended. They are sometimes sent complimentarily with purchases of preserved microscope slides.
Snellen eye test chart	1/C	23c	1	This can often be borrowed from an optometrist or a physician.
sphygmomanometer	1/C	22b	2	This can often be borrowed from a physician or nurse. It is also available at some department stores and drugstores.
stereomicroscopes	2/C	several	4	These are very nice luxury items (also called dissection microscopes). Usually hand lenses work just as well.
sterilizer, autoclave	1/C	10a	3	A pressure cooker designed for canning may be used.
stethoscopes	4/C	21a, 22b	2	These can often be borrowed from a physician or nurse.
test tubes	1/S	4, 7, 10a	2	These are usually sent free with purchases of bacteria.
thermometers	3–5/C	several	1	Outdoor or room thermometers are suitable for some experiments. Wider-range thermometers are necessary for others.
transfer loop	1/C	10a	2	See note B.*
tuning forks (128 cps, 256 cps, and assorted cps)	2/C	23c	2	
visuals				
human muscles diagram	1/C	20c	3	
human skeleton diagram	1/C	20b	3	

* Notes for Materials Lists are on pages A18–A20.

Laboratory Equipment—Preserved Microscope Slides

Material	Quantity	Laboratory Exercise	Priority	Notes
algae				A few slides of an individual type are better than no slides of that kind. The quantities recommended here would be ideal; however, fewer could be used if students are told to work other sections of the exercise while slides are in use. The slides needed in the largest quantity are the desmids (1b), diatoms (1b), and *Allium* root tips (5a), since doubling up on the use of these slides will be difficult.
desmids, mixed	1/3S	1b, 11	1	
diatoms, mixed	1/3S	1b, 11	1	
dinoflagellates (freshwater)	1/5S	11	2	
Protococcus	1/5S	11	3	
Spirogyra	1/5S	11	1	
Spirogyra in conjugation	1/5S	11	1	
animal and human				
beef tapeworm (*Taenia saginata*)				
bladders in meat	1/5S	15c	2	
proglottid	1/5S	15c	2	
scolex	1/5S	15c	2	
blood, human	1/5S	22a	1	
bone, dry ground, c.s.	1/5S	20b	1	
crustaceans, various (*Daphnia*, copepods, ostracods, etc.)	1 each/C	16a	4	
embryo, whitefish	1/2S	5a	4	
feathers, down and contour	1/5S	18a	3	
Grantia, c.s. and l.s.	1/5S	15a	1	
Grantia, spicules	1/5S	15a	2	
hookworm (*Necator americanus*)	1/5S	15c	3	
hydra, c.s.	1/3S	15b	2	
hydra, plain and budding	1/3S	15b	1	
hydra, with ovaries	1/5S	15b	3	
hydra, with testes	1/5S	15b	3	
muscle, cardiac	1/5S	20c	2	
muscle, skeletal (striated)	1/5S	20c	1	
muscle, visceral (smooth)	1/5S	20c	2	
skin, human, c.s.	1/5S	20c	3	
Trichina worm (*Trichinella spiralis*)	1/5S	15c	3	

Material	Quantity	Laboratory Exercise	Priority	Notes
bacteria types† (three types on a single slide)	3/C	10a	2	
colored threads	1/5S	1b	1	
fungi				
Aspergillus	1/5S	12	3	
Coprinus, c.s.	1/5S	12	2	
Coprinus, l.s.	1/5S	12	2	
lichen, c.s.	1/C	12	2	
Penicillium	1/5S	12	1	
Rhizopus nigricans	1/5S	12	1	
R. nigricans zygotes	1/5S	12	3	
plants				
Allium root tips, l.s.	1/2S	5a	1	
leaf, c.s. (dicot recommended)	1/5S	13b	1	
Ranunculus stem, c.s	1/5S	13b	1	
Ranunculus young root, c.s.	1/5S	13b	1	
Zea stem, c.s.	1/5S	13b	3	
protozoans				
amoebas	1/5S	11	1	
euglenas	1/5S	11	2	
paramecia	1/5S	11	1	
paramecia in fission	1/C	11	4	
Plasmodium	1/5S	11	4	
Stentor	1/C	11	4	
Vorticella	1/C	11	4	

† requires at least 940×

Laboratory Equipment—Preserved Specimens

Material	Quantity	Laboratory Exercise	Priority	Notes
algae				May be collected and preserved in some areas. See note F.* Plastic mounted specimens may also be used. Often these are available in group mounts.
Chondrus	1/C	11	3	
Corallina	1/C	11	3	
Fucus	1/C	11	1	
kelp	1/C	11	1	
Protococcus	1/C	11	2	
animal and human				
Ascaris	1/C	15c	4	Plastic mounts are recommended. Sometimes slaughterhouses or veterinarians can supply these organisms for you to preserve. See note H.*
bird feathers				These can be supplied by anyone with chickens or a pet bird. Also sold in craft stores.
contour	1/S	18a	1	
down	1/S	18a	1	
flight	1/S	18a	1	
coral	1/C	15b	3	Dried specimens are available in some resort areas. Mounted specimens containing the organism are recommended.
crayfish life cycle (showing male and female)	1/C	9, 16a	3	Plastic mounted specimens are recommended. See note H.*
crustaceans, various				Preserved, mounted specimens are recommended. See note H.*
barnacle	1/C	9, 16a	4	
crab	1/C	9, 16a	4	
shrimp	1/C	9, 16a	4	
fur, mammal	1/C	18b	2	A game enthusiast can supply this. Rodent or cat fur is good.
grasshopper, lubber (*Romalea microptera*)	1/2S	16b	2	Purchase specimens intended for dissection and store in a closed jar.
insect collection	1/C	9, 16c	3	Insect collections can be easily made. See note G.*
jellyfish	1/C	15b	4	Plastic mounted specimens are recommended. See note H.*
skeleton, frog	1/C	Final	1	This is better purchased rather than supplied by students.
skeleton, human	1/C	20b	2	Charts or models may be used.
skull, mammal	several	18b	3	These may be found outdoors and cleaned or purchased. Museum replicas are adequate; sets may be available.
sponge	1/C	15a	2	Dried sponges can be purchased at some resort areas, craft stores, or cosmetic departments. Plastic mounts of entire sponges are also recommended.
tapeworm	1/C	15c	4	Plastic mounts are recommended. Sometimes slaughterhouses or veterinarians can supply these organisms for you. See note H.*
various animals	several	9	1	The items above and similar suitable ones can be used.

*Notes for Materials Lists are on pages A18–A20.

Material	Quantity	Laboratory Exercise	Priority	Notes
fungi				
bracket fungi	1/C	12	1	
lichens, dried	1/C	12	1	
mushrooms	1/C	12	1	
puffballs	1/C	12	1	
plant				
herbarium	1/C	13a–b	2	Pressed, dried specimens can be purchased, or fresh specimens can be collected and mounted. See note I.*
preserved specimens	several	13a	2	Plastic mounts of mosses, liverworts, and similar plants can be purchased, or specimens can be collected and preserved. See note F.*

*Notes for Materials Lists are on pages A18–A20.

Consumables

Available Locally—Nonperishable

Material	Quantity	Laboratory Exercise	Priority	Notes
alcohol, isopropyl	2 pints/C	7, 15d, 21a, 22a, others	1	Having several pint bottles handy is recommended.
baking soda	1 box/C	4, 19	4	
corks	5/C	3a	1	They should be small enough to fit the nuts. See Exercise 3a.
cotton, sterile	1 bag/C	10a, 11, 22a	1	Cotton balls are good.
cotton-tipped swabs	1 box/C	3a–b, 23b, others	1	
dish soap, liquid	1 bottle	7	1	
Epsom salts	1 small jar/C	15c	1	
fertilizer, plant	1 jar/C	19	4	Liquid types are best.
glycerine or methyl cellulose	1 small jar/C	11	3	This is available in drugstores.
iodine (tincture of)	1 bottle/C	3b	1	This is available in drugstores.
lens paper	1 pack/ microscope	several	1	Type used to clean eyeglasses is recommended.
lime, powdered	1 oz/C	19	4	You can obtain lime at a hardware store or a garden supply store.
marker, permanent (felt-tipped)	1/C	several	1	Use markers to print names on plastic bags.
paper towels		many	1	The type found in many public restrooms is acceptable.
pens, washable ink	2/C	23b	3	Overhead projector pens can be used.
plastic bags	1/S	15d, 16a, 17b, Final, others	1	Small, resealable bags are needed to store partially dissected specimens.
salt	1 lb/C	3b, 7, 25	1	Noniodized salt is recommended.
sugar cubes	1/S	23b	2	
sugar (sucrose), granulated	1 cup/C	2	1	
tissues	1 box/C	1b	1	
toothpicks	2/S	11, 22a	1	
vanilla extract	1 small bottle/C	23b	2	
vinegar (dilute acetic acid)	1 small bottle/C	4, 15b, 19	3	
water, distilled	1 gal/ exercise/C	2, 7, 10a, others	1	
wax pencil	1/C	2	1	This can be obtained at an office supply store.

Consumables Available Locally—Perishable

Material	Quantity	Laboratory Exercise	Priority	Notes
banana	1/C	3b	2	Obtain fresh bananas from the grocery.
egg, chicken (raw)	1/2S	18a	2	
fish, living	1/C	17a	1	See pages A4–A5. Fish are available at pet shops.
flowers, fresh specimens	1/S	14	2	Pick flowers in your own garden or obtain from a florist. Roses, gladioli, or other simple flowers are best. Avoid daisies, carnations, and similar flowers.
fruit, fresh specimens (pome, drupe, true berry, modified berry, and pod)	several	14	2	See text, page 391, for examples of types.
lettuce or geranium leaves, fresh specimens	1/S	13b	1	Obtain these fresh from garden or grocery.
onion	1/C	3a	1	White or yellow (not red) is best.
plant material, dried (from pond)	several	19	2	During late summer, collect handfuls of pond weeds and emerging vegetation from a pond. See Exercise 19.
plants, living	several	13a–b	1	See pages A4–A5.
seeds	several	14	2	See teacher's notes for Exercie 14 regarding kinds and sources.
twigs, dormant, and dormant buds	several	13b	1	Collect several specimens during winter months. See Exercise 13B.
water, pond		11, 19	2	It is best to obtain it from a local pond. Pond water should contain organisms.
water, spring (sterile)	1 gal/ exercise/C	15b–c, 19	1	Spring or well water obtained locally should be boiled. Tap water that has been treated with chemicals used to prepare water for an aquarium may be substituted for spring water. (StartRight by Jungle is recommended and is available from pet shops and scientific supply houses.)
yeast	1 pkg/C	12	2	Use packaged dry, active yeast from the grocery. See Exercise 12 for directions on culturing.

Consumables Available from Suppliers of Scientific Materials—Nonperishable

Material	Quantity	Laboratory Exercise	Priority	Notes
agar	5 g/C	10a	4	See note B.*
agar, nutrient	25 g/C	10a–b	2	This is available as a dehydrated powder that keeps indefinitely.
blood lancets	1/S	22a	1	These are sometimes available at drugstores. Buy only individually wrapped, sterile lancets. See teacher's notes for lab regarding the use of blood in high-school classes.
capillary tubes	3/C	22a	2	These should be uniform in diameter, about 4 inches long. They are almost impossible to make yourself.
carmine powder	1 small jar/C	11	4	
dissection specimens				Order specimens that are not preserved in formaldehyde. Medium-sized specimens are recommended.
crayfish	1/2S	16a	1	
earthworms	1/2S	15d	1	
frogs	1/S	Final	1	Order a few extra frogs in case of defects.
yellow perch	1/2S	17b	1	
ether	25 mL/C	15d	4	Ether is used as anesthetic for earthworms (may use chloroform). It is occasionally available in drugstores.
formaldehyde (formalin)	1 L/C	several	2	See note F.*
hydrion test paper (pH test paper)	1 roll/C	4, 19	4	These may occasionally be obtained at pet shops.
hydrochloric acid	100 mL/C	19	4	
immersion oil	1 bottle/C	1b, 10a, others	4	This oil is needed to use oil-immersion microscopes.
methylene blue	1 bottle/C	3a–b, 12	1	It is sometimes available at pet shops as a fish remedy.
mouthpieces for lung volume bag	4/C	21a	3	
peptone	5 g/C	10a	2	See note E.*
phenol red indicator	120 mL/C	7	2	This is sometimes sold as phenolsulfonphthalein solution. You may use 0.02% or 0.04% solution.
Tallquist hemoglobin scale	1/C	22a	1	
test strips for glucose in urine	24–30 strips/C	2	1	Clinistix by Bayer Diagnostic or a similar product is available at most drugstores and serves well for this experiment.

*Notes for Materials Lists are on pages A18–A20.

Consumables Available from Suppliers of Scientific Materials—Perishable

Material	Quantity	Laboratory Exercise	Priority	Notes
cultures				
algae		19	3	
Protococcus	1 culture/C	11	2	
Spirogyra	1 culture/C	11	2	
bacteria				
Bacillus cereus	1 culture/C	10a–b	2	Order this to arrive one week before lab date and begin the culturing process upon arrival. See note B.*
Bacillus subtilis	1 culture/C	10a	2	
Rhodospirillum rubrum	1 culture/C	10a	2	
Sarcina lutea	1 culture/C	10a	2	
Sarcina subflava	1 culture/C	10a	2	
fungi				
bread mold (*Rhizopus*)	1 culture/C	12	2	Cultures keep well. Usually a culture can be obtained from your own kitchen. See Exercise 12 and note C.*
Penicillium notatum	1 culture/C	12	3	
protozoans		19		Order these to arrive one to two days before lab. Cultures do not keep well. See note D.*
amoebas	1 culture/C	11	3	
euglenas	1 culture/C	11	1	
paramecia	1 culture/C	11	1	
live specimens				
Anacharis (Elodea, *Egeria*)	1 bunch/C	3b, 4	1	Obtain early to be sure of a supply. Sources include local ponds, pet shops, or scientific supply houses. See note C* and notes for Exercises 3b and 4.
chicken eggs, fertilized	12/C	25	4	These are best when obtained from a local hatchery. See teacher's notes for Exercise 25.
Daphnia or brine shrimp	1 culture/C	15b, 19	1	Cultures keep well. See note D.*
earthworms	6/C	15d	2	Bait shops may have large specimens. If large (12-inch) specimens can be dug up, use them.
flour beetles (*Tribolium*)	1 culture/C	16c	3	Wild varieties are available and may be cultured with proper equipment. See note E.* They are also available from suppliers of scientific materials. See note C.*
fruit flies (*Drosophila*)	1 culture/C	16c	3	
hydrae	1 culture/C	15b	1	Cultures keep well. See note D.*
planaria	1 culture/C	15c	1	Cultures keep well. See note D.*

*Notes for Materials Lists are on pages A18–A20.

Material	Quantity	Laboratory Exercise	Priority	Notes
perishable chemicals				
antibiotic disks	1 set/C	10b	2	These will last for several years if refrigerated. See note B.*
beef extract	1 tube/C	10a	2	This must be refrigerated.
blood sera, human anti-A and anti-B	1 vial each/C	22a	3	Occasionally a local medical lab will provide blood-testing serum that is too old for clinical use but is acceptable for the classroom.
invertase	1 g/C	2	1	This must be refrigerated. (See notes for Exercise 2.)

*Notes for Materials Lists are on pages A18–A20.

Notes to Materials Lists

A

Ideally, one microscope should be provided for every two students in the class. Most of the exercises in this book can be accomplished with one microscope per three students, or even one per four students, although the students will get considerably less accomplished per unit of time in the laboratory. Unless there is one microscope for every two students, some of the exercises may have to be cut down or omitted.

The standard school microscope, equipped with 10× and 44× objectives and a 10× eyepiece (resulting in magnifications of 100× and 440×), is ideal for these exercises. The 4× objective (40× magnification) is not useful. Having one or two microscopes with a 100× objective (oil-immersion power, 1000×) along with the 10× and 44× objectives is desirable. Microscopes with these powers are available very inexpensively as toys. These toy microscopes, however, are not recommended. They are not built to take the wear and tear of school use. A more significant problem is their poor resolution (ability to be focused). Better microscopes are sturdy and give good lens resolution.

Microscopes can be obtained from suppliers of scientific materials. You may save money by purchasing them in quantity. Used microscopes are sometimes available at optical instrument repair shops (see Microscopes or Optical Equipment in the Yellow Pages for a medium to large city). Often schools replacing their microscopes sell their old ones to such establishments, which then overhaul them and sell them at prices considerably below retail.

About every two to five years, depending upon the usage you give them, microscopes should be taken to an optical repair shop for cleaning and adjustment. This preventive service will help to protect your investment.

B

The bacteria cultured for Exercises 10a and 10b can be cultured outside an incubator in warm areas (near heaters).

Petri dishes and nutrient agar are most economically purchased separately. After the dehydrated nutrient agar is prepared, the entire petri dish (with agar in it) is sterilized in an autoclave or sterilizer.

Autoclaves are frequently found in local medical laboratories or physicians' offices. These places are sometimes willing to sterilize petri dishes and media for educational purposes. Some heavy-duty pressure cookers (about $40) will work just as well as the expensive autoclaves ($2000 to $6000). If you do not have access to an autoclave or sterilizer, you may be able to obtain sealed, sterile petri dishes containing nutrient agar from a supplier of scientific materials.

Nutrient broth (formula given in teacher's notes for Exercise 10a) can also be purchased in sterile test tubes from some suppliers. Some suppliers will even send *Bacillus cereus* already in a broth culture, which is all you need for Exercise 10b. Antibiotic sensitivity disks, necessary for Exercise 10b, often come in collections and can be purchased from supply houses. A collection, however, is far more than you can profitably use before the antibiotics deteriorate (even with refrigeration). If your school is small, try to obtain a few antibiotic sensitivity disks from a local medical laboratory or through a physician.

C

Even if you have several classes, one culture of these organisms should supply all you need for all your classes.

D

Students will be using these organisms and most often disposing of them. Be sure to order the size of culture necessary for your class, and if you have several classes, order properly-sized cultures for each class.

E

Cultures of both fruit flies and flour beetles are available from suppliers of scientific materials. They can, however, be collected and cultured inexpensively. To make a good medium for culturing and collecting fruit flies, bring a mixture of 500 mL of water and 15 g of agar to a boil. Slowly add 135 mL of corn syrup or molasses. Mix 100 g of cornmeal in 250 mL of cold water. Add the cornmeal mixture to the hot agar-syrup mixture and boil for 5 minutes. Add a drop or two of mold inhibitor. Pour the mixture into small narrow-necked bottles to a depth of about 1 inch and stopper them with cotton. Sterilize the culture bottles in an autoclave or sterilizer (pressure cooker) at 15 pounds of pressure for 15 minutes. Set the culture bottles at an angle as the medium hardens (to increase surface area). Refrigerate until needed.

To obtain fruit flies, open the jar and set it on an open window ledge or on a porch in the shade during the spring, summer, or fall. Place a piece of paper for the flies to crawl on inside the jar. When several flies are inside the bottle, replace the stopper.

Every few weeks you will need to transfer several fruit flies to a new culture. Tilt the culture jar on its side so that the surface of the medium faces downward. Tap the jar a few times to get the flies to land on the side. (Flies landing upside down on the medium often stick to it and die.) Place a piece of ether-saturated cloth inside the bottle and quickly recap it. As soon as the flies are etherized (not moving on the sides of the bottle), pour them out of the bottle and sort them. Before they have a chance to recover, place several of the flies into a new culture bottle while the bottle is on its side. Be sure to place something in each bottle for the adult flies to crawl on.

Flour beetles are occasionally found in flour, cake mixes, crackers, cereals, or other dry, flour-based foodstuffs that have remained on the shelf for a long time. In a gallon jar with a securely fastened cloth top, place two dozen adult flour beetles and about half a jar of medium (made of half white flour, half wheat flour, and some brewer's yeast). If the mixture becomes dry, add a slice of potato, which should be replaced as it becomes moldy or dry. Every so often a new culture will need to be prepared; otherwise overcrowding will result in cannibalism and aberrant forms among the beetles.

F

Algae, fungi, and plant specimens are easy to collect but always seem to turn up out of season. Mushrooms spring up after a midsummer rain, but the laboratory exercise dealing with fungi is usually covered around Thanksgiving. Spotting a nice puffball, noting pond scum or balls of *Nostoc* colonies, finding a beautiful clump of moss with sporophytes, seeing young male and female pinecones, or locating fern fronds with sori may make a teacher mutter, "If only I had had this when we were studying it." Even if you do not know their exact genus and species, you can collect and preserve examples of these and similar specimens for effective classroom use.

Plants, algae, and the softer fungi are easily preserved in the agent F.A.A., which can be made following either of the two formulas given below.

F.A.A. will cause most green specimens to turn pale yellow-green to white. To prevent this, add a few crystals of copper sulfate to the F.A.A. before putting the specimen in. When the specimen regains its original color, transfer it to a jar of plain F.A.A.

The harder, more woody specimens (such as most bracket fungi, lichens, and even mosses) can be dried and, if handled carefully, kept in good condition.

It is often best to mount larger specimens on glass plates in jars. This procedure makes classroom viewing easier and prevents students from shaking the jar in order to see the other side of the specimen. Use several loops of monofilament fish line to secure the specimen to a glass plate that just fits into the jar you wish to use. Fill the jar with F.A.A. and seal it to prevent evaporation.

An insect collection is relatively easy to make. Methods for collecting insects vary with habitats and range from simple nets to elaborate electrical contraptions. Most can easily be built from scrap parts. It is recommended that you obtain a couple of books that discuss collecting and preserving insects if you are seriously considering making a major insect collection.

A killing jar is often recommended. A good way to make a killing jar is to put holes in the lid of a small jar of sodium cyanide and attach the small jar (or plastic film canister) upside down inside a larger jar (attached to the lid). Insects placed in the larger jar soon die. Sodium cyanide is often available at drugstores. Its vapors are very poisonous to animals and man and must be handled with great care. A cotton ball saturated with fingernail polish remover works almost as well. (Beetles are often best killed in small jars of alcohol, for they seem to be able to survive long periods in a sodium cyanide killing jar.)

Insects may be mounted by using long pins to attach them to a display area. They are usually displayed in a box with a glass lid for easy viewing. The box should be airtight, if possible, and should have mothballs secured inside it in order to prevent tiny living insects from destroying the preserved insects. If you require students to complete an insect collection, some may be willing to donate specimens to your permanent collection after grading.

Most animals are best preserved in formalin. The following suggestions may prove helpful.

- *Invertebrates except arthropods.* Parasitic flatworms, roundworms, and earthworms should be placed in water and heated until they are limp and motionless and then preserved in 6 to 8 percent formalin. Heating snails slowly in water often causes them to come out of their shells. The dead snails may then be placed in 6 to 8 percent formalin.
- *Arthropods.* The carapace of a crayfish or similar crustacean must be punctured with a knife or small nail so that the preservative can enter the body. Crustaceans should be placed in 6 to 8 percent formalin. Spiders are best preserved by dropping them into 85 percent alcohol or by using the same method for killing and mounting them as for the insects.
- *Vertebrates.* Puncture the bodies of fish in at least one place and then place them in a 5 to 6 percent formalin solution for about a week. Since larger animals dilute the preservative, the fish should then be taken out and placed in fresh 5 to 6 percent formalin for keeping; otherwise they may spoil. Amphibians also should be punctured to permit the preservatives to enter. The preservative will need to be changed after two weeks or so. Reptiles may be preserved in about the same way as amphibians, but if a tablespoon of sugar is added for each quart of formalin, they retain their color better. Birds and mammals may also be preserved in 7 to 8 percent formalin; however, for teaching purposes, taxidermic preservation is

Formalin-Acetic Acid-Alcohol (F.A.A.) Preservative

Ingredients	
Alcohol* (ethyl or grain), 50%	90 mL
Formalin† (commercial)	5 mL
Glacial acetic acid	5 mL
or	
Alcohol* (ethyl or grain), 70%	85 mL
Formalin (commercial)	10 mL
Glacial acetic acid	5 mL

*Rubbing (isopropyl) alcohol is usually 70% and should be diluted (70 mL alcohol with 30 mL water) for use in the first formula. It can be substituted full strength in the second formula.

†Formalin is a 37% solution of formaldehyde with some methanol. Formaldehyde is a carcinogen and should be handled with great care. It is recommended only for the preservation of specimens that will be observed in sealed glass containers. It is not recommended for student use. Use only in well-ventilated areas and when wearing goggles, gloves, and protective clothing. Formaldehyde requires special disposal procedures. Carefully follow instructions that come with the formalin for safe use and proper disposal.

recommended. Internal organs (such as brains and hearts) may be preserved in formalin, which should be changed after two weeks for long-term storage. If the organ is large, formalin should be injected into it.

I

A classroom herbarium is a very useful teaching aid. Complete instructions for herbariums may easily be found in most libraries. Here are some basic instructions. Collect plant specimens and place them in plant presses. Plant presses can be purchased, but they are easy to build. Specimens are placed between folds of newspapers, which are placed between heavy blotter papers, which are placed between sheets of corrugated cardboard (serving as ventilators). These units are then stacked (sometimes several feet high) and placed between the end boards of the plant press. Pressure is applied by weights or straps while the specimens dry. Drying can take place in a normal room (unless humidity is high), over heaters, in boiler rooms, or in dryer ovens. If the specimens are succulent, the blotters may need to be changed. Allow the entire plant press to cool before releasing pressure (to prevent curling of the specimens). Specimens should be pressed until moisture can no longer be felt on the specimen or blotter and the specimen does not curl when left uncovered.

Specimens should be mounted with glue or permanent tape to 11″ × 16″ heavy white acid-free paper. Attach a label in the lower right-hand corner of the paper; the label should indicate the scientific name of the plant, its common name or names, notes concerning the habitat and location where the specimen was found (city or area, county, state), date of collection, and the collector's name. Herbarium mounts should be stored lying flat in a closed box containing mothballs to prevent damage by insects.

Special glues, papers for mounting specimens, cellophane bags for protecting mounted specimens, drying ovens, boxes for storing herbarium mounts, and even mounted herbarium specimens are available from scientific suppliers.

Lab 15b—Life Processes Chart

Organism: Hydra **Phylum:** Cnidaria **Class:** Hydrozoa **Genus:** *Hydra*

Structure	Function
Movement	
basal disk	This attachment site at the base of the hydra can release to allow it to move in a somersaulting motion.
	Long contractile fibers at the bases of the cells in the epidermis and gastrodermis enable the hydra to bend.
Body Covering	
epidermis	The epidermis (the outer cell layer) is composed primarily of protective epithelium interspersed with cnidoblasts.
cnidoblasts	Batteries of stinging cells containing nematocysts line the tentacles.
Support	
epidermis, gastrodermis	The epidermis and the gastrodermis (the internal cell layer) surround the gastrovascular cavity.
mesoglea	The jellylike mesoglea fills the space between the two layers and provides support.
Nutrition	
nematocysts	The nematocysts sting and paralyze the victim.
tentacles	The tentacles draw the food toward the mouth.
gastrovascular cavity	Within the gastrovascular cavity, enzymes secreted by gland cells begin extracellular digestion.
gastrodermis	Cells of the gastrodermis ingest small food particles for intracellular digestion.
Respiration	
no structures	Individual cells exchange gases directly with their environment.
Circulation	
no structures	Nutrients reach all cells by diffusion through the thin body walls.
Excretion	
no structures	Wastes are excreted directly from individual cells into the environment or indirectly from cells of the gastrodermis.
Responses	
nerve net	The nerve net is a series of nerve fibers extending throughout the body wall that coordinate feeding and defensive movements.
Reproduction—Asexual	
budding	Budding is the gradual emergence and eventual separation of a new hydra from the side of the parent.
regeneration	Regeneration of hydras may involve the production of new individuals from severed sections of the original hydra.
Reproduction—Sexual	
ovaries	The ovaries appear as swellings on the side of the hydra and produce eggs.
testes	The testes also appear as swellings but produce sperm.
	An egg squeezes through an opening in the body wall to lie on the outer surface and is fertilized by sperm. The zygote undergoes division, forms a cyst, is released into the water, and soon develops into a new hydra.
Other Notes	Hydras are commonly found in quiet lakes or ponds. The hydra is a typical polyp, having a mouth and tentacles at one end and a basal disk at the other.

Lab 15c—Life Processes Chart

Organism: Planarian **Phylum:** Platyhelminthes **Class:** Turbellaria **Genus:** *Dugesia* *(not in text)*

Movement	
ciliated cells	Ciliated cells on the ventral surface propel the planarian over a layer of secreted slime.
muscle layers	Contractions of the muscle layers beneath the epidermis contribute to larger movements.
Body Covering	
epidermis	The epidermis (the outer cell layer) provides a protective covering.
Support	
mesoderm	The mesoderm, located between the ectoderm and gastroderm, contributes to maintaining the planarian's characteristic shape.
Nutrition	
mouth	Digestive enzymes are released through the mouth.
pharynx	The pharynx is everted, extending through the mouth to suck up small bits of food.
intestine	The intestine is lined by the gastroderm and secretes enzymes to digest food extracellularly. Other gastroderm cells ingest particles for intracellular digestion.
Respiration	
no structures	Individual cells exchange gases directly with the environment or the extensive digestive tract.
Circulation	
no structures	Diffusion among cells accomplishes all necessary circulation.
Excretion	
tubule network	Excretion occurs largely by diffusion, assisted by a mesodermal network of tubes ending in flame cells.
flame cells	Cilia in the flame cells beat vigorously to set up a current in the tubes, eliminating wastes and excess water.
Responses	
brain, eyespots, sensory organs	The brain, an anterior mass of nervous tissue, has branches leading to the eyespots and other sensory organs.
longitudinal and transverse nerve cords	Two longitudinal nerve cords extend the length of the planarian's body. Transverse nerve cords assist in coordination.
Reproduction—Asexual	
regeneration	When the planarian is cut, new planarians regenerate from the individual sections.
Reproduction—Sexual	
ovaries/testes	The ovaries produce eggs, while the testes, found on separate planarians, produce sperm. After cross-fertilization, young planarians emerge from fertilized eggs in less than one month.
Other Notes	Planarians inhabit freshwater lakes and streams. They vary in color from black or brown to white.

Lab 15c—Life Processes Chart	
Organism: *Ascaris* **Phylum:** Nematoda **Class:** Rhabditea *(not in text)* **Genus:** *Ascaris*	
Movement	
longitudinal muscles	Four longitudinal muscle bands can contract, producing a thrashing motion.
Body Covering	
epidermis *cuticle*	The cellular epidermis covers the *Ascaris's* body and secretes a noncellular, protective cuticle.
Support	
epidermal fibers	Epidermal fibers help maintain the roundworm's shape.
organs, fluid	The fluid and organs between the epidermis and the digestive tube provide support.
Nutrition	
pharynx	The pharynx sucks food through the mouth into the digestive tract.
intestine	The intestinal wall absorbs digestible material.
anus	Indigestible material passes through the anus.
Respiration	
no structures	Each cell obtains oxygen from its immediate environment. Fluid between the epidermis and the digestive tract brings dissolved gases close to all cells.
Circulation	
no structures	Nutrients from the intestine diffuse into the fluid beneath the epidermis. This fluid circulates as the worm moves.
Excretion	
lateral excretory canals, excretory pore	Wastes are eliminated by two lateral excretory canals through a single excretory pore just below the mouth.
Responses	
anterior nerve ring	A ring of nervous tissue around the pharynx receives sensory stimuli and initiates responses.
nerve cords	Dorsal and ventral nerve cords extend the length of the *Ascaris*.
Reproduction—Asexual	
none	
Reproduction—Sexual	
ovaries/testes	The female possesses ovaries; the male possesses testes. Both organs are long, coiled tubes. After fertilization, the female releases the eggs into the host's intestine.
Other Notes	*Ascaris* may reach twelve inches in length. Males are smaller than females and have a posterior hook. The *Ascaris*'s life cycle includes stages in the host's intestine, bloodstream, and lungs.

Lab 16a—Life Processes Chart	
Organism: Crayfish **Phylum:** Arthropoda **Class:** Malacostraca *(not in text)* **Genus:** *Cambarus*	
Movement	
internal muscles	The internal muscles move the exoskeleton.
Body Covering	
exoskeleton	The exoskeleton, made of chitin, maintains the crayfish's form and supports internal organs. The crayfish must molt its exoskeleton in order to grow.
Support	
exoskeleton	The rigid exoskeleton provides support and serves in muscle attachment.
Nutrition	
esophagus, stomach	Food entering the mouth passes through the esophagus to the stomach.
gastric mill	Chitinous teeth in the gastric mill (a part of the stomach) grind food.
digestive glands	The digestive glands complete the breakdown of small particles of food.
intestine, anus	Coarse particles pass through the intestine and out of the anus.
Respiration	
gills	Feathery gills are located in two chambers along the thorax. Blood flowing through the gills exchanges gases with the water that is pumped over the gills.
Circulation	
heart, arteries	The dorsal heart pumps blood through arteries to spaces around body organs.
sternal sinus, pericardial sinus	This blood collects in the ventral sternal sinus and travels to the pericardial sinus to begin the cycle again.
Excretion	
green glands	The green glands extract wastes from the blood and eliminate the wastes through a pore near the mouth.
Responses	
brain	The brain is composed of a pair of anterior ganglia.
ventral nerve cord	The ventral nerve cord carries nerve impulses through the length of the crayfish.
sensory organs	(The eyes, antennas, and antennules are discussed in the exercise.)
statocysts	The statocysts sense the crayfish's position.
Reproduction—Asexual	
none	There is no asexual reproduction. Regeneration produces new limbs, not new crayfish.
Reproduction—Sexual	
ovaries/testes, seminal receptacles, oviducts	The male reproductive swimmerets transfer sperm to the female's seminal receptacles. The sperm fertilize the eggs as they pass out of the oviducts. Egg clusters cling to the female's swimmerets until the young hatch.
Other Notes	Crayfish inhabit freshwater lakes and streams around the world. They reach about six inches in length. Their colors range from white to orange to brown or black. Their lifespan ranges from three to eight years.

Lab 16b—Life Processes Chart	
Organism: Grasshopper **Phylum:** Arthropoda **Class:** Insecta **Genus:** *Romalea*	
Movement	
jointed legs	Three pairs of jointed legs, including the very muscular last pair, equip the grasshopper for walking and jumping.
hind wings	The membranous hind wings are used for flying.
Body Covering	
exoskeleton	The exoskeleton forms a tough but flexible protection against chemicals and predators.
forewings	The leathery forewings cover the delicate hind wings.
Support	
exoskeleton	The rigid exoskeleton provides support and serves in muscle attachment.
Nutrition	
mandibles	Grasshoppers chew plant material with the mandibles.
maxillae	The maxillae bring chewed food to the mouth.
salivary glands	Salivary glands add their secretions to food passing into the esophagus.
crop	The crop stores food.
gizzard	The gizzard grinds food with chitinous plates.
midgut, gastric ceca	The midgut, or stomach, absorbs particles digested by juices from the gastric ceca.
intestine, rectum, anus	The intestine passes unabsorbed particles to the rectum and anus.
Respiration	
tracheae	The tracheae, a complex network of tubules, bring air directly to the cells.
spiracles	The tracheae open to the exterior at the spiracles. Inspiration and expiration occur with abdominal contractions.
Circulation	
heart	The heart pumps blood toward the head, through the thoracic and abdominal cavities, and back to the heart.
Excretion	
Malpighian tubules	The Malpighian tubules absorb wastes from blood flowing through the abdomen and pour them into the digestive tract for elimination.
Responses	
brain	The brain connects to the anterior ganglion.
ventral nerve cord	The ventral nerve cord transmits impulses the length of the body.
sensory organs	The sensory organs include the antennae (smell), receptors on the mouthparts (taste), tactile hairs (touch), compound and simple eyes (sight), and the tympanum (hearing).
Reproduction—Asexual	
none	
Reproduction—Sexual	
ovaries/testes	The ovaries (female) and the testes (male) are in the abdomen.
seminal receptacle	The female's seminal receptacle stores sperm.
ovipositor	The female deposits fertilized eggs through her ovipositor.
Other Notes	Grasshoppers live throughout the world. They may cause extensive crop damage.

Lab 17a—Life Processes Chart	
Organism: Yellow Perch **Phylum:** Chordata **Class:** Osteichthyes **Genus:** *Perca*	
Movement	
fins	(Fins have been discussed in the section on external structures of a yellow perch.)
air bladder	The air bladder controls buoyancy.
muscles	Muscular bands in the fish's trunk and tail produce a whipping motion.
Body Covering	
scales	The skin is covered by rows of overlapping scales.
mucous glands	Mucous glands secrete mucus, hindering parasites and decreasing friction.
chromatophores	Chromatophores are cells in a fish's skin that help to produce the coloration of the fish.
countershading	Countershading is a type of coloration in fish that aids in protection from predators.
Support	
bony skeleton	An internal bony skeleton supports the perch. The skull and vertebral column are completely bone. Other skeletal parts may be cartilaginous.
Nutrition	
pharynx, esophagus, stomach	Food passes from the mouth through the pharynx and esophagus to the stomach, where it is stored.
intestine	Digestion begins in the intestine.
anus	Any substance not digested will leave the digestive tract through the anus.
pyloric ceca	The pyloric ceca absorb small particles or secrete digestive juices.
liver	A large liver joins the digestive tract near the stomach.
gallbladder	The gallbladder is connected to the liver.
Respiration	
gills	The gills are composed of gill filaments supported on the gill arch. As blood flows through the gills, gases are exchanged with the passing water.
opercula	Water flowing through the mouth and across the gills exits through the opercula.
gill rakers	Gill rakers prevent debris from passing onto the gills.
Circulation	
heart (atrium and ventricle), ventral aorta	The heart consists of two chambers. The atrium receives deoxygenated blood. The ventricle pumps blood through the ventral aorta to smaller arteries supplying the gills.
dorsal aorta	The dorsal aorta branches to supply the body with blood.
pericardial cavity	The pericardial cavity is an anterior portion of the fish's body cavity.
bulbus arteriosus	The bulbus arteriosus joins the ventricle to the ventral aorta.
Excretion	
kidneys	The kidneys filter wastes from the blood and pass them, along with excess water, to the urinary bladder.
urinary bladder	The urinary bladder discharges fluid nitrogenous wastes through the urogenital opening.
urogenital opening	The urogenital opening releases liquid wastes and eggs or sperm.
Responses	
cranial nerves	The cranial nerves bring impulses to the brain.
spinal nerves	The spinal nerves bring impulses to the spinal cord.
olfactory sacs	The olfactory sacs detect tiny amounts of dissolved substances.
lateral line	(This has been discussed in the exercise.)
brain	The brain has typical vertebrate divisions (the optic lobes and cerebellum are the largest).
Reproduction—Asexual	
none	
Reproduction—Sexual	
ovaries/testes	The female's ovaries (called roe) produce numerous eggs. The male's testes produce milt (sperm). The female spawns, and the male covers the eggs with milt.
yolk	Fertilized eggs develop into embryos, which feed on the eggs' yolks until they hatch.
Other Notes	The yellow perch is the most common pan fish in North America.

Lab 22a
Methods of Finger Pricking

The following methods, if practiced faithfully, are adequate to supply the blood needed for this laboratory exercise and to prevent the spread of infection. Because of the possibility of infection, it is recommended that the teacher be the one to do the finger pricking either on himself or on volunteers.

I. Preliminary steps
- Be sure both the pricker and the donor thoroughly wash and dry their hands. The pricker should wear gloves.
- Select a finger from the nondominant hand.
- Use gauze soaked in alcohol to clean the fingertip that is to be pricked. Allow the alcohol to evaporate from the fingertip.
- "Milk" the finger so that the fingertip is bright pink.

II. Blood collection
- Follow these instructions if you are using a manual lancet.
  - While the finger is being held, quickly and with enough force to break the skin, jab the lancet into the finger. The lancet is made so that the wound will not be too deep.
  - Dispose of the lancet. **Do not use it again, even on the same person.**
  - Allow the first small drop of blood to come, and then wipe it away with sterile gauze.
  - To obtain blood for your experiment, "milk" the finger. If the blood is slow to appear, you may need to prick the finger again—your jab was probably not hard enough.
- Follow these instructions if you are using a spring-loaded lancet.
  - Cleanse the finger as described above.
  - Follow the instructions for the device that you have purchased. Usually it involves cocking the lancet, gently pressing it against the finger, and then releasing the spring. This type of lancet is designed so that it can be used only once. The lancet retracts so that it prevents injuries. Many of the science suppliers shown on our website (www.bjup.com, under Resources Online) sell these devices.
  - Follow the instructions above for collecting the blood specimen.

III. The follow-up
- When you have all the blood required, place sterile gauze over the wound and hold it there until the bleeding stops.
- If you need more blood and have waited more than two minutes since you made the puncture, you will have to make a new puncture.
- The amount of blood shed for this class is not enough to make even the most anemic person faint. If students feel they may pass out because of the sight of blood, have them sit down.

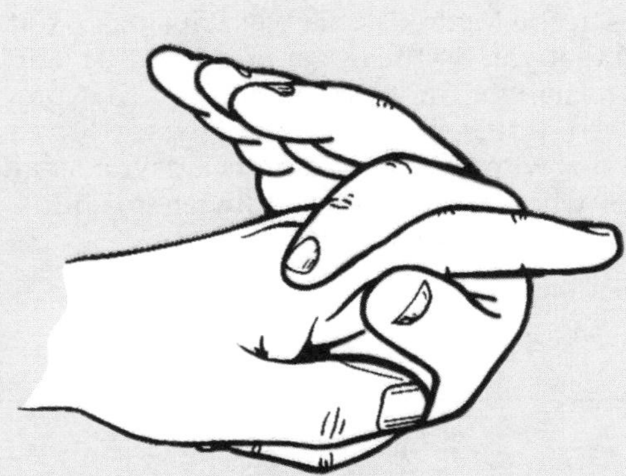

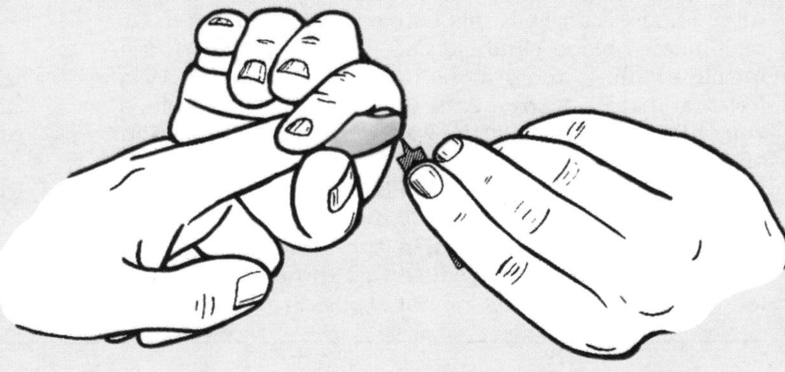

Milking the finger (left) and pricking the finger (right)

Procedures for Handling Blood in the High-School Classroom

Although these procedures should be more than are necessary for handling normal blood, it is recommended that you check with your local health department or environmental protection agency to determine the local statutes for defining and disposing of potentially infectious waste and sharp instruments (the lancets). The statutes are designed to prevent a person from becoming infected with contaminated blood. You may want to adopt some or all of these procedures as precautions.

- All who are to handle blood or blood-contaminated equipment should wear gloves.
  - It is recommended that students not be required to handle fresh blood.
  - When students are to observe fresh blood (as in the observation of a blood typing or a blood-clotting experiment), they should be instructed not to touch the blood.
- All glassware (slides or watch glasses) or other nondisposable equipment contaminated by blood should be thoroughly washed.
  - The equipment should be placed in a strong solution of bleach immediately after its use.
  - When the equipment is to be washed, strong soap and high heat should be used. If possible, the equipment should be sterilized.
- Blood-contaminated objects (gauze, alcohol pads, etc.) should be collected in disposable containers that can be sealed. These containers should be sturdy enough that those handling the trash will not inadvertently become contaminated. The lancets should be collected into puncture-proof containers prior to disposal.
- Excess fresh blood should be washed down a drain with plenty of water. The entire sink and surrounding area should then be cleaned with a strong bleach or appropriate bactericidal cleaning solution.
- The counter or tables where fresh blood has been used should be cleaned immediately with a strong bleach or appropriate medical cleaning solution. Keep in mind that bleach may discolor some metal surfaces.

Blood Sources

- Simulated blood can be used for the typing exercise, but not for the clotting section. Several different biological supply houses carry kits that contain simulated blood. Use of simulated blood eliminates all of the potential risks of infection, injury, and disposal of blood-contaminated materials and sharp instruments. If you use simulated blood, you will need to modify the exercise to the specifications of the kit that you purchase.
- You may choose to use your own blood for the demonstrations of blood typing, hemoglobin count, and blood clotting. Follow the procedures in the Methods of Finger Pricking box. It is recommended that those procedures be followed so that students are not exposed to fresh blood.
- You may choose to have students volunteer to be "blood donors." If you do this, it would be wise to get the written consent of the parents before the procedure is done. Follow the procedures in the Methods of Finger Pricking box. It is recommended that you do the finger pricking, that you be the only one to handle the fresh blood, and that procedures be followed so that students are not exposed to each other's blood. It is wise to ask the donors a day or so after the experiment whether their pricked finger still hurts. If so, they may need medical attention.

Lab 25

Important Events in Chick Embryo Development

Elapsed time	Developing structures
Day 1	
18 hours	Alimentary canal
20 hours	Vertebral column
21 hours	Nervous system
22 hours	Head
24 hours	Eyes
Day 2	
35 hours	Ears
42 hours	Heart starts to beat
Day 3	
50 hours	Amnion
60 hours	Nose
62 hours	Legs
64 hours	Wings
70 hours	Allantois
Day 4	Tongue
Day 5	Reproductive organs
Day 6	Beak and egg tooth
Day 8	Feathers
Day 13	Scales and claws
Day 19	Yolk sac begins to enter body
Day 20	Yolk sac completely drawn into body
Day 21	Chick hatches

Suggested Questions for Frog Lab Quizzes

Some of these questions assume that there are specimens for the students to observe. You should be able to determine what the specimen is by the answer given. Additional questions that you may wish to use can be found in Chapter 17 of *BIOLOGY for Christian Schools* prepared tests or the Testbuilder program.

Muscle, Bone, and Skin Quiz

- True or False? Some frogs have deadly poisons in their skin.
  True

- Name the structures in the skin of the frog that account not only for a frog's color but also for its ability to change colors. chromatophores

- What is the only muscle you learned that is not visible on a skinned frog? internal oblique

- Which of these is not found in the frog? D
  A ilium
  B. radioulna
  C. clavicle
  D. tibiotarsals

Systems-Functions Quiz

- Name the heart chamber labeled *A* and tell how many exist in the frog's heart. ventricle, one

- Name the microscopic structures that accomplish the main function of the organ labeled *C*. nephrons

- Name the system indicated by letter *D* and tell what other structure accomplishes the same function.
  respiratory, skin or mouth lining

Frog Master Quiz

- The large collecting veins entering the sinus venosus of the frog's heart are the C
  A. aortic arches.
  B. bulbus arteriosus.
  C. venae cavae.
  D. carotid arches.

- A folded membrane that connects the intestine to the dorsal body wall is the C
  A. vasa efferentia.
  B. pancreas.
  C. mesentery.
  D. nictitating membrane.

- The tiny tubes that carry sperm into the kidneys of a frog are the B
  A. venae cavae.
  B. vasa efferentia.
  C. ureters.
  D. eustachian tubes.

- Estivation is D
  A. a type of frog reproduction.
  B. a winter hibernating state.
  C. a means of locomotion in some frogs.
  D. a period of summer inactivity.

- The digestive, reproductive, and excretory systems of the frog all terminate in a common chamber called the B
  A. sinus venosus.
  B. cloaca.
  C. kidney.
  D. urinary bladder.

- Fat bodies are found A
  A. above the kidneys.
  B. under the muscular layer.
  C. around the small intestine.
  D. above the spleen.

- The frog's pelvic girdle is made up of the ischium, the ilium, and the C
  A. atlas.
  B. clavicle.
  C. urostyle.
  D. suprascapula.

- The frog's teeth are used primarily for B
  A. chewing.
  B. holding prey.
  C. biting.
  D. all of these.

- As a frog matures, its diet C
  A. remains carnivorous.
  B. is normally herbivorous.
  C. changes from herbivorous to carnivorous.
  D. changes from carnivorous to herbivorous.

- A thin covering that keeps the frog's eyeball moist while the frog is on land is the B
  A. web membrane.
  B. nictitating membrane.
  C. tympanic membrane.
  D. mesentery.

- The origin of the gastrocnemius is D
  A. the patella.
  B. the calcaneus.
  C. the proximal femur.
  D. the distal femur.

- The function of the mylohyoid is to D
  A. close the mouth.
  B. open the mouth.
  C. move the tongue.
  D. raise the floor of the mouth.

- One of the frog's two sets of teeth is called C
  A. molars.
  B. deciduous.
  C. vomerine.
  D. incisors.

- Which limbs do tadpoles develop first? A
  A. hind limbs
  B. forelimbs
  C. simultaneous development
  D. depends on the species

- The opening in the mouth that leads to the trachea is called the A
  A. glottis.
  B. eustachian tube.
  C. vocal chamber.
  D. epiglottis.

- True or False? The absence of claws on the toes is an amphibian characteristic. True

- True or False? Both frogs and toads are members of the order Caudata. False

- True or False? Some amphibians are legless. True

- A frog that breathes by means of gills is called a/an tadpole.

Essay Questions

(Their values should vary.)

- Describe the metamorphosis of the frog's circulatory system. Deal with only the circulatory system. List and describe the structures that change.

- Describe the metamorphosis of the frog's respiratory system. Deal with only the respiratory system. List and describe the structures that change.

- List three differences between a frog skeleton and a human skeleton. For each difference you list, give the corresponding structures (or lack of structures) of both the human and the frog.

- The frog lacks a rib cage and certain muscles that the human uses for breathing. Explain how a frog is able to move air into and out of its lungs without those structures. Also tell how a frog can spend hours underwater without refilling its lungs.